Biological & Inorganic Copper Chemistry Volume I

Biological & Inorganic Copper Chemistry Volume I

Proceedings of the Second Conference on Copper Coordination Chemistry held at the State University of New York at Albany, July 23-27, 1984

Edited by

Kenneth D. Karlin

Department of Chemistry
State University of New York at Albany

and

Jon Zubieta

Department of Chemistry
State University of New York at Albany

Adenine Press, P.O. Box 355
Guilderland, New York 12084

Adenine Press
Post Office Box 355
Guilderland, New York 12084

Cover illustration: Structure of a tetrachloro-*o*-catecholato- and phenoxo-bridged dicopper(II) complex, by K.D. Karlin, Y. Gultneh, T. Nicholson and J. Zubieta as a model for intermediates in coper-catalyzed oxidation of catechols

Library of Congress Cataloging-in-Publication Data

Conference on Copper Coordination Chemistry
   (2nd : 1984 : Albany, N.Y.)
   Biological & inorganic copper chemistry.

   Includes bibliographies and indexes.
   1. Copper proteins—Congresses. 2. Copper—
Congresses.   3. Coordination compounds—Congresses.
I. Karlin, Kenneth D., 1984-   .   II. Zubieta, Jon,
1945-   .   III. Title.   IV. Title: Biological and
inorganic copper chemistry.
QP552.C64C65 1984   546'.65   85-32334
ISBN 0-940030-11-X (v. 1)
ISBN 0-940030-15-2 (v. 2)

Made in New York, USA

Preface

These volumes explore the relationships of the biological and inorganic roles of copper by presenting contributions from spectroscopists, biochemists and inorganic coordination chemists. The books have evolved from the scientific discussions of the Second Conference on Copper Coordination Chemistry held at the State University of New York at Albany, July 23-27, 1984.

A previous volume in this series, published in 1983, provides an introduction to the field of the bioinorganic and general catalytic chemistry of copper. The evolution of our understanding of the role of copper in these processes has so accelerated that a mass of significant new chemistry has been developed since the publication of this original volume. The past three years have witnessed a refinement of structural and spectroscopic implications of the metal binding sites in type 1 and 2 copper proteins, with relevant structural analogues evolving in sophistication. Likewise, the rapid progress in the development of binuclear copper systems has profound implications upon the nature of the interaction of molecular oxygen with copper both in enzymes and in abiological systems.

The persistent theme of these volumes is that the evolution of the coordination chemistry of copper provides the fundamental insights required for the detailed understanding of the structural and spectroscopic properties of copper sites in proteins and of the interactions of molecular oxygen with reduced copper.

E.I. Solomon prefaces the volume with an overview of the role of copper coordination chemistry in the development of fundamental concepts of both biological and abiological catalysis, spectroscopy, and structural chemistry.

The volume opens with contributions exploring the chemical and spectroscopic properties of a variety of copper-containing proteins. The fine details of the type 1 or blue copper binding site are discussed in contributions by D.R. McMillen and A.G. Sykes. Applications of nuclear magnetic resonance spectroscopy and EXAFS to the elucidation of the copper(II) sites in superoxide dimutase are presented by C. Luchinat and N.J. Blackburn, while the role of zinc(II) and the essential arginyl residue of Zn/Cu SOD is examined by J.S. Valentine.

R.A. Scott and S.P. Cramer discuss structural studies of the binuclear copper site of cytochrome c oxidase. The functional diversity of binuclear copper sites is illustrated in the contrasting role of hemocyanin, where the copper site cooperativity is explored in a discussion by C.A. Reed. The binding of Cu(II) to Poly(L-Lysine) is discussed by F.T. Greenaway. The strategy of chemical modification of metal sites in proteins is the unifying theme of presentations by M.M. Morie-Bebel, D.M. Dooley, and J.M. Rifkind, who apply this technique in investigations of proteins as diverse as laccase, superoxide dimutase and modified hemoglobin.

The second major subdivision of the volume describes recent developments in the exciting area of medicinal applications of copper chemistry. The specific antitumor activity of copper preparations and the possible mechanisms of this activity are represented by contributions from S.-H. Chiou and coworkers and from W.E. Antholine and D.H. Petering. J.R.J. Sorenson and coworkers present an overview of the medicinal uses of copper complexes. Site-specific metal mediated Haber-Weiss mechanism in paraquat toxicity is proposed by R. Kohn and M. Chevion.

The first volume concludes with the discussion of the physical and spectroscopic properties of copper complexes and provides the bridge between the study of biological materials and the fundamental physico-chemical principles gleaned from small molecule or "model" studies. The general magnetic and electronic properties of a variety of copper (II) complexes are developed in detail by the contributers. Magnetic interactions in chain compounds and EPR properties of cluster compounds are discussed by W.E. Hatfield and G. Kokoszka respectively. O. Kahn discusses spin polarization effects in ligand bridged copper (II) ions. Novel analytical applications of electron paramagnetic resonance provide the focus of contributions by J.S. Hyde and W.E. Antholine and by H. Gampp and A.D. Zuberbühler. Electronic and magnetic properties associated with diverse phenomena-mixed-valence complexes, cooperative Jahn Teller interactions and antiferromagnetic coupling, are examined by D.N. Hendrickson, D. Reinen and C.P. Landee, respectively.

The second volume focuses on the synthesis and characterization of copper complexes that mimic some aspects of the structural or functional roles of copper proteins or of abiological copper catalysts. A major theme of the presentations is the persistence of analogies between the biological and the simple chemical catalytic systems.

The "activation" of molecular oxygen provides the topic for the introductory section of the volume. Contributions by J.S. Thompson and L. Wilson focus on the reversible reactions of dioxygen with mononuclear copper complexes. Binuclear complexes which mimic tyrosinase or hemocyanin activity represent exciting new chemistry in the presentations of S.M. Nelson, T.N. Sorrell, and K.D. Karlin. Copper catalyzed oxidation of phenols, an important industrial process, is explored in synthetic systems by J.E. Lyons and D.A. Haitko. The reactivity of copper clusters toward dioxygen is developed by G. Davies, while the mechanistic feature of the reactions of α-diketones with metallic copper are presented by G. Speier.

The second major subdivision presents the general topic of copper coordination chemistry with an emphasis on protein models. Models for copper sites in cytochrome c oxidase are discussed by J.K. Hurst and H. Toftlund. Binuclear complexes are discussed in relation to type 3 copper proteins, to synthetic copper binding polymers, and to a variety of homo- and hetero-binuclear systems by J. Reedijk, K.S. Murray and E. Sinn, respectively. The more general inorganic and structural properties of copper(II) complexes are developed in contributions by D.E. Fenton, J.M. Latour and G. Davies.

The volume concludes with a discussion of organometallic copper complexes, species of general interest in the development of organic synthetic processes. G. Van Koten focuses on the structural chemistry of organocuprate reagents. Polyhydride clusters are employed in numerous synthetic processes; K.G. Caulton discusses the rational synthesis of copper polyhydride species. The theme of aggregation is pursued by G. Doyle in a contribution on the synthesis of other types of copper containing clusters.

The contributions to these volumes are representative of the current trends in the development of the bioinorganic and more classical coordination chemistry of copper and reflect our major thesis that underlying the apparent diversity of physico-chemical data there exists a unity of fundamental chemical design. Once again, we hope that these volumes will serve as a useful compendium of the most recent research trends in this area and as a focus for discussion and further research activity.

The 1984 Copper Symposium and these volumes were only made possible through the generous support of a variety of University, State, and industrial sources. We wish to thank the SUNY Conversations in the Discipline Program, the SUNYA Office of the Vice President for Research, and the Research Foundation of the State of New York for financial assistance. We were particularly gratified by the supportive response from industry and wish to thank Allied Corporation, Bioanalytical Systems Inc., Bristol-Myers Company, Exxon Research & Engineering Co., Galbraith Laboratories, General Electric, International Copper Research Association, Inc., the Standard Oil Company (SOHIO), Sun Tech Inc., and Texaco Co. We hope that the fruitful collaboration between the University and industrial sectors represented by the success of this endeavor continue to fluorish in years to come.

Finally, we would like to thank the contributors, who met our numerous deadlines without protest and who dealt stoically with the delays occasioned by editorial miscues. In conclusion, K.D.K. thanks Nancy and Matthew for their patience and affection and J.Z.thanks Susan, Chloe and Christa for bearing up when the long hours were showing.

Kenneth D. Karlin
Jon Zubieta
November, 1985
State University of New York (SUNY) at Albany

Foreword

The coordination chemistry of copper has played a major role in the development of both basic concepts of physical inorganic chemistry and important catalytic reactions, particularly those involving dioxygen and carbon monoxide activation. Since the 1950's, detailed spectroscopic and magnetic studies on high symmetry transition metal complexes have provided the experimental framework for ligand field theory. Strong emphasis has been placed on copper (II) as the d^9 (one hole) configuration allows a most rigorous correlation to theory. A few key studies of particular note are: The temperature dependence of the EPR spectrum of copper (II) doped in $Zn(H_2O)_6 \cdot SiF_6$, which first clearly demonstrated that a Jahn-Teller effect was active; the use of EPR on square planar copper (II) complexes to obtain g values, hyperfine and superhyperfine coupling parameters, which in turn gave experimental estimates of the covalent mixing in the anti-bonding "d" molecular orbitals of these complexes; the dependence of the $d \Rightarrow d$ transition energies on geometry and ligand type, provided an accurate test of the ligand field approximation of separating radial and angular contributions to the energies and further allowed the investigation of possible chemical insight from the values of these radial integrals; further, the $d \Rightarrow d$ combined with the charge transfer transitions in high symmetry copper complexes have enabled an experimental evaluation of various levels of molecular orbital calculations for metal ions (extended Huckel, HF-SCF-LCAO at different levels of approximation and SCF-X α -SW); finally, the classic magnetochemistry studies of cupric acetate monohydrate and related binuclear copper(II) complexes have led to deep insight into antiferromagnetic coupling, superexchange pathways, and magneto structural correlations (i.e. changes in exchange coupling with bridging geometry and ligand type).

The reactivity of copper active sites play critical roles in heterogeneous, homogeneous and enzymatic catalysis. In heterogeneous catalysis, the conversion of synthesis gas to methanol at low temperature and pressure is achieved through a copper-promoted ZnO catalyst. This catalyst is also used commercially in the water gas shift reaction. In addition, cuprous oxide has been found to be an effective selective oxidation catalyst which uses dioxygen to oxidize propylene, apparently through a π-allyl intermediate. Little is known about the oxidation state, ligation or geometry of any of these surface copper active sites. Even less is known on a molecular level about the copper chloride catalyst systems involved in the apparently homogeneous oxidation of organic molecules with dioxygen. At this point, the most well defined active sites are those found in copper proteins. High resolution crystal structures are now available for Cu-Zn superoxide dismutase and the Blue Copper proteins, and structures are underway on hemocyanin, ascorbate oxidase, and ceruloplasmin. For hemocyanin, tyrosinase and laccase, chemical and spectroscopic studies have led to the generation of spectroscopically effective models for their active sites; hemocyanin and tyrosinase containing a binuclear copper unit involved in reversible oxygen binding and oxygenation, and laccase a trinuclear copper site which appears to be important in the irreversible reduction of dioxygen to water.

It is clear from the contributions to these volumes and from the proceedings of the "Albany Meeting" which are the basis for this series, that the areas of copper coordination chemistry including spectroscopy, synthesis and catalysis, have come together and are providing fundamental geometric and electronic structural insight into these active sites on a molecular level. The first volume of this set includes physical inorganic studies on protein active sites and parallel studies on small molecule high-symmetry complexes which serve as electronic structural analogues. The second volume focuses on the synthesis and characterization of structurally defined copper complexes which model specific features of the active site and allow one to systematically investigate structural contributions to reactivity. As is demonstrated by the depth and quality of the papers in this collection, much attention is now focused toward active sites in copper proteins and structure-function correlations are rapidly developing. These should encourage parallel molecular level studies of copper coordination chemistry related to the less well defined active sites in heterogeneous and homogeneous catalytic systems in the near future.

Edward I. Solomon
Stanford University
November, 1985

CONTENTS

Volume I

Medicinal Copper Chemistry

Physical Characteristics of Copper Compounds

CONTENTS

Volume II

Dioxygen Chemistry and Catalysis

Coordination Chemistry; Protein Models

Biological & Inorganic Copper Chemistry,
ISBN 0-940030-11-X, Eds., K. D. Karlin & J. Zubieta, Adenine Press, ©Adenine Press, 1985

The Blue Copper Binding Site:
From the Rack or Tailor-Made?

David R. McMillin and Helen R. Engeseth
Department of Chemistry
Purdue University
West Lafayette, Indiana 47907

Abstract

A commonly held view is that the protein conformation dictates a strained geometry for Cu(II) in blue copper proteins so as to foster high electrode potentials and facile electron transfer. Taking a somewhat different point of view, we suggest that the structure of the blue copper site ought to be well adapted for binding copper in order to promote the specific uptake of copper. If this is true, the binding site of stellacyanin should be similar to those of azurin and plastocyanin since the small blue proteins have probably evolved from a common ancestor. Recent results are consistent with this expectation. The disulfide linkage of stellacyanin has been reassigned, and Cys-87, which is homologous with the cysteine ligands of azurin and plastocyanin, is available to bind copper. ^{113}Cd NMR studies have confirmed the fact that the metal binding sites of azurin and stellacyanin are very similar, but they do not allow us to identify the fourth ligand of stellacyanin unequivocally. There is, however, considerable indirect evidence implicating a disulfide donor which is, in the electronic sense, analogous to methionine sulfur. Studies of the denaturation of native azurin, apoazurin and metal-substituted derivatives of azurin indicate that, compared with most other metal ions, Cu(II) binds quite strongly to the protein. The ligand field stabilization energy seems to be an important factor in determining the affinity for first row transition metal ions, and the deviation from tetrahedral symmetry appears to bias the site toward copper binding.

Introduction

The type 1, or blue, copper site occurs in a number of proteins which have been a source of continuing interest to coordination chemists and biochemists alike. By comparison with ordinary copper complexes, blue copper centers exhibit some unusual properties, the most distinctive of which is an intense visible absorbance in the region of 615 nm ($\epsilon \approx 4500\ M^{-1}cm^{-1}$). This absorption is responsible for the intense coloration and has now been convincingly assigned to sulfur-to-copper charge-transfer (1-3). Another spectroscopic signature is found in the so-called parallel region of the epr spectrum where the hyperfine splitting from the copper nucleus is unusually narrow (4). The reason(s) for the reduced hyperfine splitting is (are) still being debated (5,6). The sites are also remarkable in that they exhibit a very stable Cu(II)−thiolate linkage; small molecule complexes of thiolates with Cu(II) tend to be unstable with respect to disulfide formation (7,8). Other notable properties of blue copper sites are 1) the fact that their reduction potentials are relatively positive (3) and 2) the evidence from EXAFS studies which suggests that the effective coordination number of the Cu(II) forms may be as low as three (9,10).

The electron is the only known substrate of the blue copper sites, and the small blue copper proteins are generally thought to function as electron transferases. This role is rather well established for plastocyanin which forms part of the photosynthetic apparatus (11). Azurin appears to function in the electron transport system of certain bacteria which are cultured anaerobically (12). Its physiological partners may include a cytochrome and a nitrite reductase (12,13). Blue copper sites are also found in enzymes like laccase which contain multiple redox-active metal centers (4). There the role of the blue site is to mediate the flow of electrons during catalysis (14,15).

The molecular structures are available for a plastocyanin (16) and for azurins from two different species (17,18), and they appear to be well suited for an electron-transfer function. The plastocyanin structure is the most refined, and it involves four ligands arranged in a distorted tetrahedral fashion. Two imidazole nitrogens and cysteine sulfur are found 2.0-2.1 Å removed from the Cu(II). A methionine sulfur is bound at a significantly longer distance, 2.9 Å (16). At the higher pH values, the coordination environment is very similar in the reduced form (19). In the azurin structures a similar ligand arrangement is found except that a fifth electron donor, a peptide oxygen, may be close enough to interact with the copper (17,18). If the interaction proves to be significant, the copper environment might better be described as a distorted trigonal bipyramid.

Understanding the functional significance of structure in blue copper proteins is a difficult and largely unsolved problem. This insight can come only from reactivity studies and through comparisons with other systems, not from knowledge of atom distributions. There are numerous factors to consider, e.g., whether the protein is involved in regulating its own synthesis, how recognition of physiological reaction partners is achieved, etc. In this paper we focus on two specific factors which pertain to the chemistry of the metal binding site.

Structure Considerations and Redox Function

The protein structure surely influences the redox reactivity of the copper center. Some time ago, the concept of a "rack mechanism" was developed to explain how protein conformation could heighten the reactivity of biologically active centers (20), and it has been noted that the same idea can also account for unique spectroscopic properties of metalloenzymes (21). In the case of the blue copper site, a common view is that the protein conformation dictates a strained geometry for Cu(II) (3,21,22). As a consequence these centers exhibit facile outer-sphere electron transfer kinetics (23,24) and relatively positive reduction potentials (3).

Support for the existence of strain in the Cu(II) form is available in the form of ligand field analysis Gray and Malmström have assigned a figure of 70 kJ mol⁻¹ studies of the Ni(II) analogues (3,26) and from the report that the coordination geometry is very similar in the Cu(II) and the Cu(I) forms of plastocyanin (19).

However, the strain effect may not be of overriding importance. It has been pointed out that the reduction potentials of the blue copper sites are not especially high (27). According to a recent analysis of redox potentials, the strain in the blue copper site would typically be ca. 0.3 eV or about 30 kJ mol⁻¹ (7). On the basis of a ligand field analysis Gray and Malmström have assigned a figure of 70 kJ mol⁻¹ (21). It can also be noted that rapid electron transfer has been observed for copper systems where significant structural reorganization is likely to attend the change in oxidation state (28-31).

Structure Considerations and Copper Selection

Another possibility—one which is not easily reconciled with the existence of severe strain in the copper binding—is that the structure of the blue copper site discriminates against other metals and promotes the specific uptake of copper. This function would appear to be an appropriate one because zinc and iron are more abundant than copper in the biological mileau and should compete for the metal binding sites in copper-containing proteins. In principle the selectivity could be based on kinetics or thermodynamics (32). To fix ideas, we will assume that the selectivity is thermodynamically controlled. The current view is that the small blue copper proteins have evolved from a common ancestor (33). If this is true and the blue copper site is highly adapted for the specific uptake of copper, one might expect that each ligand would have a unique role in binding copper and that the residues which serve as ligands would be strictly conserved. There are reports that this is not the case. Although stellacyanin shows considerable homology with azurin and plastocyanin, it has been reported that the ligating cysteine is not conserved (34). Moreover, methionine, one of the copper ligands in azurin and plastocyanin, is not found in stellacyanin (35). However, recent results from our lab suggest the disparity between stellacyanin and the other small blue copper proteins is not as great as it might appear.

Location of the Free Cysteine in Stellacyanin

As can be seen from Figure 1, Cys-87 of stellacyanin corresponds to the cysteine ligand of azurin when the protein sequences are aligned. The same cysteine is implicated when the primary structures of stellacyanin and plastocyanin are compared (33). But, Cys-87 has, along with Cys-93, been reported to be involved in a disulfide bridge (34). The assignment was based on the fact that Cys-59 of denatured apostellacyanin was the residue that combined with a radio-labeled electrophile (34). This seemed peculiar to us since Cys-59 occurs in a region of the sequence which bears little homology with the other blue proteins.

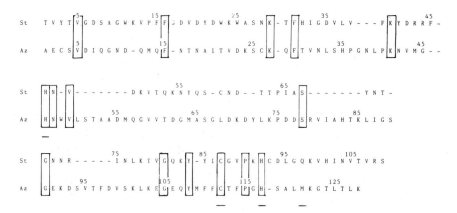

Figure 1. Amino acid sequence comparison of azurin (Az) and stellacyanin (St). Conserved residues are enclosed in rectangles, and the ligands of azurin are underlined. The original references and the one-letter symbols for the amino acids are compiled in the *Atlas of Protein Sequence and Structure,* Ed., M. Dayhoff, National Biomedical Research Foundation, Washington, D. C., Vol. 5, Suppl. 2, pp. 50-65 (1976).

For this reason, we reinvestigated the thiol assignment using a milder procedure and less basic conditions (36). In our analysis we denatured apostellacyanin at pH 7 in the presence of 4-vinylpyridine. After blocking the lysine residues, we exposed the protein to trypsin which cleaved the protein at the Arg-X linkages. Two of the 3 possible fragmentation patterns that could have resulted are shown in Figure 2. Analysis showed that a heavy and a light fragment were obtained, a result which is inconsistent with the presence of a disulfide bridge between Cys-87 and Cys-93. Moreover, the 4-vinylpyridine label was found in position 87. We also found evidence that a disulfide switch occurred when the labeling was carried out at higher pH as in the previous work (34). This possibility might have been anticipated since Cys-87 and Cys-93 are near neighbors in the chain; therefore a bridge between

FRAGMENTATION PATTERNS

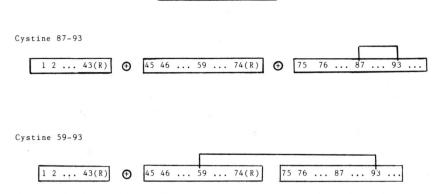

Figure 2. Schematic presentation of two fragmentation patterns. After proteolysis fragments with C-termini Arg-43, Arg-74 and Ser-107 are present. Only in the disulfide 87-93 form do the three fragments migrate independently. The other two possible linkages give rise to a heavy and a light fragment.

these residues is likely to be statistically favored in the unfolded protein. We conclude that the ligating cysteine is, in fact, Cys-87.

The Fourth Ligand of Stellacyanin

Even with the revised disulfide assignment, stellacyanin is still anomalous in that it does not contain methionine. Three of the copper ligands in stellacyanin have been identified. ^{1}H NMR spectroscopy has implicated two histidine residues (37), and the visible absorbance implicates a thiolate donor from cysteine (2,3). Thus it might be argued that the key ligands of the blue copper site are present in stellacyanin. The significance of the fourth ligand in plastocyanin is in doubt since the X-ray structure shows the internuclear distance to be quite long, ca. 2.9 Å (16,19). Moreover, the methionine sulfur has little impact in the EXAFS spectrum even when an oriented crystalline sample is used (10). On the other hand, the methionine group does influence the ligand field spectrum (3,25).

In part with the aim of learning more about the metal environment in stellacyanin, we have prepared the cadmium derivatives of several small blue copper proteins and measured their [113]Cd NMR spectra (38). The ionic radii presented in Table I show that the Cd(II) ion is only slightly larger than Cu(I) or Cu(II). This, coupled

Table I
Radii of Four-Coordinate Ions

Ion	Shannon/Prewitt pm	Pauling pm
Cu(II)	71	
Cu(I)	74	96
Zn(II)	74	74
Cd(II)	92	97
Hg(II)	110	110

with the fact that both Cd(II) and Cu(I) are d^{10} ions, argues that the coordination environment of cadmium in the blue copper site should be representative of at least the Cu(I) forms of the proteins. This is significant because previous studies of the cadmium derivatives of various zinc proteins have shown the [113]Cd chemical shift to be a sensitive probe of the ligand environment (39). In particular the chemical shift depends on the number, type and distribution of bound donor atoms. Table II contains the [113]Cd chemical shifts of the cadmium derivatives of several blue copper proteins and selected zinc proteins where the coordination geometry is roughly tetrahedral in each case. It can be seen that replacing an oxygen or nitrogen donor by a thiolate sulfur gives rise to a characteristic downfield shift, and that the chemical shifts of the copper proteins are completely consistent with the presence of a single thiolate ligand. This finding and several other observations support the hypothesis that the cadmium binds at the blue copper site (38). The chemical shift difference of ca. 50 ppm between the plastocyanin and azurin derivatives is perhaps surprising

Table II
Chemical Shifts of Selected ^{113}Cd-Substituted Proteins

Protein	Donor Set[a]	σ^b vs $Cd_{(aq)}^{2+}$ ppm
Superoxide dismutase	N_3O	311
Pseudomonas azurin	N_2SS*	372
Alcaligenes azurin	N_2SS*	379
Stellacyanin	$N_2SS*(?)$	380
Spinacea plastocyanin	N_2SS*	432
Alcohol dehydrogenase plus imidazole	N_2S_2	519
Alcohol dehydrogenase, structural site	S_4	751

[a]N, imidazole nitrogen; O, oxygen; S, thiolate sulfur; S*, neutral sulfur (thioether or disulfide?)
[b]Ref. 38 and references therein.

in view of the similar coordination geometries which have been deduced from X-ray data. More important for the present purposes is the fact that the chemical shifts of the azurin and stellacyanin derivatives correspond so closely. Even if the bond is quite long, the fourth ligand ought to have some influence on the ^{113}Cd resononace. Thus, whatever the nature of the fourth ligand, it has the same effect on the ^{113}Cd chemical shift as methionine sulfur. This would be most easily explained if it is an electronically similar donor, presumably a disulfide sulfur. We have previously argued that an electronically similar donor is required to account for the charge-transfer band at 572 nm in the absorption spectrum of stellacyanin (2). Finally, the proximity of cysteine and cystine ligands in the metal binding site would promote the disulfide switching which is so facile in the apoprotein at higher pH's.

Strain Effect on Cu(II) Binding

The results discussed thus far are consistent with the hypothesis that the blue copper site is specifically adapted for high affinity binding of copper. To test the idea further, we require quantitative data regarding the relative binding energies of different metal ions in the blue copper site. Unfortunately, directly determining the binding constants is difficult for kinetic reasons. However, since the metal tends to stabilize the folded structure of the protein, an indication of the binding energy can be obtained from studies of thermally induced denaturation using microcalorimetry (40,41).

The thermally induced denaturation of a globular protein is normally a cooperative, endothermic process which occurs at a characteristic temperature. In Figure 3A the denaturation of native azurin (*Pseudomonas aeruginosa*) is shown schematically as it is monitored by differential scanning calorimetry. The area under the deflection is the heat absorbed upon denaturation. Although it reflects the binding energy between copper and the apoprotein, the measured enthalpy is in reality a composite quantity since we do not know whether complete dissociation of the metal occurs upon denaturation nor to what extent other processes like hydrolysis of the metal

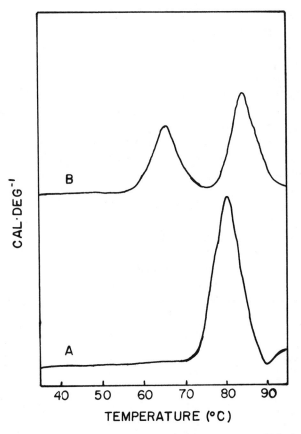

Figure 3. Calorimetric scans of native azurin (A) and apoazurin (B) in pH 8 phosphate buffer. The heating rate was 1°C per minute. After the denaturation transition, native azurin exhibits an exothermic process, presumably due to some type of precipitation phenomenon.

ion occur. A further complication is the fact that the denaturation of azurin is an irreversible process. Nevertheless, so long as the contributions from these effects are not too different from metal to metal, the heats of denaturation should vary as the binding energies.

To this end we have studied the denaturation of various derivatives of *Pseudomonas* azurin. In view of the modest size of the protein, the calorimetric scans are surprisingly complex. Figure 3B depicts a scan of apoazurin which exhibits two transitions. As metal is titrated into the apoprotein, the two transitions suffer a parallel loss of intensity. The midpoint temperature of the first transition decreases as the pH is raised from 6 to 9, while the other transition is virtually independent of pH over the same range. Since 3 of the 4 histidines of azurin are found near the binding site, this may suggest the first transition involves structure around the metal binding site. According to CD results, much of the beta sheet structure remains after heating through the first transition, suggesting that the higher temperature transition may involve the breakdown of this part of the structure. Indications are that sequential, irreversible melting phenomena occur in the apoprotein. Only one transition is resolved when Cu(II) is bound, and it occurs at an intermediate temperature (Figure 3A). The pH dependence of this transition parallels that which is observed for the low temperature transition of apoazurin. Therefore, the two processes are either cooperative or else nearly simultaneous in the native protein. When Ni(II) is bound, two transitions are cleanly resolved; in the case of Co(II) the transitions have almost merged into one. The Hg(II) derivative, like the Cu(II) form, gives only one transition. The pertinent results are summarized in Table 3. The important point to note is that the heat required to denature the metalated protein in excess of that required for the apoprotein (ΔH_d^{excess}) is substantial for the Cu(II) protein. In Figure 4 we show how ΔH_d^{excess} is predicted to vary among the Co(II), Ni(II) and Cu(II) derivatives assuming the differences in stability are due solely to the particular

Table III
Calorimetry of Azurin Derivatives[a]

System	ΔH_d cal g^{-1}	T_d °C	ΔH_d^{excess} kJ mol^{-1}
Hg(II)Az	24(2)	90(2)	700
Cu(II)Az	≳21	80(2)	≳550
Co(II)Az	21(2)	82(2)	550
Ni(II)Az	6(1)	75(2)	90
	10(1)	90(2)	150
Apoazurin	5(1)	63(2)	—
	7(1)	89(2)	—

[a]20 mM phosphate buffer, pH 8.0.

changes in ligand field stabilization energy associated with a transformation from idealized tetrahedral to octahedral coordination geometry. The model roughly accounts for the experimental results, but the Cu(II) derivative is anomalously stable. This suggests that the coordination environment of azurin deviates from tetrahedral symmetry in a way that is specifically suited to Cu(II). This could be due to the type of ligands present and/or their spatial distribution.

Conclusions

Several comments are in order regarding the properties of the blue copper sites. First there is good evidence that the copper binding site of stellacyanin is closely related to that of azurin. Although the identity of the fourth ligand in stellacyanin has not been firmly established, a disulfide sulfur is a likely possibility. Second, in light of the donor makeup the reduction potential of the blue copper site is not particularly high, strain effects being responsible for a modest elevation of the

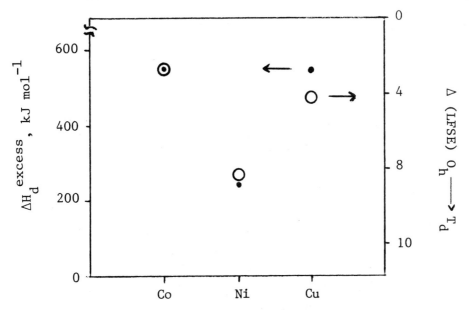

Figure 4. Correlation between ΔH_d^{excess} (•) and the ligand field stabilization energies (○). Δ(LFSE), the change in the ligand field stabilization energy in units of Dq, is calculated for the transition from a tetrahedral to an octahedral coordination environment and is a favorable process for all three metals. Dq is assumed to be the same for all three metals, and the zero of the right hand ordinate has been arbirtrarily adjusted so that the correct ΔH_d^{excess} is obtained for Co(II)Az after correcting for the change in ligand field stabilization energy.

potential (7,27). Third, while the structure of the blue copper site is well adapted for facile electron transfer, other geometries, even quite tetragonal ones, are also compatible with rapid electron transfer reactivity (28,29). Fourth, the fact that a range of metal ions can be taken up, each with distinct steric preferences, suggests that the coordination environment is capable of some structural reorganization. It is worth remembering in this context that Cu(II) complexes are frequently characterized by multiple configurations which have similar energies and which interconvert at ambient temperature. The same may be true of the blue copper site. Fifth, the calorimetry studies suggest that Cu(II) is bound very firmly in azurin; any strain which is present is clearly not an overriding factor in determining the binding affinity. Finally, it must be remembered that excessive levels of copper are harmful to cells, and as a result the concentration of free copper is quite low in biological fluids. In all probability the makeup of the blue copper site reflects a balance among: 1) the need for the appropriate reduction potential, 2) the need for facile electron transfer reactivity and 3) the need for a ligand environment with a high affinity for copper.

Acknowledgement

This work was supported by National Institutes of Health Grant GM 22764. The authors are grateful to Phillip S. Low for the use of his calorimeter.

McMillin, et. al.

References and Footnotes

1. D. R. McMillin, R. C. Rosenberg and H. B. Gray, *Proc. Natl. Acad Sci. U. S. A. 71*, 4760-4762 (1974).
2. D. R. McMillin and M. C. Morris, *Proc. Natl. Acad. Sci. U. S. A. 78*, 6567-6570 (1981).
3. H.B. Gray and E. I. Solomon in *Copper Proteins*, Ed., T. G. Spiro, John Wiley and Sons, New York, Vol. 3, pp. 1-39 (1981).
4. J. A. Fee, *Struct. Bonding 23*, 1-60 (1975).
5. A. S. Brill, *Mol. Biol., Biochem. and Biophys. 26*, 40 (1977).
6. A. Bencini and D. Gatteschi, *J. Am. Chem. Soc. 105*, 5535-5541 (1983).
7. A. W. Addison, T. N. Rao and E. Sinn, *Inorg. Chem. 23*, 1957-1967 (1984).
8. J. M. Downes, J. Whelan and B. Bosnich, *Inorg. Chem. 20*, 1081-1086 (1981).
9. L. Powers, *Biochim. Biophys. Acta 683*, 1-38 (1982).
10. R. A. Scott, J. E. Hahn, S. Doniach, H. C. Freeman and K. O. Hodgson, *J. Am. Chem. Soc. 104*, 5364-5369 (1982).
11. J. Anderson, *Mol. Cell. Biochem. 46*, 161-172, (1982).
12. M. C. Silvestrini, M. Brunori, M. T. Wilson and V. M. Darley-Usmar, *J. Inorg. Biochem. 14*, 327-338 (1981).
13. O. Farver, J. Blatt and I. Pecht, *Biochemistry 21*, 3556-3561 (1982).
14. L.-E. Andréasson and B. Reinhammar, *Biochim. Biophys. Acta 568*, 145-156 (1979).
15. F. B. Hansen, R. W. Noble and M. J. Ettinger, *Biochemistry 23*, 2049-2056 (1984).
16. J. M. Guss and H. C. Freeman, *J. Mol. Biol. 169*, 521-563 (1983).
17. E. T. Adman and L. H. Jensen, *Isr. J. Chem. 21*, 8-12 (1981).
18. G. E. Norris, B. F. Anderson and E. N. Baker, *J. Mol. Biol. 165*, 501-521 (1983).
19. H. C. Freeman in *Coordination Chemistry*, Ed., J. P. Laurent, Proceedings of the Twenty-first International Conference on Coordination Chemistry, Pergamon Press, New York, Vol. 21, pp. 29-51 (1981).
20. R. Lumry and H. Eyring, *J. Phys. Chem. 58*, 110-120 (1954).
21. H. B. Gray and B. G. Malmström, *Comments Inorg. Chem. 2*, 203-209 (1983).
22. R. J. P. Williams, *Inorg. Chim. Acta 5*, 137-155 (1971).
23. O. Farver and I. Pecht, *Met. Ions Biol. Syst. 3*, 151-192 (1981).
24. R. A. Holwerda, S. Wherland and H. B. Gray, *Annu. Rev. Biophys. Bioeng. 5*, 363-396 (1976).
25. E. I. Solomon, J. W. Hare, D. M. Dooley, J. H. Dawson, P. J. Stephens and H. B. Gray, *J. Am. Chem. Soc. 102*, 168-178 (1980).
26. H. R. Engeseth, D. R. McMillin and E. L. Ulrich, *Inorg. Chim. Acta 67*, 145-149 (1982).
27. K. D. Karlin and J. K. Yandell, *Inorg. Chem. 23*, 1184-1188 (1984).
28. E. J. Pulliam and D. R. McMillin, *Inorg. Chem. 23*, 1172-1175 (1984).
29. B. Reinhammar, *Adv. Inorg. Biochem. 1*, 91-118, (1979).
30. D. B. Rorabacher, M. J. Martin, M. J. Koenigbauer, M. Malik, R. R. Schroeder, J. F. Endicott and L. A. Ochrymowycz in *Copper Coordination Chemistry: Biochemical and Inorganic Perspectives*, Eds., K. D. Karlin, J. Zubieta, Adenine Press, Guilderland, NY, pp.167-202 (1983).
31. J. K. Yandell in *Copper Coordination Chemistry: Biochemical and Inorganic Perspectives*, Eds., K. D. Karlin, J. Zubieta, Adenine Press, Guilderland, NY, pp. 157-166 (1983).
32. J. A. Blaszak, D. R. McMillin, A. T. Thornton and D. L. Tennent, *J. Biol. Chem. 258*, 9886-9892 (1983).
33. L. Ryden and J.-O. Lundgren, *Biochemie 61*, 781-790 (1979).
34. C. Bergman, E.-K. Gandvik, P. O. Nyman and I. Strid, *Biochem. Biophys. Res. Commun. 77*, 1052-1059 (1977).
35. J. Peisach, W. G. Levine and W. E. Blumberg, *J. Biol. Chem. 242*, 2847-2858 (1967).
36. H. R. Engeseth, M. A. Hermodson and D. R. McMillin, *FEBS Lett. 171*, 257-261 (1984).
37. H. A. O. Hill and W. K. Lee, *J. Inorg. Biochem. 11*, 101-113 (1979).
38. H. R. Engeseth, D. R. McMillin and J. D. Otvos, *J. Biol. Chem. 259*, 4822-4826 (1984).
39. I. M. Armitage, and J. D. Otvos in *Biological Magnetic Resonance*, Eds., L. J. Berliner and J. Reuben, Plenum Press, New York, Vol. 4 pp. 79-144 (1983).
40. C. H. Roberts and J. F. Chlebowski, *J. Biol. Chem. 259*, 3625-3632 (1984).
41. J. F. Chlebowski and S. Mabrey, *J. Biol. Chem. 252*, 7042-7052 (1977).

Biological & Inorganic Copper Chemistry,
ISBN 0-940030-11-X, Eds., K. D. Karlin & J. Zubieta, Adenine Press, ©Adenine Press, 1985

Active Site Protonations of Blue Copper Proteins

J. McGinnis, J.D. Sinclair-Day and A.G. Sykes*

Department of Inorganic Chemistry, The University
Newcastle upon Tyne, NE1 7RU, England

Abstract

Reactivities of single blue (Type 1) copper proteins, including three different plastocyanins, azurin, stellacyanin, umecyanin and rusticyanin are considered. Whereas the plastocyanins (from parsley, spinach and the blue-green algae *Anabaena variabilis*) in the Cu(I) state exhibit protonation, with a switch-off in reactivity established as a change in coordination from $4 \Rightarrow 3$, none of the other proteins exhibit this same behavior. A comparison is made of acid dissociation pK_a values for the (protonated) plastocyanins obtained by nmr and kinetic studies. Umecyanin in the Cu(II) state exhibits a shift in peak position from 610 to 580nm as the pH changes from 8.2 to 10.8 (pK_a 9.5), which clearly reflects some change at or near the active site. The higher $E°$ for rusticyanin of 680mV is of further interest in considering active site properties.

Introduction

This paper is concerned with protonation effects which are influential at the active site of blue copper proteins. A range of proteins (1), having diverse functions which relate to the $Cu(I) \rightleftharpoons Cu(II) + e^-$ couple, is considered (Table I). Plastocyanin is

Table I
Properties of blue copper proteins

		M.Wt.	pI	$E°$ (mV)	λ_{max} (nm)	ϵ $(M^{-1}cm^{-1})$
Plastocyanin	(Spinach)[a]	10,500	4.2	370	597	4,500
	(*A. variabilis*)	11,200	>7[b]			
Azurin	(*P. aeruginosa*)	14,000	5.4	330	626	4,800
Stellacyanin	(*R. vernicifera*)	20,000[c]	9.86	184	604	4,080
Umecyanin	(horseradish root)	14,600	5.85	283	610[d]	3,400
Rusticyanin	(*T. ferro-oxidens*)	16,500	9	680[e]	597	1,950

[a]Parsley assumed to have similar values
[b]Is absorbed on CM-cellulose
[c]40% carbohydrate
[d]Shifts to 580nm, pK_a 9.5
[e]pH 2

important as a member of the photosynthetic electron transport chain which functions between photosystems II and I. Reactions of plastocyanin from two higher plants (parsley and spinach), are compared with those of plastocyanin from the prokaryotic blue-green alga *Anabaena variabilis* (2), the composition of which results in this protein having a positive charge at pH 7. Azurin is known to have an electron transport function in bacterial *Pseudomonas aeruginosa*. Similarly stellacyanin (tree sap of *Rhus vernicifera*), umecyanin (horse-radish roots) and rusticyanin (from *Thiobacillus ferro-oxidans*) are believed to be involved in redox processes (1). Oxidation states of the different proteins are referred to in an abbreviated form (using initials) e.g. UCu(I) and UCu(II) for umecyanin.

The proteins all have characteristic visible spectra with a prominent band at ~600nm, Figures 1 and 2. Absorption coefficients (ϵ) for the 600nm peak (Table I), are much higher than is normally observed for ligand-field bands, and are associated with a cysteinyl S$\Rightarrow$Cu charge-transfer process. Additional less intense bands have been identified either side of the principal band (1), (3). The proteins also have characteristic esr spectra with unusually low $A_{||}$ values (1). These spectroscopic properties have so far proved difficult to mimic in model compounds.

Guss and Freeman have determined the x-ray crystal structure of plastocyanin from poplar leaves to 1.6Å resolution (4). They report a distorted tetrahedral coordination of the Cu(II) to two histidines (His37 and 87), a cysteine (Cys84), and methionine (Met92). At pH >7 the Cu(I) state has a virtually identical structure (5)

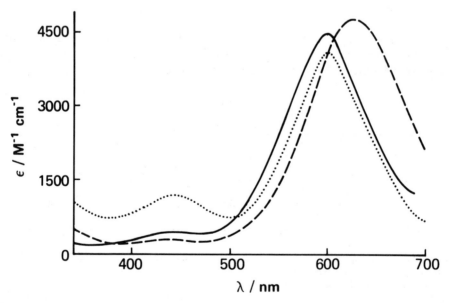

Figure 1. A comparison of u.v.-visible spectra of plastocyanin, PCu(II) (——); azurin, ACu(II) (-------); and stellacyanin SCu(II) (········).

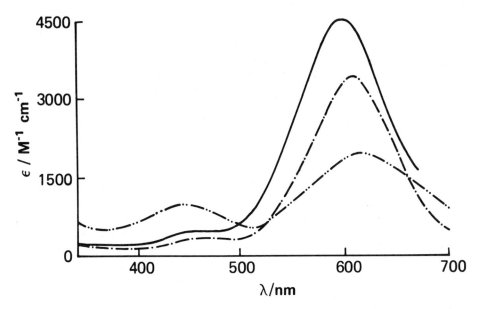

Figure 2. A comparison of u.v.-visible spectra of plastocyanin PCu(II) (——); umecyanin, UCu(II) (·-·-·-·); and rusticyanin RCu(II) (········)

making possible efficient electron transfer with minimal reorganisation requirements. At lower pH's however, protonation occurs and the Cu−N (His87) bond lengthens to 3.4Å, which is sufficient to allow the insertion of a proton (5), Figure 3. At pH 7 the long Cu−S (methionine) bond of 2.9Å for both the Cu(I) and Cu(II) forms is an unusual feature. The protonation results in the Cu moving in plane with the three remaining ligands. The change in coordination number leads to a stabilisation of the Cu(I) state, since 3-coordination is not normally encountered with Cu(II). Crystallographic (6) and exafs (7) information is also available for azurin from *Pseudomonas aeruginosa* (resolution 2.7Å). and *Alcaligenes denitrificans* (2.5Å). The effect of protonation was first observed in kinetic studies on the oxidation of parsley PCu(I) with $[Fe(CN)_6]^{3-}$ and $[Co(phen)_3]^{3+}$ (8). For these two oxidants the

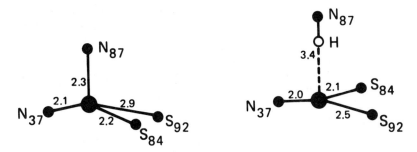

Figure 3. The active site of plastocyanin PCu(I) at pH >7 (left) and pH <4.5 (right), (5).

switch-off in redox reactivity gave pK_a's of 5.7 and 6.1 respectively. In addition a pK_a of 5.7 was reported for the oxidation of spinach PCu(I) with $[Co(phen)_3]^{3+}$. It has been puzzling that these pK_a's in the 5.7-6.1 range were not in line with the pK_a of 4.9 determined by proton nmr for spinach PCu(I) (9). Also of concern was the observation that, with $[Co(4,7\text{-}DPSphen)_3]^{3-}$ as oxidant, no similar variations in rate constants consistent with active site protonation were detected down to pH 5.1 (10). These and other related effects are now considered.

Methods and Materials

Proteins were isolated by methods previously described, and purified to literature absorption peak ratios. The plastocyanin used was obtained from parsley and spinach leaves (8), and also from the blue-green alga *Anabaena variabilis* (2), which was grown by a procedure described (2). Azurin was isolated from *Pseudomonas aeruginosa* (CAMR Microbial Products, Porton) (11), stellacyanin from an acetone powder (Saito & Co., Tokyo) from *Rhus vernicifera* (12). We are most grateful to Professor K.-G. Paul (Umea, Sweden) for the umecyanin from horseradish roots (13), and Dr. W.J. Ingledew (St. Andrews, U.K.) for rusticyanin obtained from *Thiobacillus ferro-oxidans* (14). Proteins were reduced by addition of an excess of dithionite (parsley and spinach plastocyanin) or ascorbate, followed by dialysis.

Commercial potassium ferricyanide $K_3[Fe(CN)_6]$ (BDH, Analar) was used without further purification. Other complexes, together with details of absorption peaks λ/nm $(\epsilon/M^{-1}cm^{-1})$ used for characterisation purposes were: tris(1,10-phenanthroline)cobalt(III) chloride, $[Co(phen)_3]Cl_3\cdot7H_2O$, peak positions 330(4660), 350(3620), 450(100) (15); potassium tris(oxalato)cobaltate(III), $K_3[Co(C_2O_4)_3]3.5H_2O$, 245(2.2×10^4), 420(221), 596(167) (12), (16); potassium 1,2-diaminocyclohexanetetra-acetatomanganate(III), $K[Mn(CyDTA)H_2O]$, 510(345) (17); sodium tris [(4,7-diphenylsulphonate)1,10-phenanthroline]cobaltate(III), $Na_3[Co(4,7\text{-}DPSphen)_3]$, 293($1.2\times10^5$) (10), (18).

Buffers at concentrations $(1\text{-}2)\times10^{-2}M$ were made up as in previous work from this laboratory (10-12). Reactant solutions were adjusted to an ionic strength $I = 0.10M$ with NaCl. The pH (and ionic strength) of reactant solutions were adjusted prior to mixing. Runs at pH <5 were in some cases studied by the pH-jump method (8). Kinetic runs, all at 25.0°C, were monitored on a Dionex D-110 stopped-flow spectrophotometer, with the inorganic reagent always in $\geq$10-fold excess, and substantially more ($\geq10^2$-fold excess) for the *A. variabilis* PCu(I) to ensure complete reaction. Simple rate laws first-order in oxidant and reductant were shown to apply in all cases. With $[Co(phen)_3]^{3+}$ as oxidant for parsley and spinach PCu(I) concentrations adopted were such that limiting kinetics did not apply. Experimentally determined first-order rate constants (k_{obs}) were converted to second-order constants (k). Variations of rate constants with pH were fitted to equation (1)

$$\frac{k_{obs}}{[\text{oxidant}]} = \frac{k[H^+]}{K_a + [H^+]} \qquad (1)$$

which can be derived from the reaction scheme (2-3) involving protein (P) and complex (C) as previously discussed (8).

$$HP^+ \overset{K_a}{\rightleftharpoons} H^+ + P \qquad (2)$$

$$P + C \overset{k}{\Rightarrow} products \qquad (3)$$

In equation (1) k is the rate constant at pH 7.5.

Results

Oxidation of PCu(I)

Rate constants for the oxidation of parsley plastocyanin PCu(I) with $[Fe(CN)_6]^{3-}$ at pH's in the range 4.7-8.1, $I = 0.10M$, gave a pK_a of 5.5±0.1 in satisfactory agreement with the previously determined value of 5.7 (8). The nmr pK_a of 4.9 was determined using a solution 0.1M in phosphate (9). Unfortunately there is no in-

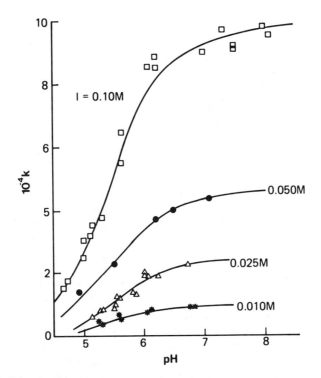

Figure 4. The effect of pH and ionic strength on second-order rate constants for the $[Fe(CN)_6]^{3-}$ oxidation of parsley PCu(I) at 25°C. Buffers used acetate pH ≤5.3; Mes pH 5.2-6.8; Tris/maleate, pH 5.2-8.0; Tris/HCl, pH 7.2-8.0.

dication as to whether the ionic strength for this study was maintained at a constant value. Possible contributions from ionic strength variations were tested for by determining pK_a values with $[Fe(CN)_6]^{3-}$ as oxidant at three additional ionic strengths, Figure 4. The pK_a values obtained (ionic strength M in brackets) were $5.6\pm0.1(0.05)$, $5.5\pm0.2(0.025)$, and $5.5\pm0.3(0.010)$, indicating no significant trend with I.

Studies of the effect of pH on rate constants for the $[Co(4,7\text{-DPSphen})_3]^{3-}$ oxidation of parsley PCu(I) were extended down to pH 4.7. As can be seen from Figure 5, rate constants do eventually decrease to a small value (probably zero). However, the decrease is much sharper than in other cases and does not conform to the simple $[H^+]$ dependence as in (1).

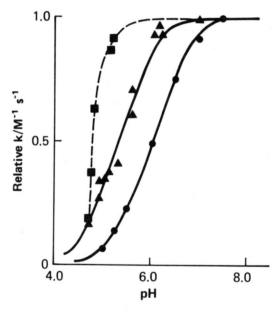

Figure 5. Showing the variation of rate constants (on a scale relative to rate constants at pH 7.5) with pH for the $[Co(phen)_3]^{3+}$ (●), $[Fe(CN)_6]^{3-}$ (▲) and $[Co(4,7\text{-DPSphen})_3]^{3+}$ (■), oxidation of parsley PCu(I) at 25°C, I = 0.10M (NaCl). Buffers used as in caption to Figure 4.

The same procedure was used to determine other pK_a's first with spinach PCu(I) and $[Fe(CN)_6]^{3-}$ (pK_a 4.9 ± 0.1), which complemented the earlier study with $[Co(phen)_3]^{3+}$ as oxidant (pK_a 5.7), Figure 6 (8). With PCu(I) from *Anabaena variabilis* a pK_a of 4.8 ± 0.1 was obtained with $[Fe(CN)_6]^{3-}$, and 5.5 ± 0.1 with $[Co(phen)_3]^{3+}$ as oxidant. A pK_a of 5.1 from proton nmr studies has been reported by Kojiro and Markley (19). Also relevant are the studies of Wright and King (14), who have determined pK_a's for French bean PCu(I) using both the kinetic method with $[Fe(CN)_6]^{3-}$ and $[Co(phen)_3]^{3+}$ as oxidants, and the nmr method. All these results are summarised in Table II.

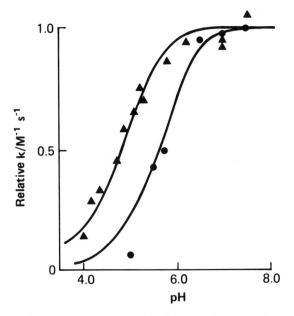

Figure 6. The variation of relative rate constants with pH for the $[Co(phen)_3]^{3+}$ (●) and $[Fe(CN)_6]^{3-}$ (▲) oxidation of spinach PCu(I) at 25°C, I = 0.10M (NaCl). Buffers used acetate, pH 4.0-5.5; Mes, pH 5.2-6.8; Tris/HCl 7.2-8.0.

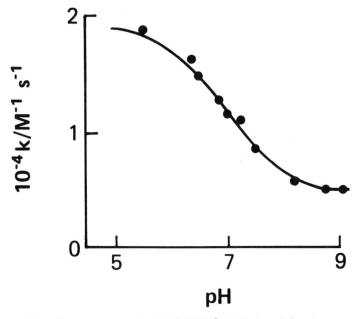

Figure 7. The variation of rate constants for the $[Fe(CN)_6]^{3-}$ oxidation of *Pseudomonas aeruginosa* azurin, ACu(I), with pH (10) at 25°C, I = 0.10M (NaCl).

Oxidation of Other Cu Proteins

Effects of pH on rate constants for the oxidations of azurin ACu(I) by $[Fe(CN)_6]^{3-}$ (Figure 7) (11), of SCu(I) and UCu(I) with $[Co(C_2O_4)_3]^{3-}$, (Figure 8) (12), (23), and RCu(I) with $[Mn(CyDTA)(H_2O)]^-$ (Figure 9) (21), have now been completed. The

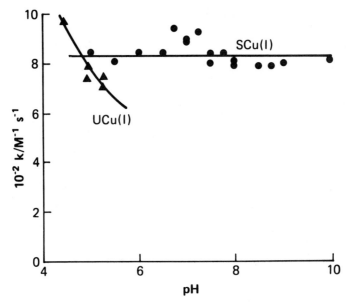

Figure 8. The variation of rate constants for the $[Co(C_2O_4)_3]^{3-}$ oxidations of *Rhus vernicifera* stellacyanin, SCu(I), (●) (12), and horseradish umecyanin, (▲) UCu(I), with pH at 25°, I = 0.10M (NaCl). Acetate buffer used in the UCu(I) study.

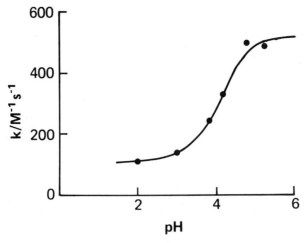

Figure 9. The variation of rate constants for the $[Mn(CyDTA)(H_2O)]^-$ oxidation of RCu(I) with pH at 25°C, I = 0.10M (NaCl). Runs at pH ≥3 were buffered using potassium hydrogen phthalate, pH 2.2-3.8; acetate, pH 3.8-5.5.

behaviour is in each case low key compared to that of PCu(I), and the trend observed characteristic of each individual protein. With RCu(I) we note that significant reactivity is retained at pH ≤ 2.

Effects of pH on UCu(II)

The peak position of UCu(II) shifts from 610nm at pH 7 ($\epsilon 3300$ $M^{-1}cm^{-1}$) to 580nm at pH 10.7 ($\epsilon 4000$ $M^{-1}cm^{-1}$) consistent with earlier observations (22). Changes are reversible (Figure 10), providing an excess of $[Fe(CN)_6]^{3-}$ ($\sim 5 \times 10^{-4}M$) is present to ensure that there is no autoreduction, and give a pK_a of 9.46 ± 0.04. Interconversions were found to be complete within mixing time ($\sim$ms) on the stopped-flow (23).

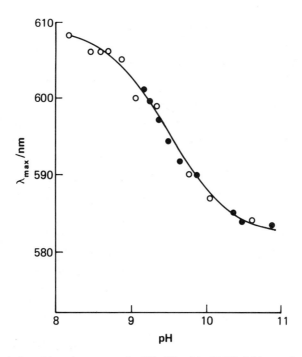

Figure 10. The variation of λ_{max} for umecyanin, UCu(II), with pH (12mM borate buffer) at I = 1.10M (NaCl) in the presence of an excess of $[Fe(CN)_6]^{3-}$ ($\sim 5 \times 10^{-4}M$) to ensure that the protein remains in the Cu(II) state. Points (O) for increasing and (X) for decreasing pH.

Discussion

The simplest protonations to envisage are those occurring at or near the active site, or those occurring near to the binding site on the protein surface. The pattern of pK_a's for parsley PCu(I) with $[Fe(CN)_6]^{3-}$ and $[Co(phen)_3]^{3+}$ as oxidants (8) has

Table II

A comparison of (acid dissociation) pK_a's for plastocyanins from different sources as determined by nmr and kinetic studies with $[Fe(CN)_6]^{3-}$ and $[Co(phen)_3]^{3+}$ respectively as oxidants.

pK_a's for plastocyanins

Plastocyanin	nmr	$[Fe(CN)_6]^{3-}$	$[Co(phen)_3]^{3+}$
Parsley		5.5	6.1
Spinach	4.9	4.9	5.7
French bean	4.85	4.6	5.4
A. variabilis	5.1	4.8	5.5

been confirmed with spinach and *Anabaena variabilis* PCu(I), Table II. Wright and King (20) have also noted similar values for French bean PCu(I). In three cases pK_a's have been determined by the nmr method (9), (19), (20), and these values are seen to be in excellent agreement with those determined by the kinetic method with $[Fe(CN)_6]^{3-}$ as oxidant. Crystallographic information obtained by Freeman and colleagues (5) has indicated that this process corresponds to an active site protonation of the PCu(I), with His87 becoming dissociated from the Cu(I) as shown in Figure 3. For each PCu(I) source the pK_a obtained with $[Co(phen)_3]^{3+}$ as oxidant is some 0.6-0.8 higher than the value for $[Fe(CN)_6]^{3-}$. It is not certain just how this effect originates, one possibility being that a secondary protonation is coupled to the active site effect. This could originate from protonation at the negatively charged region on the protein in the vicinity of Tyr83 and the negative patch of four carboxylate residues 42-45, which region incorporates the binding site for positively charged complexes such as $[Co(phen)_3]^{3+}$ (24). We note however that in the case of PCu(I) from *Anabaena variabilis* the protein has a higher pI, and carries an overall positive charge to at least pH 7. From the amino-acid sequence there is no negative patch and only residue 42 remains acidic. The similar responses of all four plastocyanins suggests that if the above explanation holds, protonation of a particular conserved residue is relevant in each case. An alternative explanation might centre around recent evidence (Guss and Freeman, personal communication) that protonated His87 can take up a second position, in addition to that illustrated in Figure 3, by rotation of the histidine through 180° as has been observed for poplar apoplastocyanin (25).

We note that the pK_a's for parsley PCu(I) appear to be higher and out of line with other values in Table II. It would be interesting to determine the pK_a by the nmr method. Should this value be in accord with the $[Fe(CN)_6]^{3-}$ value of 5.5, then a special influence is clearly operative for parsley PCu(I), which shifts the pK_a by some 0.6 compared to spinach and *Anabaena* PCu(I).

The results with $[Co(4,7-DPSphen)_3]^{3-}$ as oxidant for parsley PCu(I) indicate a trend in pK_a opposite to that observed in going from $[Fe(CN)_6]^{3-}$ to $[Co(phen)_3]^{3+}$. The fact that a switch-off in reactivity is observed removes in part the anomaly that existed with this oxidant.

The response of PCu(I) to H^+ and complete switch off in reactivity is a quite remarkable effect. With $[Fe(CN)_6]^{3-}$ for example, rate constants decrease from $\sim 10^5 M^{-1}s^{-1}$ to zero or close to zero. Quite different responses to $[H^+]$ are observed for all the other Cu(I) proteins, Figures 7-9. In the case of the RCu(I) reaction with $[Mn(CyDTA)(H_2O)]^-$ the pH profile observed (Figure 9) probably originates from a protonation of the oxidant. However, the most important feature is that RCu(I) is still reactive (and stable) at pH 2, the pH at which it normally functions. We note that UCu(I) is also stable at pH ~ 4, a pH at which PCu(I) is essentially completely protonated, and parsley plastocyanin is extensively denatured. Because PCu(I) from sources as divergent as higher plants and algae give near identical behavior, it seems likely that the effect observed relates in some way to the requirements of photosynthesis. Since protons as well as electrons are transported within the chloroplast, control of pH is undoubtedly important. The Cu active site in all other proteins considered must somehow or other be protected from protonation. At present there is insufficient structural information for us to speculate as to how this protection originates, and what particular feature is relevant.

The shift in peak position for UCu(II) with change in pH must correspond to a change at or near the active site sufficient to affect the chromophore. It is tempting to think in terms of a change in coordination attendant on the deprotonation. This could be an increase in coordination $4 \Rightarrow 5$, or exchange of an existing ligand. A further possibility is that a residue close to the active site (an amine?) deprotonates and moves sufficiently close to the Cu(II) to distort the coordination sphere. In this context, we note that the change in spectrum is no greater than that observed in going from PCu(II) to ACu(II), Figure 1. Although crystallographic studies have indicated a close structural homology between the metal centres in PCu(II) (4) and ACu(II) (6), (7), it has been noted that a carbonyl O-atom approaches to within 3.2Å (large standard deviation) of the Cu(II) in the latter (6). McMillin and colleagues (26) have suggested from Cd-113 nmr studies on the Cd(II) substituted proteins that azurin may have a slightly modified coordination with respect to plastocyanin. Consistent with the idea that in the case of UCu(II) there is movement of an adjacent group without full coordination, we note that rate constants for the $[Ru(NH_3)_5py]^{2+}$ reduction of UCu(I) decrease by only a factor of 2 on increasing the pH from 7.3 to 10.6. (23)

As already indicated (6) the reduction potential E° for the PCu(II)/PCu(I) couple increases from 360mV as the pH decreases below pH 7. At pH 5 it is 450mV and still increasing as the build-up of 3-coordinate PCu(I) continues. The exceptionally high E° for the RCu(II)/RCu(I) couple of 680mV (26) over the range pH 1-3 raises the interesting question as to whether RCu(I) is less than 4-coordinate. Further information will no doubt be forthcoming on this point.

Acknowledgements

We are grateful to SERC for post-doctoral (J.M.) and post-graduate support (J.D.S.-D).

References and Footnotes

1. For a recent review see A.G. Lappin, *Metal Ions in Biological Systems, 13,* 15 (1981).
2. A. Aitken, *Biochem. J., 149,* 675 (1975).
3. E.I. Solomon, J.W. Hare and H.B. Gray, *Proc. Nat. Acad. Sc. (USA), 73,* 1389 (1976).
4. J.M. Guss and H.C. Freeman, *J. Mol. Biol., 169,* 521 (1983).
5. H.C. Freeman, *Coordination Chemistry—21,* ed. J.L. Laurent, Pergamon Press, Oxford 1981, p. 29-51.
6. G.E. Norris, B.F. Anderson, and E.N. Baker, *J. Mol. Biol., 165,* 501 (1983).
7. T.D. Tullius, P. Frank and K.O. Hodgson, *Proc. Nat. Acad. Sci. (USA), 75,* 4069 (1978).
8. M.G. Segal and A.G. Sykes, *J. Amer. Chem. Soc., 100,* 4585 (1978).
9. J.L. Markley, E.L. Ulrich, S.P. Berg and D.W. Krogmann, *Biochem., 14,* 4428 (1975).
10. A.G. Lappin, M.G. Segal, D.C. Weatherburn and A.G. Sykes, *J. Amer. Chem. Soc., 101,* 2297 (1979).
11. A.G. Lappin, M.G. Segal, D.C. Weatherburn, R.A. Henderson and A.G. Sykes, *J. Amer. Chem. Soc., 105,* 225 (1983).
12. M.J. Sisley, M.G. Segal, C.S. Stanley, I.K. Adzamli and A.G. Sykes, *J. Amer. Chem. Soc., 101,* 2302 (1979).
13. K.-G. Paul and T. Stigbrand, *Biochim. Biophys. Acta, 221,* 255 (1970).
14. J.B. Cobley and B.A. Haddock, *FEBS Lett., 162,* 52 (1983).
15. P. Pfeiffer and B. Werdelmann, *Z. Anorg. Allg. Chem., 263,* 31 (1950).
16. J.C. Bailar and E.M. Jones, *Inorg. Synth., 1,* 37 (1939).
17. R.E. Hamm and M.A. Suwyn, *Inorg. Chem., 6,* 139 (1967) Sample in present work no H_2O's crystallisation.
18. J.V. McArdle, C.L. Coyle, H.B. Gray, G.S. Yoneda and R.A. Holwerda, *J. Amer. Chem. Soc., 99,* 2483 (1977).
19. C.L. Kojiro and J.L. Markley, *FEBS Lett., 162,* 52 (1983).
20. P.E. Wright and G. King, personal communication.
21. J. McGinnis, J. Ingledew and A.G. Skyes, unpublished work.
22. I. Sjoholm and T. Stigbrand, *Biochim. Biophys. Acta, 371,* 408 (1974).
23. S.K. Chapman, C.V. Knox, J. McGinnis, J.D. Sinclair-Day, K.-G. Paul and A.G. Sykes, unpublished work.
24. S.K. Chapman, A.D. Watson and A.G. Sykes, *J. Chem. Soc. Dalton Trans,* 2543 (1983).
25. T.P.J. Garrett, D.J. Clingeteffer, J.M. Guss, S.J. Rogers and H.C. Freeman, *J. Biol. Chem., 259,* 2822 (1984).
26. W.J. Ingledew, *Proc. Soc. Ital. Biochem.,* 84 (1976).

Biological & Inorganic Copper Chemistry
ISBN 0-940030-11-X, Eds., K. D. Karlin & Zubieta, Adenine Press, © Adenine Press, 1985

NMR Studies on Copper(II) Containing Biological Molecules

Ivano Bertini and Claudio Luchinat
Department of Chemistry
University of Florence
Italy

Abstract

We have developed a theoretical treatment for the interpretation of paramagnetic nuclear relaxation in macromolecules. Such treatment includes the effect of the hyperfine coupling tensor of the unpaired electron with the copper $I = 3/2$ nuclear spin and accounts for all the experimental water proton relaxation data on copper(II) proteins. The analysis of the data provides structural information and an estimate of the electronic relaxation time.

In the presence of magnetic coupling with a fast relaxing paramagnetic ion the electronic relaxation times of copper(II) are drastically reduced, allowing the detection of isotropically shifted NMR signals from the copper ligands. By substituting the native zinc(II) ion in superoxide dismutase with high spin cobalt(II) we have provided an enzyme derivative which is successfully monitored in its copper(II) containing active site through ^1H NMR spectroscopy. It is for example shown that a histidine is removed from coordination upon anion binding.

Introduction

Copper(II) is essential to living systems and is present in a variety of biologically relevant macromolecules, most often linked to the presence of specific catalytic activity for a redox process (1,2). Copper(II) is also often substituted in vitro for the native metal ion in metalloproteins (3). All of the above derivatives are investigated through spectroscopic techniques, taking advantage of the electronic properties of the metal ion; electron spin resonance and electonic spectroscopies are widely employed. Furthermore, the paramagnetism of the ion alters the NMR properties of nearby nuclei through unpaired electron-nucleus coupling; this property can be exploited to obtain further information on the structure and dynamics of the systems. In particular, water proton relaxation measurements as a function of magnetic field (NMRD) can give a detailed picture of the hydration of the active site metal ion, provided that the theory of the electron-nucleus interaction is understood. We will give here an account of the specific development of such theory for the case of copper(II) containing macromolecules, with the aim to rationalize the "anomalies" observed in the experimental NMRD data (4), and to discuss how relevant chemical information can be extracted from relaxation measurements. We will also show that magnetic coupling phenomena may turn copper(II) into an NMR shift reagent.

Relevant electronic properties of copper(II) in macromolecules

Copper(II) has a $3d^9$ electronic configuration, which gives rise to a ^2D free-ion ground term. In the low symmetry environments typical of its natural coordination compounds the five-fold orbital degeneracy of such term is completely removed, leaving five Kramer's doublets well spaced in energy. In particular, the separation between the ground doublet and the first excited doublet is always found to be as large as several thousands wavenumbers. Therefore, as far as the electronic properties and the electron-nucleus coupling phenomena are concerned, these can be analyzed entirely in terms of the magnetic properties of the ground state, which is the only appreciably populated state at room temperature. The influence of spin-orbit coupling and of the hyperfine coupling with the metal nucleus can be effectively taken into account with a spin Hamiltonian of the type

$$\hat{H}_o = \mu_B B_o \cdot g \cdot \hat{S} + \hat{I} \cdot A \cdot \hat{S} \tag{1}$$

where I is the ^{63}Cu or ^{65}Cu nuclear spin operator. The two isotopes have both $I=3/2$, and interact practically to the same extent with the electron spin.

Of particular relevance in the analysis of the electron-nucleus coupling is the understanding of the electronic relaxation processes; in fact, the electronic relaxation time τ_s is often the relevant correlation time for the electron-nucleus interaction. Given the electronic configuration of copper(II) in low symmetry environments, relaxation mechanisms of solid state type such as Orbach and Raman processes (5,6), requiring the presence of low-lying excited states, are expected to be relatively ineffective. Among the mechanisms proposed for solutions (7), spin rotational mechanisms decrease in efficiency with increasing rotational correlation time, τ_r, and therefore are hardly relevant for macromolecules; on the other hand, modulation of g or A tensors anisotropy brought about by rotation or fluctuations in the geometry of the chromophore can account for electronic relaxation times of the right order of magnitude (10^{-9}-10^{-8} s) of those observed in such copper(II) containing systems.

Table I

Best fit parameters for NMRD data at 25°C on solutions of copper(II)-containing proteins

	G (pm^{-6})	τ_s (s)	θ (deg)
Cu$_2$TRN	7.2×10^{-16}	5.7×10^{-9}	50
CuBCA II	3.9×10^{-15}	1.9×10^{-9}	53
CuBCA II + N$_3^-$	4.7×10^{-15}	2.6×10^{-9}	50
CuBCA II + HCO$_3^-$	1.2×10^{-15}	2.1×10^{-9}	52
Cu$_2$Zn$_2$SOD	1.7×10^{-15}	1.8×10^{-9}	20

overall contribution of the contact term is negligible (9). It has also been shown that the dipolar interaction of water protons with the unpaired electron can be described with very good approximation by considering the electron as a point dipole centered on the metal ion (10).

The theory for nuclear relaxation induced by point dipole interaction between two isolated $S=1/2$ and $I=1/2$ spins has been developed in the fifties by Solomon (11). Such theory does not include possible effects of g tensor anisotropy and hyperfine coupling with the metal nucleus, which are both present in the spin Hamiltonian for copper(II) ions (equation 1), and therefore cannot be applied as such to the present systems. Since the theoretical tools for including these effects are available (12), we have explicitly calculated the field dependence of T_{1M}^{-1} for protons interacting with copper(II) in a macromolecule.

In anisotropic systems, the nucleus feels the paramagnetic center in different ways depending on the relative values of the correlation times operative (13-17). The most likely situation of slow tumbling of the molecule with respect to the electronic relaxation time has been chosen (18,19). Furthermore, it is assumed that the exchange rate of water from the copper(II) coordination sphere, τ_M, is fast with respect to the nuclear longitudinal relaxation enhancement but slow with respect to both molecular rotation and electronic relaxation; this condition is also easily met. In summary:

$$T_{1M}^{-1} < \tau_M^{-1} < \tau_r^{-1} < \tau_s^{-1} \qquad (2)$$

From the general equation for T_{1M}^{-1} (12)

$$T_{1M}^{-1} = \sum_\gamma \frac{1}{\hbar^2} \int_0^\infty \frac{\langle [\hat{I}_z, \hat{H}_{dip}^\gamma(t)][\hat{H}_{dip}^{-\gamma}(0), \hat{I}_z] \rangle e^{i\gamma\omega_I t}}{\langle \hat{I}_z^2 \rangle} \, dt \qquad (3)$$

the Hamiltonian for the nucleus-electron spin dipolar interaction $\hat{H}_{dip}^\gamma(t)$ can be expressed as

$$\hat{H}_{dip}^\gamma(t) = e^{\frac{i}{\hbar}\hat{H}_o t} \hat{H}_{dip}^\gamma(0) \, e^{-\frac{i}{\hbar}\hat{H}_o t}$$

with $\hat{H}_o$ given by equation 1 and

$$\hat{H}_{dip}^\gamma(0) = \hat{A}^{-\gamma}\hat{F}^\gamma \qquad (4)$$

$\hat{A}^{-\gamma}$ contains nuclear spin operators and $\hat{F}^\gamma$ contains electron spin operators. The problem is then reduced to the evaluation of expectation values of the type

$$\langle \hat{F}^\gamma(t)\hat{F}^{-\gamma}(0) \rangle \qquad (5)$$

and therefore to the diagonalization of the energy matrix of $\hat{H}_o$. The effect of g anisotropy has been analyzed separately (i.e. retaining only the first term in $\hat{H}_o$) and found to introduce only small deviations from the Solomon behavior for g anisotropies typical of copper(II) systems (19). Such result is analogous to that obtained for fast rotating systems (14). Therefore, in all subsequent calculations an isotropic g value of 2 has been used in $\hat{H}_o$. To evaluate the effect of hyperfine coupling an axial A tensor has been chosen (19). Analytical solutions could be obtained for the limit cases $A_\perp = A_\parallel$ (isotropic A), and $A_\perp = 0$. For the general case of $A_\parallel > A_\perp > 0$ the field dependence of T_{1M}^{-1} has been calculated numerically.

Analysis of the experimental data

As in the Solomon equation (11), the T_{1M}^{-1} values obtained from the above treatment are functions of 1) a geometrical factor G related to the metal proton distance and to the number of interacting protons ($G = \sum_i r_i^{-6}$); 2) the electronic relaxation time τ_s; 3) the magnetic field. Furthermore, they depend on the values of $A_\perp$, $A_\parallel$, and of the angle θ formed between the z axis of the A tensor and the metal proton vector. Figure 1 shows the experimental water proton T_{1M}^{-1} values as a function of magnetic field (NMRD) for solutions of copper(II) substituted bovine carbonic anhydrase (CuBCA II) and of its adducts with N_3^- and HCO_3^- (20). The solid lines are best fit curves obtained using the experimental $A_\parallel$ values, reasonable estimates of $A_\perp$, and G, τ_s, and θ as parameters. For comparison purposes, the dashed lines show the best fit curves to the Solomon equation. It is apparent that, unless only the high field region is considered (20), the data cannot be analyzed in terms of the Solomon equation. Highly satisfactory fittings using our treatment are also obtained for the NMRD data on superoxide dismutase (Cu_2Zn_2SOD) (19) and copper substituted transferring (Cu_2TRN) (21), underlining the general validity of our approach. The best fit values of G, τ_s, and θ for all of the above derivatives are reported in Table I.

Table I
Best fit parameters for NMRD data at 25°C on solutions of copper(II)-containing proteins

	G (pm^{-6})	τ_s (s)	θ (deg)
Cu_2TRN	7.2×10^{-16}	5.7×10^{-9}	50
CuBCA II	3.9×10^{-15}	1.9×10^{-9}	53
CuBCA II + NO_3^-	4.7×10^{-15}	2.6×10^{-9}	50
CuBCA II + HCO_3^-	1.2×10^{-15}	2.1×10^{-9}	52
Zn_2Cu_2SOD	1.7×10^{-15}	1.8×10^{-9}	20

The θ values should be better regarded as empirical parameters, for the following reasons: 1) when more than one proton interacts with the paramagnetic center each one has its own θ angle. ii) if the system is not axial, a second angle would be in principle needed to define the position of the proton with respect to the A tensor. These drawbacks, however, are absolutely minor as far as the G value is concerned. Therefore, the excellent agreement of the theory with the experimental data allows confidence in the numerical values of the structural parameters reported in Table I. A regularly coordinated water molecule (metal-oxygen distance of about 200 pm)

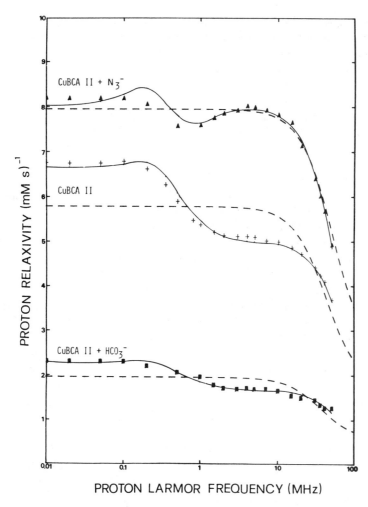

Figure 1. Water proton NMRD data at 25°C for solutions of CuBCA II and of its adducts with N_3^- and HCO_3^-. The full lines represent best fit curves obtained by inclusion of the hyperfine coupling with the metal nucleus ($A_{\parallel} = 124 \times 10^{-4}$ cm^{-1}, $A_{\perp} = 40 \times 10^{-4}$ cm^{-1} for the N_3^- adduct, and $A_{\parallel} = 131 \times 10^{-4}$ cm^{-1}. $A_{\perp} = 20 \times 10^{-4}$ cm^{-1} for the other two derivatives). For comparison purposes the dashed lines show the "best fit" curves obtained with the Solomon equation. In this case unreasonable τ_s values ($\sim 10^{-11}$s) are obtained.

corresponds to a G value of about 4×10^{-15} pm^{-6}. With this in mind, both the native and azide-ligated CuBCA II derivatives are shown to contain water directly coordinated to the copper center; apparently in the latter system both the N_3^- ion and water are simultaneously present in the coordination sphere. In the adduct with HCO_3^-, which is a substrate of the native enzyme, the lower G value points to a different coordination site for the latter anion, possibly with water semicoordinated in a fifth coordination position (metal-oxygen distance of about 260 pm). In Cu_2Zn_2SOD water is known from the X-ray structure to occupy the apical position of a distorted square pyramidal chromophore. Indeed, the G value is again consistent with a semicoordinated water (metal-oxygen distance of 240 pm). The very low G value observed in Cu_2TRN might indicate absence of water from the first co-ordination sphere, or a water molecule that exchanges so slow not to be detected. The observed paramagnetic contribution might come from a solvent proton hydrogen bonded to a donor atom of one of the ligands; for instance, a single proton at 320 pm would be consistent with the observed G value. Indeed, very similar results are obtained for the oxovanadium(IV) derivative of transferrin (21), where the only solvent-accessible position is likely to be occupied by the VO oxygen.

The use of copper(II) as a shift reagent

Paramagnetic metal ions are usually divided in shift reagents and relaxation reagents, according to their relative ability of inducing isotropic shifts and relaxation enhancement (and hence line broadening) on nearby nuclei. For macromolecules, under the usual experimental conditions the line broadening effect is proportional to the electronic relaxation times. The relatively long electronic relaxation times of copper(II) make the ion a good relaxation reagent but prevent its use as a shift reagent. However, when copper(II) is exchange-coupled to a paramagnetic metal ion with short electronic relaxation times, its electronic relaxation time may be reduced. Qualitatively, the presence of a nearby metal ion strongly coupled to the lattice is expected to provide an additional and efficient relaxation pathway for the electronic spin associated with copper(II). In the simple case of isotropic exchange coupling described by the Hamiltonian

$$\hat{H} = J\,\hat{S}_1 \cdot \hat{S}_2 \tag{6}$$

the electronic relaxation time of the copper(II) ion will be close to that of the fast relaxing metal ion M in the limit $J > \hbar\tau_{s(M)}^{-1}$. In the intermediate case $\hbar\tau_{s(Cu)}^{-1} < J < \hbar\tau_{s(M)}^{-1}$, it will be descibed by an equation of the type (22)

$$\tau_{s(Cu)}^{-1}(J) = \tau_{s(Cu)}^{-1}(0) + \frac{J^2}{\hbar^2}\,\tau_{s(Cu)}(0) \tag{7}$$

Equations describing the overall effect of exchange coupling on the T_{1M}^{-1} of nuclei close to the copper center have been developed and successfully tested (22) on a model system constituted by the adduct between bis-ethylenediamine-copper(II) and hexacyanoferrate(III); the two ions are bridged by a cyanide ligand (23).

Although the exchange coupling constant J for such system is small, it is still apparently larger than $\hbar\tau_{s(Cu)}^{-1}$, so that the electronic relaxation time of copper(II) is dramatically reduced. Since this phenomenon is quite general, it is conceivable to exploit it on suitable copper(II) containing biological molecules. A quite appropriate natural system is superoxide dismutase, whose active site copper(II) ion is bridged to a zinc(II) ion through a histidine imidazolate moiety. The zinc ion can be substituted with high spin cobalt(II) without altering the enzymatic properties of

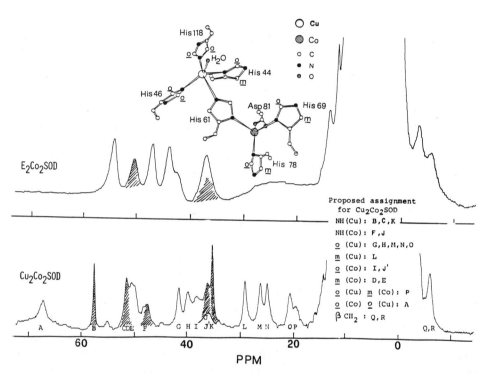

Figure 2. 300 MHz ^{1}H NMR spectra of cobalt(II)-copper deprived SOD (E$_2$Co$_2$SOD) and of Cu$_2$Co$_2$SOD. The shaded signals disappear in D$_2$O. The assignment of the signals is also indicated, with reference to the chromophore shown in the inset.

the molecule (24). The exchange coupling constant is relatively small, as judged from magnetic susceptibility measurements at room temperature (25), but apparently sufficiently large to reduce $\tau_{s(Cu)}$ so that the EPR signal of copper(II) is broadened beyond detection (24). Therefore, in this system copper(II) should be as good as high spin cobalt(II) as a shift reagent (26). The 300 MHz ^{1}H NMR spectrum of such derivative (Cu$_2$Co$_2$SOD) is shown in Figure 2, together with the spectrum of the copper-deprived cobalt(II) derivative (E$_2$Co$_2$SOD) for comparison purposes (25). The assignment of the signals to the various protons of the cobalt and copper

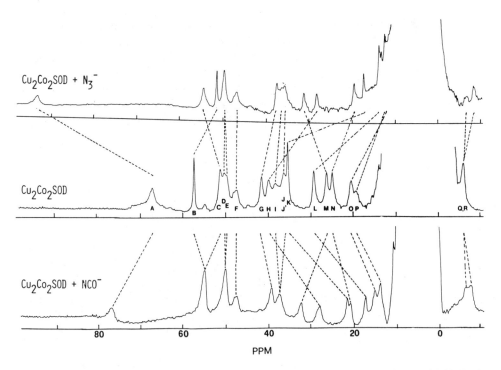

Figure 3. 300 MHz ^{1}H NMR spectra of water solutions of Cu_2Co_2SOD and of its adducts with N_3^- and CNO^-. Signals K, L, and O, assigned to the NH, m-H, and o-H protons of His 44, respectively, undergo a dramatic decrease in isotropic shift upon anion binding.

ligands (inset) has been performed through deuteration and T_1 measurements. It appears that several signals of protons belonging to the copper chromophore are even narrower than those of analogous protons of the cobalt comparison purposes (25). The assignment of the signals to the various protons of the cobalt and copper ligands (inset) has been performed through deuteration and T measurements. It appears that several signals of protons belonging to the copper chromophore are even narrower than those of analogous protons of the cobolt chromophore. Indeed, if the electronic relaxation times of the two systems are the same, the nuclear relaxing efficiency of copper(II) is smaller owing to its smaller $S(S+1)$ value. We have therefore a means of monitoring the active site nuclei and of using them as a reporter of chemical changes occurring under various conditions. As an example, binding of anions like azide, cyanate and thiocyanate is shown (Figure 3) to dramatically reduce the isotropic shift of three signals assigned to the ring protons of His 44, one of the copper(II) ligands. This is strongly indicative of removal of His 44 from coordination (25). Apparently, a rearrangement of the chromophore occurs upon anion binding, which does not necessarily imply coordination of the anion in the apical position occupied by a water molecule in the native enzyme (27,28). Coordination of a hydroxide ion at high pH (29) results in similar changes in the NMR spectrum.

References and Footnotes

1. *Metal Ions in Biological Systems XIII,* Ed., H. Sigel, Marcel Dekker, New York (1981).
2. *Metal Ions in Biology III,* Ed., T.G. Spiro, John Wiley and Sons, New York (1981).
3. I. Bertini and A. Scozzafava in *Metal Ions in Biological Systems XII,* Ed., H. Sigel, Marcel Dekker, New York, p. 31 (1981).
4. S.H. Koenig and R.D. Brown, *Ann. N.Y. Acad. Sci. 222,* 752 (1973).
5. R. Orbach, *Proc. Phys. Soc. (London) A77,* 821 (1961).
6. D. Kivelson, *J. Chem. Phys. 45,* 1324 (1966).
7. W.B. Lewis and L.O. Morgan, *Trans. Met. Chem. 4,* 33 (1968).
8. Z. Luz and R.G. Shulman, *J. Chem. Phys. 43,* 3750 (1965).
9. S.H. Koenig and R.D. Brown in *ESR and NMR of Paramagnetic Species in Biological and Related Systems,* Eds., I. Bertini and R.S. Drago, D. Reidel, Dordrecht, p.89 (1980).
10. L. Nordenskiöld, A. Laaksonen and J. Kowalewski, *J. Am. Chem. Soc. 104,* 379 (1982).
11. I. Solomon, *Phys. Rev. 99,* 559 (1955).
12. R. Kubo and K. Tomita, *J. Phys. Soc. (Japan) 9,* 888 (1954).
13. U. Lindner, *Ann. Physik (Leipzig) 16,* 319 (1965).
14. H. Sternlicht, *J. Chem. Phys. 42,* 2250 (1965).
15. H. Pfeifer, D. Michel, D. Sames and H. Sprinz, *Mol. Phys. 11,* 591 (1966).
16. I. Bertini, C. Luchinat, M. Mancini and G. Spina, *J. Magn. Reson. 59,* 213 (1984).
17. N. Benetis, J. Kowalewski, L. Nordenskiöld, H. Wennerström and P.-O. Westlund, *Mol. Phys. 48,* 329 (1983).
18. I. Bertini, C. Luchinat, M. Mancini and G. Spina in *Magneto-Structural Correlations in Exchange Coupled Systems,* Eds., R.D. Willett, D. Gatteschi and O. Kahn, D. Reidel, Dordrecht, p. 421 (1985).
19. I. Bertini, F. Briganti, C. Luchinat, M. Mancini and G. Spina, *J. Magn. Reson. 62,* 000 (1985).
20. I. Bertini, E. Borghi, G. Canti and C. Luchinat, *J. Inorg. Biochem. 18,* 221 (1983).
21. I. Bertini, F. Briganti, R.D. Brown, S.H. Koenig and C. Luchinat, submitted.
22. I. Bertini, G. Lanini, C. Luchinat, M. Mancini and G. Spina, *J. Magn. Reson., 62,* 000 (1985).
23. I. Bertini, C. Luchinat, F. Mani and A. Scozzafava, *Inorg. Chem. 19,* 1333 (1980).
24. L. Calabrese, G. Rotilio and B. Mondovi, *Biochim. Biophys. Acta 263,* 827 (1972); J.A. Fee, *J. Biol Chem. 248,* 4229 (1973).
25. I. Bertini, G. Lanini, C. Luchinat, L. Messori, R. Monnanni and A. Scozzafava, *J. Am. Chem. Soc., 107,* 000 (1985).
26. I. Bertini and C. Luchinat, *Adv. Inorg. Biochem. 6,* 000 (1985).
27. I. Bertini, C. Luchinat and A. Scozzafava, *J. Am. Chem. Soc. 102,* 7349 (1980).
28. I. Bertini, E. Borghi, C. Luchinat and A. Scozzafava, *J. Am. Chem. Soc. 103,* 7779 (1981).
29. I. Bertini, C. Luchinat and L. Messori, *Biochem. Biophys. Res. Commun. 101,* 577 (1981).

Biological & Inorganic Copper Chemistry,
ISBN 0-940030-11-X, Eds., K. D. Karlin & J. Zubieta, Adenine Press, ©Adenine Press, 1985

Structural Studies on Non-blue Copper Proteins. Comparison of EXAFS with X-ray Crystallography using Interactive Molecular Graphics

N. J. Blackburn,
Department of Chemistry, University of Manchester
Institute of Science and Technology
P.O. Box 88, Manchester M60 1QD, UK

and

S. S. Hasnain
Daresbury Laboratory
Warrington, Cheshire WA4 4AD, UK

Abstract

EXAFS data for the native, reduced and cyano forms of bovine erythrocyte superoxide dismutase have been collected and analysed. The bond lengths determined for the native enzyme have been superimposed on the crystallographic coordinates of Tainer et. al. (J. Mol. Biol. (1982), 181) using interactive molecular graphics. The results show that the splitting of the Cu-C_β distances (where $C_\beta = C_2$ and C_5 of the imidazole ring) are most probably real and reflect asymmetrical coordination of the histidine residues. The data for cyano SOD are consistent with reorientation of the copper coordination geometry such that CN^- binds equatorially displacing an imidazole group to an axial position. Preliminary results on dopamine-β-monooxygenase and plasma amine oxidase are also reported.

Introduction

The copper containing enzymes, superoxide dismutase, dopamine monooxygenase and plasma amine oxidase while functionally diverse are often classified together as 'non-blue' or 'type 2' on the basis of the similarity of their optical and EPR spectroscopic properties to those of simple mononuclear complexes (1). X-ray absorption spectroscopy offers a further method of examining the structural relationships within this class of copper proteins. In this paper we summarise the results of EXAFS studies, which provide evidence of structural homologies and have identified imidazole coordination in all three enzyme systems. In the case of native superoxide dismutase where a crystal structure is available to 2Å resolution (2,3), comparison of EXAFS and crystallographic coordinates using molecular graphics has provided extra insights into the local structure of the active site.

33

Results and Discussion

1. Bovine erythrocyte superoxide dismutase (SOD)

This enzyme catalyses the dismutation of the superoxide anion according to the equation

$$2O_2^- + 2H^+ \Rightarrow O_2 + H_2O_2$$

Recent refinement of the crystal structure (2,3) has produced a clear view of the structure of the metal sites: the copper ligands, (N atoms of imidazoles of His-44, -46, -61 and -118) show an uneven tetrahedral distortion from a square plane with the fifth axial co-ordination position occupied by solvent (4,5). His-61 forms a bridge to the zinc, the other ligands of which are N atoms of His-69 and 78 and an oxygen of Asp-81. The geometry around zinc is tetrahedral with a strong distortion towards a trigonal pyramid having the buried Asp-81 at the apex.

1.1 Copper site of the native enzyme

The interpretation of the EXAFS data for the copper site of (oxidised) bovine erythrocyte superoxide dismutase in aqueous phosphate buffer (0.010 M, pH 7.4) indicates an immediate coordination environment in close agreement with the crystallographic results, namely four imidazole groups with $Cu-N = 1.99$ Å and one solvent water molecule with $Cu-O = 2.24$ Å as ligands to copper (Table I, Fig. 1). The $Cu-N$ bond lengths are slightly shorter than the crystallographic value of 2.1 Å, determined as the average over the four copper sites of the asymmetric unit. However, the value determined by EXAFS agrees closely with $Cu-N$ distances reported for similar Cu(II) imidazole complexes, especially $[Cu(Himid)_4](NO_3)_2$ (6) the EXAFS of which has been successfully interpreted with 4 $Cu-N$ distances of 1.98 Å as compared to the crystallographic value of 2.01 Å. Furthermore, the

Table I

Parameters used to simulate the EXAFS associated with the copper K-edge of oxidised, reduced and cyano superoxide dismutase in aqueous phosphate buffer (0.01 M)

	Oxidised			Reduced			Cyano		
	Atom	$2\sigma^2/(\text{Å})^2$	R/(Å)	Atom	$2\sigma^2/(\text{Å})^2$	R/(Å)	Atom	$2\sigma^2/(\text{Å})^2$	R/(Å)
1st Shell	$4N_\alpha$ 1O	0.01	1.99 2.24	$3N_\alpha$	0.01	1.94	$3N_\alpha$ 1C $1N_\alpha$	0.01	1.96 2.00 2.24
2nd Shell	$4C_\beta$ $4C_\beta$	0.01	2.96 3.16	$3C_\beta$ $3C_\beta$		2.98 3.08	$3C_\beta$ $3C_\beta$	0.02	2.90 3.30
3rd Shell	$4N_\gamma$ $4C_\gamma$	0.01	3.90 3.80	$3N_\gamma$ $3C_\gamma$	0.01	3.90 3.80	$3N_\gamma$ $3C_\gamma$	0.025	3.80 3.78

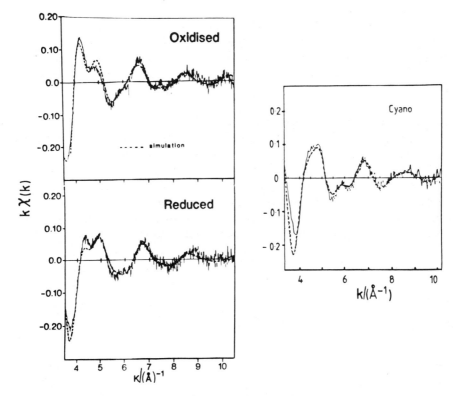

Figure 1. EXAFS associated with the copper K-edge of oxidised, reduced and cyano superoxide dismutase.

Cu$-$N value obtained for the enzyme in aqueous solution is within 0.01 Å of that obtained for the lyophillised derivative (7).

The EXAFS interpretation of the aqueous enzyme also locates a single oxygen atom at 2.24 Å. Both crystallography (2) and water proton relaxation studies (4,5) provide strong evidence for the presence of solvent in an axial type position. The distance found for this oxygen as the fifth ligand is consistent with an axially coordinated water molecule in a five coordinate structure (8) but is too short for a CuN_4O_2 structure involving two axial water molecules, where Cu$-$OH$_2$ bond lengths are typically 2.6 Å (9).

An interesting feature of the analysis of the EXAFS of the Cu site of SOD is the need to split the Cu$-$C$_\beta$ distances by 0.2 Å (where C$_\beta$ represents the C$_2$ and C$_5$ carbon atoms of the imidazole rings). The magnitude of the splitting is found to correlate with the intensity and degree of resolution of the low energy shoulder on the second EXAFS peak (k = 5.5-6.5 Å^{-1}). This effect can be seen by comparing the values of the splittings (Table I) with the EXAFS profiles of the oxidised, reduced and cyano derivatives (Fig. 1). While it is possible that the effect results from multiple scattering processes which are inadequately accounted for by the theory, no splitting is apparent in tetrapyrrole systems (10). A more satisfactory explanation is that the splittings are real and result from asymmetric coordination of the imidazole rings. Such structures are known for copper imidazole model systems particularly in complexes where the proton attached to the distant (noncoordinating) N atom of the imidazole group H-bonds to the anionic counter ion e.g. $[Cu(Himid)_6](NO_3)_2$ (11).

The magnitude of the splittings observed in the enzyme derivatives should then reflect the degree of H-bonding of the imidazole groups with other protein residues in the active site pocket. Furthermore, the ability to resolve the splittings offers the exciting possibility of deriving information on the orientation of the rings relative to the metal centre. Accordingly we have used interactive molecular graphics to fit the EXAFS distances to the crystallographic coordinates of Tainer et al (2) by carrying out translations and rotations of the imidazole groups whilst keeping all other protein residues fixed at their crystallographic positions. Figure 2 shows the

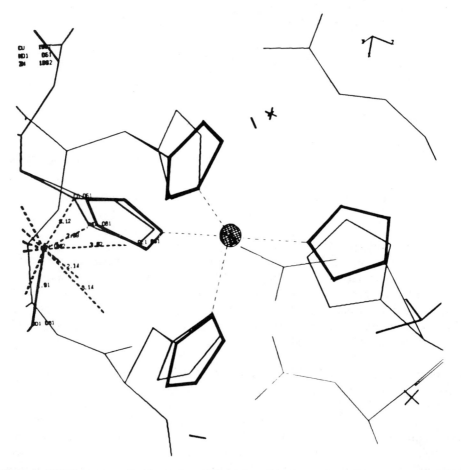

Figure 2. EXAFS positions of imidazole rings (shown in heavy black) superimposed on the crystallographic coordinates of Tainer et al. (2) for copper atom #1001. The data were generated using the graphics program FRODO.

EXAFS positions of the imidazole groups superimposed on the crystallographic positions for one particular orientation. The results have shown that asymmetrical coordination of imidazole is not unreasonable and is indeed observed for some rings at the resolution of the crystallographic refinement.

1.2 Copper Site of the Reduced Enzyme

Features on the copper K-absorption edge and the X-ray Absorption Near Edge Structure (XANES) of oxidised and reduced bovine erythrocyte superoxide dismutase in aqueous phosphate buffer, show clear differences in relative intensity, suggesting a stereochemical change at the copper accompanying reduction. The interpretation of the EXAFS for the reduced form of the enzyme has been most successful for three coordinate Cu(I) involving only imidazole coordination. However, and of more significance, the value of the Cu−N bond lengths of 1.94 Å in the reduced form of the enzyme is itself indicative of a coordination number lower than that in the oxidised form since reduction of the copper is expected to lengthen the Cu−N bonds, unless the coordination number is decreased. Thus $[Cu^{II}(N\text{-methylimida-zole})_4][BF_4]_2$ (12) and $[Cu^I(N\text{-methylimidazole})_4][ClO_4]$ (13) involve Cu−N distances of 2.006 and 2.054 Å, respectively. 3 coordinate Cu(I) complexes on the other hand exhibit Cu−N(pyridine) first shell distances in the range 1.89-1.93 Å (see refs 14 & 15 for a fuller discussion of this point).

The EXAFS results thus provide the first direct structural information on the copper site of reduced superoxide dismutase and are fully consistent with previous proposals based on redox titration data (16,17) and ^{113}Cd nmr spectra (18) that an imidazole group dissociates from the copper on reduction. EXAFS gives no indication as to which imidazole is lost although Fee (19) suggests that it is the bridging ligand to zinc.

1.3 Cyano−SOD

The EXAFS of cyano SOD is not easy to interpret unambiguously but is best fit by three 'equatorial' type imidazole groups at 1.96 Å, CN⁻ at 2.00 Å and a more distant 'axial' imidazole at 2.24 Å (Fig. 1 table 1). These results support previous proposals based on other spectroscopic data that CN⁻ binding reorients the coordination sphere such that one imidazole ligand is displaced from an essentially equatorial to an axial position with CN⁻ occupying the vacant equatorial site. The value of 2.00 Å is longer than the Cu(II)−CN distances documented by crystallography (although examples of Cu^{II}-cyano complexes are rare). For example, distorted trigonal bipyramidal $[Cu(phen)_2CN](NO_3)H_2O$ (20) and $[Cu(bipy)_2CN](NO_3)2H_2O$ (21) have Cu−C = 1.935Å and 1.974Å respectively. However if coordinated CN⁻ in superoxide dismutase was also H-bonded to the protonated Arg-141 in the active site cavity, a lengthening of Cu−C bond would not be unexpected, Fig. 3. This proposal is in accord with the observation that chemical modification of arginine residues decreases the CN⁻ binding constant (22). It is also consistent with a recent observation from this laboratory that evacuation or lyophilisation causes dissociation

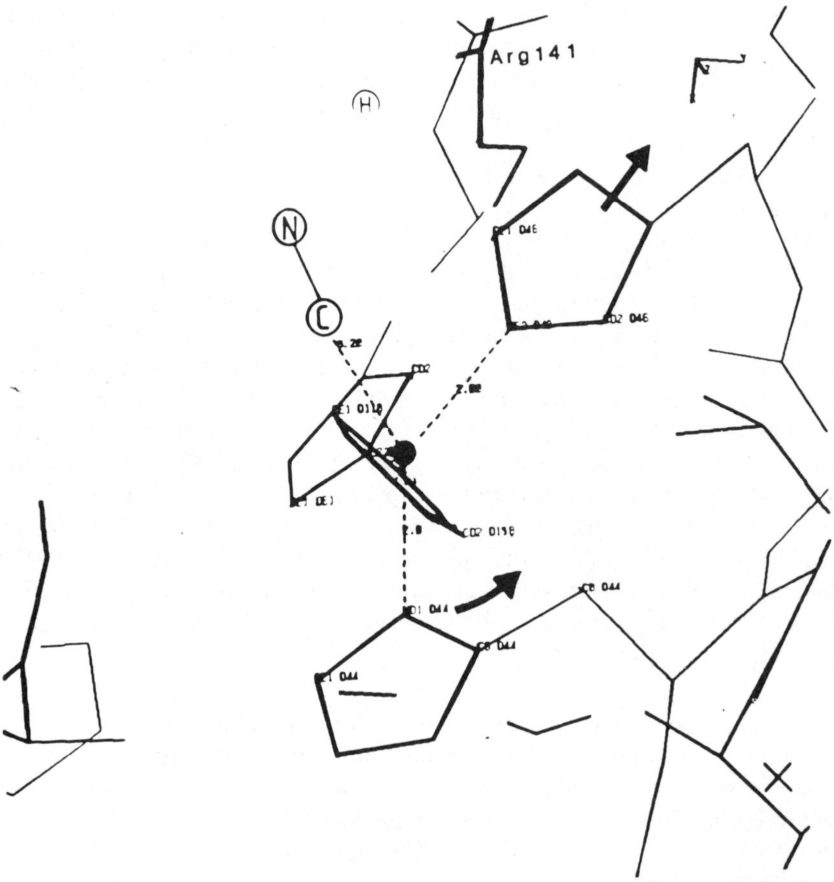

Figure 3. Possible structure of cyano superoxide dismutase showing proposed H-bonding interaction with Arg-141. Suggested movement of imidazole rings are shown by arrows.

of the cyanide ligand from the enzyme as HCN, with a pH dependence which implicates a group with a $pK_a > 10.5$ as the source of the proton.

2 Dopamine-β-monooxygenase (DβM) and monoamine oxidase (MAO)

DβM catalyses the hydroxylation of dopamine to nor adrenalin, an important step in the modification of transmitter molecules (25,26).

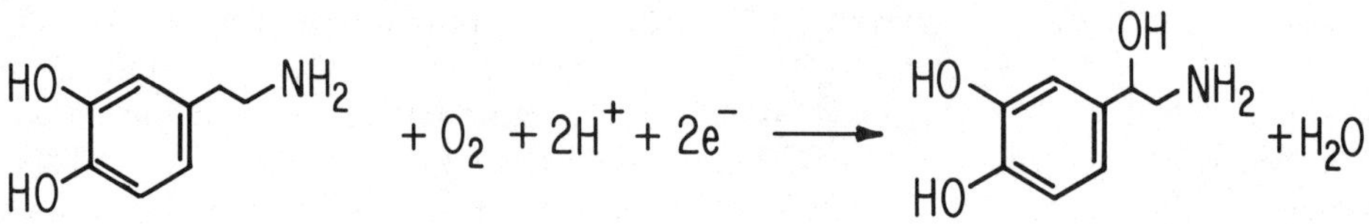

MAO catalyses the oxidative conversion of biogenic amines to the corresponding aldehyde.

$$RCH_2NH_2 + O_2 + H_2O \Rightarrow RCHO + H_2O + NH_3$$

Due to the high molecular weight of these enzymes the copper is much more dilute (1 Cu per 77000 & 90,000 respectively for the preparations of DβM and MAO used in this study). The more limited quality of the data therefore renders our conclusions more tentative. However, the EXAFS study clearly shows that in each case Cu is coordinated to $\geq$ 3 imidazoles and the structures of the catalytic sites in these enzymes are thus closely related. For dopamine monooxygenase best fits are obtained by 4 imidazoles (or 3 imidazoles and one O) at 2.01 Å and a solvent molecule at 2.3 Å. When combined with EPR data (25) these results are consistent with a square pyramidal site.

Acknowledgement

We would like to thank the SERC for financial support and the Daresbury Laboratory for provision of facilities. We are especially grateful to Professor T. Blundell and Dr. Peter Linley of the Birkbeck College, University of London for use of the Molecular Graphics facility.

References and Footnotes

1. R. Malkin and B. G. Malmstrom, *Adv. Enz., 33,* 177, (1970).
2. J. A. Tainer, E. D. Getzoff, K. M. Beem, J. S. Richardson and D. C. Richardson, *J. Mol. Biol.,* 181-217 (1982).
3. J. A. Tainer, E. D. Getzoff, J. S. Richardson and D. C. Richardson, *Nature, 306,* 284-286, (1983).
4. J.A. Fee and B. P. Gaber, *J. Biol. Chem., 247,* 60-65 (1972).
5. N. Boden, M. C. Holmes and P. F. Knowles, *Biochem J., 177,* 303-309, (1979).
6. D. L. McFadden, A.T. McPhail, C. D. Garner and F. E. Mabbs, *J. Chem. Soc. Dalton Trans.* 47-52, (1976).
7. N. J. Blackburn, S. S. Hasnain, G. P. Diakun, P. F. Knowles, N. Binsted and C. D. Garner, *Biochem. J. 213,* 765-768, (1983).
8. K. D. Karlin, Y. Gultneh, J. G. Hayes and J. Zubieta, *Inorg. Chem., 23,* 521-523, (1984).
9. W. Vreudgdenhill, P. J. M. W. L. Birker, R. W. M. ten Hoedt, G. C. Verschoor and J. Reedijk, *J. Chem. Soc. Dalton Trans.,* 429-432, (1984).
10. M. F. Perutz, S. S. Hasnain, P. J. Duke, J. L. Sessler and J. E. Hahn, *Nature, 295,* 535-538, (1982).
11. D. L. McFadden, A. T. McPhail, C. D. Garner and F. E. Mabbs, *J. Chem. Soc., Dalton Trans.* 263-268, (1975).
12. S. R. Acott, W. Clegg, D. Collison and C. D. Garner, personal communication.
13. W. Clegg, S. R. Acott and C. D. Garner, *Acta Cryst. C. 40,* 768-769, (1984).
14. N.J. Blackburn, S. S. Hasnain, N. Binsted, G. P. Diakun, C. D. Garner, and P. F. Knowles, *Biochem. J. 219,* 985-990, (1984).
15. K. D. Karlin, J. C. Hayes, Y. Gultneh, R. W. Cruse, J. W. McKown, J. P. Hutchinson and J. Zubieta, *J. Am. Chem. Soc. 106,* 2121-2128, (1984).
16. J. A. Fee and P. E. diCorletto, *Biochemistry, 12,* 4893-4899, (1973).
17. G. D. Lawrence and D. T. Sawyer, *Biochemistry, 18,* 3045-3050, (1979).
18. D. B. Bailey, P. D. Ellis and J. A. Fee, *Biochemistry, 19,* 591-596, (1980).

Blackburn and Hasnain

19. J. A. Fee in Metal Ions in Biological Systems Vol. 13, (Copper Proteins) (Sigel H. ed.) pp. 259-298, Marcel Dekker, New York, (1981).
20. O. P. Anderson, *Inorg. Chem., 14,* 730-734, (1975).
21. S. Tyagi and B. J. Hathaway, *J. Chem. Soc. Dalton Trans.,* 199-203, (1983).
22. O. Bermingham-McDonogh, D. M. De Freitas, A. Kumamoto, J. E. Saunders, D. M. Blech, C. L. Borders Jr., and J. S. Valentine, *Biochem. Biophys. Res. Comm. 108,* 1376-82, (1982).
23. T. Skotland and T. Ljones, *Inorg. Perspect. Biol. Med., 2,* 152-180, (1979).
23. J. J. Villafranca, in Metal Ions in Biology, Vol. 2, (Copper Proteins) (ed. T.G. Spiro) pp. 264-281, John Wiley and Sons, New York (1981).
25. N. J. Blackburn, D. Collison, J. Sutton and F. E. Mabbs, *Biochem. J., 220.* 447-454. (1984).

Biological & Inorganic Copper Chemistry,
ISBN 0-940030-11-X, Eds., K. D. Karlin & J. Zubieta, Adenine Press, ©Adenine Press, 1985

Copper EXAFS of Cytochrome *c* Oxidase. Structure of the *a₃*-Cu$_B$ Binuclear Site

Robert A. Scott[a], James R. Schwartz[a],
and Stephen P. Cramer[b]
[a]School of Chemical Sciences,
University of Illinois, Urbana, IL 61801
[b]Exxon Research and Engineering,
Annandale, NJ 08801

Abstract

Copper extended x-ray absorption fine structure (EXAFS) data on several samples of resting state cytochrome *c* oxidase prepared by a number of different procedures in a number of different laboratories are compared. Despite visual differences in the Fourier transforms, the EXAFS data of all the samples are shown to be the same within experimental error. A peak in the Fourier transform at a phase-shifted distance (R′) of *ca.* 2.7 Å is shown to be only assignable to an Fe scatterer. This is interpreted as the heme *a₃* Fe-Cu$_B$ interaction in the binuclear O_2-interaction site, yielding a Cu-Fe distance of 3.02(2) Å.

Introduction

Cytochrome *c* oxidase resides in the inner mitochondrial membrane and is responsible (as the terminal enzyme of the respiratory chain) for using electrons from cytochrome *c* to reduce O_2 to H_2O in an energy-conserving reaction (1). The enzyme contains four structurally and spectroscopically distinct metal active sites per monomer: heme *a,* heme *a₃,* Cu$_A$, and Cu$_B$. Electrons from cytochrome *c* initially go to heme *a* (probably a bis-imidazole heme A prosthetic group) and possibly Cu$_A$ (responsible for the g2 electron paramagnetic resonance (epr) signal), after which they are transferred (intramolecularly) to the heme *a₃*-Cu$_B$ binuclear site, the site at which O_2 is reduced to H_2O. The enzyme will be referred to herein as cytochrome *aa₃* or simply *aa₃*.

Our limited knowledge of the structural details of the metal active sites in *aa₃* comes mainly from x-ray absorption spectroscopy (XAS) and extended x-ray absorption fine structure (EXAFS) investigations (2-8). Two separate groups have been involved in the EXAFS studies on cytochrome *aa₃*, often obtaining different results. For example, Fourier transforms (FT's) of Cu EXAFS of resting state enzyme obtained by Powers, Chance, and coworkers (6,7) exhibit a single major peak at R′ = 1.5 Å, whereas similar FT's obtained by Scott, Cramer, and coworkers

(5,8) usually show a split main FT peak with maxima at $R' \approx 1.4, 1.9$ Å. These data were obtained on purified aa_3 prepared by different techniques raising the possibility that the EXAFS data are preparation-dependent. We have examined cytochrome aa_3 samples prepared by four different methods in a number of different laboratories and show here that, even though the appearance of the FT varies considerably, any differences observed are within the experimental error of the data.

The heme a_3-Cu_B binuclear site has been proposed by Powers, *et al.* (6,7) to consist of Fe and Cu separated by *ca.* 3.8 Å with a thiol bridge in the resting state enzyme. In the resting state Cu EXAFS presented here, we observe an FT peak at $R' \approx 2.7$ Å which is shown to be only assignable to Cu-Fe scattering. This peak is observed in all the enzyme preparations examined and is sensitive to the redox state of the enzyme. We therefore assign it to the Fe-Cu vector in the heme a_3-Cu_B site and calculate the Fe-Cu distance to be *ca.* 3.0 Å.

Materials and Methods

A list of the eight cytochrome aa_3 samples and their purification procedures and origins is presented in Table I. Previously published EXAFS data were collected on

Table I

Cytochrome aa_3 samples examined

Sample	Temperature (K)[a]	Purification Method [Reference]	Origin
Hb/U[b]	4,190	Hartzell/Beinert [9]	Urbana
HB/M	195	Hartzell/Beinert [9]	Madison[c]
HB/P	190	Hartzell/Beinert [9]	Pasadena[d]
vB/A	190	van Buuren [10]	Amsterdam[e]
K/B[b]	4	King [11]	Bern[f]
Y/E	4	Yonetani[12]	Essex[g]

[a] Temperature of XAS data collection;
[b] Two samples were examined;
[c] From the laboratory of H. Beinert;
[d] From the laboratory of S. I. Chan;
[e] This sample was a gift from B. F. van Gelder to H. Beinert;
[f] From the laboratory of A. Azzi;
[g] From the laboratory of M. T. Wilson

samples prepared by the Hartzell/Beinert method (5,8) and by the Yonetani method (6,7). All XAS data were collected at the Stanford Synchrotron Radiation Laboratory (SSRL) on the wiggler beam line VII-3 under dedicated operation at 3.0 GeV and *ca.* 60 mA. Each data set consists of an average of *ca.* 15 20-minute scans of samples *ca.* 1.5-2.0 mM in Cu. Data were collected by fluorescence excitation techniques using a multi-element array of scintillation detectors and Ni filters (13).

For data analysis involving Cu-N and Cu-S interactions, Cu EXAFS data on two model compounds were obtained. $[Cu(imid)_4]^{2+}$ (imid ≡ imidazole) was examined as a 20 mM frozen (4 K) aqueous solution by fluorescence techniques for extraction of Cu-N information. $[Cu(14\text{-ane-}S_4)](ClO_4)_2$ (14) was examined as a room temperature solid by transmission techniques as a model for Cu-S interactions.

Extraction of the EXAFS from raw XAS data was done using standard techniques (15,16). Curve-fitting of the EXAFS data was performed using a hybrid empirical/ theoretical technique described in detail elsewhere (16). This method uses complex Fourier backtransformation to extract (non-parameterized) empirical amplitude and phase functions from EXAFS data of the appropriate shells of model compounds, then uses these functions to fit the EXAFS data of the enzyme samples. The proper threshold energy (E_0) for each shell was estimated by performing the model compound complex backtransform phase function extraction at a series of E_0 values (used to define the k-scale of the original EXAFS) and comparing the empirical phase function with the appropriate theoretical function (17). The E_0 giving the best match was assumed to be the proper one. The empirical amplitude function was then extracted from the model compound by complex backtransform assuming the known N_s (number of scatterers in the shell) and an arbitrary σ_{as}^2 (the Debye-Waller relative mean square deviation in R_{as}, the absorber(Cu)-scatterer distance). All Debye-Waller factors for the enzyme fits are then reported as $\Delta\sigma_{as}^2$ values (relative to the model compound σ_{as}^2 for that shell). In general, the high degree of positive correlation between N_s and $\Delta\sigma_{as}^2$ requires that one be fixed, while the other is optimized. We have chosen to fix the value of N_s (for each fit) to be an integer (or half-integer for a two-copper enzyme such as aa_3) and vary $\Delta\sigma_{as}^2$. The accuracy of the fit is then judged by examining a goodness-of-fit parameter and by ascertaining the physical reasonability of the optimized $\Delta\sigma_{as}^2$. The distances (R_{as}) for each shell can be optimized simultaneously with the $\Delta\sigma_{as}^2$ values. For fits treating more than one shell, ΔE_0 is usually varied for all shells or for all but one shell.

Mathematically, the EXAFS expression used for the fits is given by

$$\chi(k) = \sum_s \frac{B_s N_s |f_s(\pi,k)|}{kR_{as}^2} \exp(-2\sigma_{as}^2 k^2)\sin[2kR_{as} + \alpha_{as}(k)] \tag{1}$$

The amplitude and phase functions (for each shell) are given by $|f_s(\pi,k)|$ and $\alpha_{as}(k)$, respectively, and B_s is a scale factor useful for correcting theoretical amplitude functions. Complex backtransformation of a single FT peak yields $\chi'(k)$ (filtered EXAFS) that contains both real and imaginary components. These can be used to generate the functions $A(k)$ and $\Phi(k)$ (16):

$$A(k) = [(\chi'_{re}(k))^2 + (\chi'_{im}(k))^2]^{1/2} \tag{2}$$

$$\Phi(k) = \tan^{-1}[\chi'_{im}(k)/\chi'_{re}(k)] \tag{3}$$

which make up the filtered EXAFS data:

$$\chi'_{re}(k) = A(k)\sin[\Phi(k)] \tag{4}$$

Assuming the filtered EXAFS is made up of just a single shell of the original $\chi(k)$, the amplitude function ($|f_s(\pi,k)|$) and phase function ($\alpha_{as}(k)$) for that shell can be easily calculated from $A(k)$ and $\Phi(k)$ using Eq. (5,6):

$$A(k) = \frac{B_s N_s |f_s(\pi,k)|}{k R_{as}^2} \exp(-2\sigma_{as}^2 k^2) \tag{5}$$

$$\Phi(k) = 2k R_{as} + \alpha_{as}(k) \tag{6}$$

and assuming a knowledge of N_s, σ_{as}^2, and R_{as} for that shell (B_s is assumed to be unity).

For the Cu-Fe fits, an appropriate model compound has not yet been examined so that the theoretical amplitude and phase functions (17) were used. Less information regarding scatterer number and Debye-Waller factor is available from these fits since no means is available for estimating B_s. However, the Cu-Fe distance is still precisely determined and information about the phase function is useful in identifying the scatterer type (*vide infra*).

Comparison of EXAFS Among Different Preparations

The Fourier transforms of the Cu EXAFS data from the eight resting state cytochrome aa_3 samples listed in Table I are compared in Fig. 1. The appearance of the FT's of

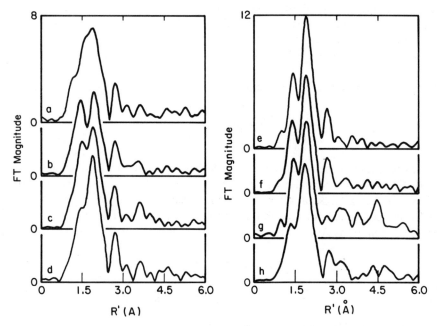

Figure 1. Fourier transforms (k^3-weighted, $k = 3.0$-13.0 Å^{-1}) of Cu EXAFS of eight resting state samples of cytochrome aa_3. The samples (see Table I for codes) are: (a) HB/Ua; (b) HB/M; (c) vB/A; (d) HB/P; (e) K/Bb; (f) K/Ba; (g) Y/E; (h) HB/Ub. (a)-(d) were collected at *ca.* 190 K, (e)-(h) at 4 K.

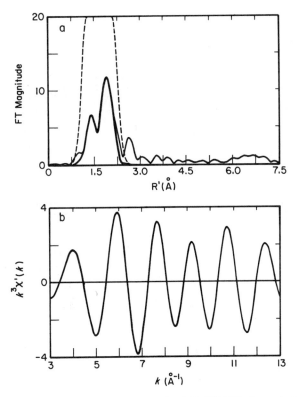

Figure 2. Example of Fourier filter of first two shells of Cu EXAFS of sample K/Bb. The FT window (dashed line) of (a) covers the range from $R' = 1.10$-2.30 Å with half-Gaussian edges of width 0.20 Å and the result of filtering is shown in (b).

the samples examined at *ca.* 190 K varies considerably among samples. Less difference is observed among the samples examined at 4 K. Thus, in examining different samples of resting state cytochrome aa_3, either one or two main FT peaks can be observed. This alone can explain the differences noted between previously published data (5-8). However, even for single-peak FT's, significant asymmetry is observed, indicating the presence of two shells (which are actually resolved into two FT peaks in many cases). As reported previously (5,8), these shells are best assigned to Cu-N(C,O) (the lower R' peak) and Cu-S interactions. These first two shells may be filtered out (as shown in Fig. 2) and curve-fit to Cu-N and Cu-S shells as described above. The results of fits to the individual samples (18) show insignificant variation in the Cu-N distance and Cu-S distance among samples but some variation in $\Delta\sigma_{as}^2$ for both Cu-N and Cu-S shells.

To determine whether these variations are significant, some estimate of the errors involved is necessary. The major source of experimental error for EXAFS on dilute systems such as metalloproteins is usually the noise in the raw EXAFS data. For this reason, a useful comparison is the deviation among the calculated (best fit

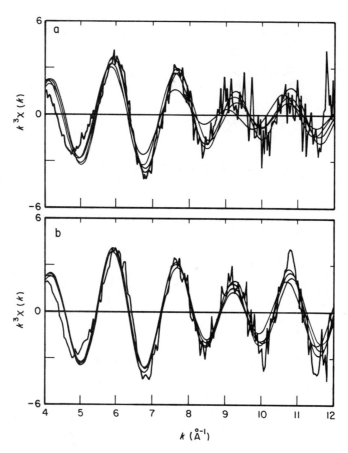

Figure 3. Comparison of individual curve-fitting results (smooth curves) with the raw Cu EXAFS data for resting state cytochrome aa_3 samples. (a) Data collected at ~190K: Fits are for samples HB/Ua, HB/M, HB/P, vB/A; raw data from sample HB/Ua. (b) Data collected at ~4 K: Fits are for samples K/Ba, K/Bb, Y/E, HB/Ub; raw data from sample K/Bb. In both cases, the spread in the fits is very comparable to the noise in the data.

Table II

Curve-fitting results for resting state cytochrome aa_3 Cu EXAFS

T (K)	Cu-N			Cu-S			ΔE_0 (eV)	f
	R_{as} (Å)	N_s	$\Delta\sigma_{as}^2$ (Å²)	R_{as} (Å)	N_s	$\Delta\sigma_{as}^2$ (Å²)		
191	1.96(2)	(2.0)	+0.0030(13)	2.30(1)	(2.0)	−0.0008(13)	−11(2)	0.360
	1.97(2)	(2.5)	+0.0042(10)	2.31(1)	(1.5)	−0.0026(12)	−14(2)	0.289
	1.98(1)	(3.0)	+0.0050(7)	2.33(1)	(1.0)	−0.0050(10)	−17(1)	0.245
4	1.94(1)	(2.0)	+0.0020(12)	2.29(1)	(2.0)	−0.0032(4)	−12(1)	0.394
	1.95(1)	(2.5)	+0.0035(11)	2.30(1)	(1.5)	−0.0048(4)	−14(1)	0.355
	1.97(1)	(3.0)	+0.0046(10)	2.31(1)	(1.0)	−0.0070(4)	−17(1)	0.398

EXAFS) ($\chi_{calc}(k)$) for different samples against the actual noise in the data. Figure 3 shows this comparison for both the 190 K and 4 K data. This is not a completely valid comparison since the fits correspond to only the first two shells of EXAFS. However, in virtually every region of *k*-space, the overall range of $\chi_{calc}(k)$ for different samples is very comparable to the random noise in the raw data. This type of comparison is usually obscured by the Fourier filtering of raw EXAFS data, which is necessary to remove shells not to be fit, but which has the added effect of disguising moderate amounts of noise.

The conclusion is that all the resting state cytochrome *aa*$_3$ samples examined (at a given temperature) give the same EXAFS (within experimental error), notwithstanding visual differences in the FT's. Given this, the curve-fitting results may be averaged together (for each temperature) and estimated standard deviations (esd's) calculated yielding information about the precision of the results. These averages are listed in Table II for three separate fits (for each temperature). The different fits assumed

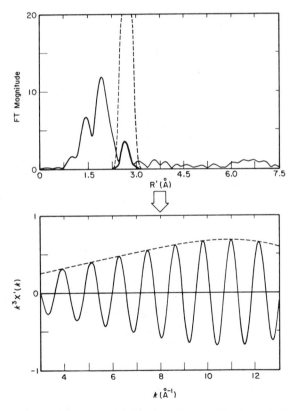

Figure 4. Example of Fourier filter of third shell of Cu EXAFS of sample K/Bb. The FT window (dashed line) of (a) covers the range from R′ = 2.45-2.95 Å with half-Gaussian edges of width 0.10 Å and the result of filtering is shown in (b). Note that the amplitude envelope of the filtered EXAFS shown in (b) has a maximum at $k \approx 11$ Å^{-1}.

different numbers (N_s) of N(C,O) and S ligands. The results may be summarized as follows. The average Cu-N(C,O) distance is 1.96(2) Å and the average Cu-S distance is 2.31(1) Å (the esd's correspond to *precision* not accuracy). The $\Delta\sigma_{as}^2$ values for Cu-N(C,O) are positive indicating more static disorder in these distances than in the model, [Cu(imid)$_4$]$^{2+}$. The difference in $\Delta\sigma_{as}^2$ between 190 K and 4K is insignificant, suggesting a fairly strong bond. For Cu-S, $\Delta\sigma_{as}^2$ values are significantly more negative at 4 K, indicating a large dynamic contribution to the Cu-S Debye-Waller factor. (This is reflected in the relative heights of the Cu-N and Cu-S FT peaks at 4 K *versus* 190 K in Fig. 1.) The goodness-of-fit parameters (f) suggest two possible stoichiometries: 5 N(C,O), 3 S per 2 Cu; or 6 N(C,O), 2 S per 2 Cu.

The a_3-Cu_B Binuclear Site

Another common feature of the FT's in Fig. 1 is the presence of a significant "third shell" peak at $R' \approx 2.7$ Å. This peak is clearly visible in all the FT's except for sample Y/E, in which the increased noise in the data appears to mask it. For the other seven samples, this third shell was Fourier-filtered as exemplified in Fig. 4. The k^3-weighted amplitude envelope of the filtered data is maximal at $k \approx 11$ Å^{-1}, reminiscent of a heavy scatterer.

Assignment of Third Shell Peak as Cu-Fe

It is instructive to consider the possible assignments of the FT peak at $R' \approx 2.7$ Å (the "third shell" peak). Other than a Cu-Fe interaction, the only realistic assignments involve outer shells of protein-derived ligands. Since there is strong evidence from labeling studies on yeast cytochrome aa_3 (19) for the assignment of histidine and cysteine as contributors to the Cu-N and Cu-S interactions, respectively, we will consider these ligands as examples. For histidine coordination through the imidazole N_3, C_2 and C_4 are known to give rise to a FT peak at $R' \approx 2.8$ Å (20). C_β of cysteine might also contribute a similar peak if the cysteine side chain is rigid enough. For other protein ligands, C atoms would again be expected as scatterers in this FT region.

If the third shell peak in the aa_3 FT was due mainly to imidazole C_2 and C_4, C_5 and N_1 would be expected to contribute a peak of about equal intensity in the region between 3.0 and 4.0 Å (20). Figure 5 compares the aa_3 FT (of sample K/Bb) with the FT of the model compound [Cu(imid)$_4$]$^{2+}$ (in aqueous solution). The [Cu(imid)$_4$]$^{2+}$ FT has been scaled to match the aa_3 FT intensity in the $R' \approx 3.0$-4.0 Å region. This comparison illustrates that the aa_3 third shell peak is much larger than would be expected if it were mainly contributed by imidazole C_2 and C_4.

This argument is based solely on FT magnitude. More information concerning the atomic number of the scatterer is available in the phase of the EXAFS oscillation giving rise to the FT peak. As already discussed, the phase function $\alpha_{as}(k)$ of the scatterer associated with the third shell peak can be extracted by complex backtransformation of that FT peak using Eq. (6). The same phase function extraction can be done on the equivalent peak in the [Cu(imid)$_4$]$^{2+}$ FT. Comparison of the

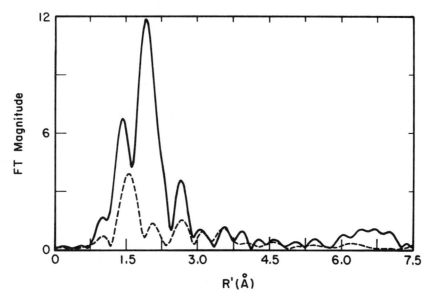

Figure 5. Comparison of Fourier transforms of Cu EXAFS of sample K/Bb (solid line) and $[Cu(imid)_4]^{2+}$ (dashed line) both at 4 K. The $[Cu(imid)_4]^{2+}$ FT is reduced by a scale factor (of 3.75) to match peak amplitudes in the R′ = 3.0-4.0 Å region. Note that the aa_3 FT peak at R′ = 2.7 Å is too large to be due to outer C shells of imidazoles.

phases will determine whether a Cu-C FT peak can be mistaken for a Cu-Fe FT peak. In order to do the $\alpha_{as}(k)$ extraction, a value for the distance, R_{as}, must be used in Eq. (6). In order to get a self-consistent value of R_{as} for all the aa_3 and $[Cu(imid)_4]^{2+}$ data sets, the third shell filtered EXAFS (see Fig. 4b) were curve-fit using the-oretical amplitude and phase functions (17) for Cu-Fe. In these fits, N_s was arbi-trarily fixed at 0.5 (one Fe per two Cu) and R_{as}, ΔE_0, B_s, and σ_{as}^2 were optimized. For each data set, Eq. (6) was then used with the best fit value of R_{as} to extract $\alpha_{as}(k)$. These $\alpha_{as}(k)$ are plotted for all seven aa_3 samples analyzed and compared to the result for $[Cu(imid)_4]^{2+}$ in Fig. 6. The spread in the aa_3 phase functions gives a good indication of the overall error involved in this determination. The phase function for $Cu[(imid)_4]^{2+}$ is clearly different from the aa_3 phase functions and well outside the experimental error. Thus, the third shell aa_3 FT peak is not realistically assignable to outer shell C atoms (at least, as represented by imidazole C_2, C_4 atoms).

Another piece of evidence involves the behavior of the third shell peak as a func-tion of cytochrome aa_3 oxidation state. Our previously published data (8) indicate that this FT peak almost completely disappears in the fully reduced enzyme. Since only minor (*ca.* 0.05 Å) changes are observed in the first shell (Cu-N,S) distances, the outer shell C contributions should not be significantly affected by reduction of the copper sites. Thus, the drastic change in the third shell FT peak upon reduction of cytochrome aa_3 also represents evidence against the assignment of this peak as Cu-C.

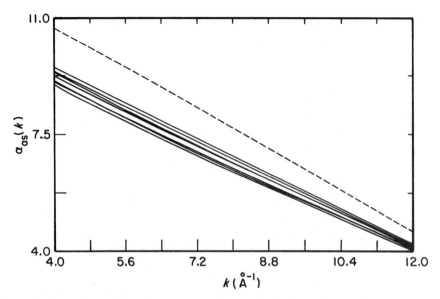

Figure 6. Comparison of phase functions ($a_{as}(k)$) derived from the R′ ≈ 2.7 Å FT peaks of seven cytochrome aa_3 samples (solid lines) and $[Cu(imid)_4]^{2+}$ (dashed line) all at 4 K. The cytochrome aa_3 samples are those listed in Table I (except for Y/E).

The weight of the evidence overwhelmingly supports the assignment of the R′ ≈ 2.7 Å peak in the resting state cytochrome aa_3 FT as a Cu-Fe interaction. The obvious conclusion is that this represents the presence of the Fe of heme a_3 in the vicinity of Cu_B.

Fe_{a3}-Cu_B Distance

The results of curve-fitting the Fourier-filtered third shell peaks of the cytochrome aa_3 FT's as Cu-Fe interactions are summarized in Table III. As discussed above, fitting with theoretical amplitude and phase functions in the absence of model compounds results in less information obtainable from the fits. This is a result of the required scaling of the theoretical amplitude function with the scale factor B_s (see Eq. (1)). Without model compounds, B_s must be treated as unknown, making the amplitude-related parameters (N_s, σ_{as}^2) relatively uninformative (on an absolute scale). In the fits represented in Table III, initial optimizations were performed varying R_{as}, σ_{as}^2, B_s, and ΔE_0 (holding N_s fixed at 0.5). Then, B_s was averaged for the seven aa_3 samples and this average B_s was used (and not optimized) for the final fits so that σ_{as}^2 values could be compared between the two temperatures (190 K, 4 K).

The most important result obtained from these fits is the Cu-Fe distance of 3.02(2) Å. As the esd shows, this value was consistently obtained for all samples. It is, however, *ca.* 0.8 Å lower than the Fe_{a3}-Cu_B distance reported by Powers, *et al.* (6,7). ΔE_0 was consistently determined to be −7(2) eV (corresponding to E_0 = 8993 eV). Without a Cu-Fe model compound, however, we cannot determine whether this

Table III
Cu-Fe curve-fitting results for cytochrome aa_3

T (K)	R_{as} (Å)	N_s	σ_{as}^2 (Å)	B_s[a]	ΔE_0 (eV)	f
191	3.03(1)[b]	[0.5][c]	0.0020(8)	[0.35]	−7(1)	0.056
4	3.01(2)	[0.5]	0.0018(4)	[0.35]	−6(2)	0.059

[a]This scale factor was the average of the values obtained for each data set in an optimization varying R_{as}, σ_{as}^2, B_s and ΔE_0.
[b]Numbers in parentheses are esd's.
[c]Numbers in square brackets are not optimized.

value is reasonable. Somewhat surprisingly, σ_{as}^2 does not decrease significantly on decreasing the temperature from 190 K to 4 K. This would seem to indicate a fairly rigid structure for the binuclear site in resting state cytochrome aa_3.

Conclusion

Comparison of Cu EXAFS of eight samples of resting state cytochrome aa_3 prepared by four different preparations in six different laboratories in Europe and USA indicate that any differences observed in the EXAFS or Fourier transform are within the experimental error of the raw data. It is our opinion that this result fully explains differences observed in the published Cu EXAFS data of two groups (5-8). The "first shell" copper ligands include 5-6 N(C,O)-containing ligands with an average Cu-N(C,O) distance of 1.96(2) Å and 2-3 S-containing ligands with an average Cu-S distance of 2.31(1) Å (somehow distributed between Cu_A and Cu_B). In combination with other evidence, our best guess at the ligand distribution is $Cu_A(N_2S_2)$, $Cu_B(N,O)_4$. No evidence is found for the existence of a short (*ca.* 2.1 Å) Cu-S bond as required for the presence of a blue copper (6,7).

A "third shell" FT peak (at $R' \approx 2.7$ Å) is consistently observed in the Cu FT of resting state cytochrome aa_3 samples. Detailed analysis of this peak indicates that it can only be assigned to the Cu_B-Fe_{a3} interaction, yielding a Cu_B-Fe_{a3} distance of 3.02(2) Å. This is significantly shorter than the Cu_B-Fe_{a3} distance of 3.80 Å reported by Powers, *et al.* (6,7), and we do not consistently observe a FT peak assignable to a scatterer at that distance. The Cu-Fe FT peak does not get significantly larger at 4 K (compared to 190 K), suggesting a fairly rigid structure for the binuclear site. It should be noted that 3.0 Å is a fairly common M-M' distance for binuclear complexes exhibiting strong antiferromagnetic exchange coupling (21) as found in resting state cytochrome aa_3 (22).

Acknowledgement

The following are acknowledged for providing resting state cytochrome aa_3 samples for this study: H. Beinert, A. Azzi, S. I. Chan, and M. T. Wilson. D. B. Rorabacher is thanked for the sample of [Cu(14-ane-S_4)](ClO_4)$_2$ and T. Smith for the sample of

Scott, et. al.

[Cu(imid)$_4$](NO$_3$)$_2$. XAS studies under RAS at Illinois were supported by NIH Biomedical Research Support Grant RR07030. The work was done at SSRL which is supported by the Department of Energy, Office of Basic Energy Sciences; and the NIH, Biotechnology Resource Program, Division of Research Resources.

References and Footnotes

1. For a review see: B. G. Malmström in *Metal Ion Activation of Dioxygen,* Ed., T. G. Spiro, Wiley, New York, chapt. 5 (1980).
2. V. W. Hu, S. I. Chan and G. S. Brown, *Proc. Natl. Acad. Sci. USA 74,* 3821 (1977).
3. V. W. Hu, S. I. Chan and G. S. Brown, *FEBS Lett. 84,* 287 (1977).
4. L. Powers, W. E. Blumberg, B. Chance, C. H. Barlow, J. S. Leigh, Jr., J. Smith, T. Yonetani, S. Vik and J. Peisach, *Biochim Biophys. Acta 546,* 520 (1979).
5. R. A. Scott, S. P. Cramer, H. B. Gray, R. W. Shaw and H. Beinert, *Proc. Natl. Acad. Sci, USA 78,* 664 (1981).
6. L. Powers, B. Chance, Y. Ching and P. Angiolillo, *Biophys. J. 34,* 465 (1981).
7. B. Chance, L. Powers and Y. Ching in *Mitochondria and Microsomes,* Eds., C. P. Lee, G. Schatz and G. Dallner, Addison-Wesley, London, p. 271 (1981).
8. R. A. Scott in *The Biological Chemistry of Iron,* Eds., H. B. Dunford, D. H. Dolphin, K. N. Raymond and L. C. Sieker, D. Reidel, Boston, p. 475 (1982).
9. Procedure I of C. R. Hartzell, H. Beinert, B. F. van Gelder and T. E. King, *Meth. Enzymol. 53,* 54 (1978).
10. Procedure III of C. R. Hartzell, H. Beinert, B. F. van Gelder and T. E. King, *Meth. Enzymol. 53,* 54 (1978).
11. Procedure II of C. R. Hartzell, H. Beinert, B. F. van Gelder and T. E. King, *Meth. Enzymol. 53,* 54 (1978).
12. T. Yonetani, *J. Biol. Chem. 235,* 845 (1960).
13. S. P. Cramer and R. A. Scott, *Rev. Sci. Instrum. 52,* 395 (1981).
14. This sample was a gift from D. B. Rorabacher: M. D. Glick, D. P. Gavel, L. L. Diaddario and D. B. Rorabacher, *Inorg. Chem. 15,* 1190 (1976).
15. R. A. Scott in *Structural and Resonance Techniques in Biological Research,* Ed., D. L. Rousseau, Academic Press, New York, vol. 2, chapt. 4, 295.
16. R. A. Scott, *Meth. Enzymol.* submitted for publication.
17. B.-K. Teo and P. A. Lee, *J. Am. Chem. Soc. 101,* 2815 (1979).
18. R. A. Scott, J. R. Schwartz and S. P. Cramer, manuscript in preparation.
19. T. H. Stevens, C. T. Martin, C. Wang, G. W. Brudvig, C. P. Scholes and S. I. Chan, *J. Biol. Chem. 257,* 12106 (1982).
20. M. S. Co, R. A. Scott and K. O. Hodgson, *J. Am. Chem. Soc. 103,* 986 (1981).
21. S. E. Groh, *Israel J. Chem. 15,* 277 (1976).
22. M. F. Tweedle, L. J. Wilson, L. García-Iñiguez, G. T. Babcock and G. Palmer, *J. Biol. Chem. 253,* 8065 (1978).

Biological & Inorganic Copper Chemistry,
ISBN 0-940030-11-X, Eds., K. D. Karlin & J. Zubieta, Adenine Press, ©Adenine Press, 1985

Studies of Copper-Zinc Superoxide Dismutase: The Role of Zinc and of the Essential Arginyl Residue

Joan Selverstone Valentine, James A. Roe, Alison Butler, and Duarte Mota de Freitas

Department of Chemistry and Biochemistry and Molecular Biology Institute,
University of California, Los Angeles,
Los Angeles, California, 90024 USA

Abstract

Differential scanning calorimetry (DSC) has been used to monitor and to characterize the thermally-induced unfolding of the apoprotein derived from bovine Cu,Zn-superoxide dismutase (SOD) and Zn-substituted derivatives. Apo-SOD was found to melt monophasically with a T_m of 57 °C. The derivatives containing zinc were found to be considerably more stable thermally, the two-zinc derivative melting at 72 and the four-zinc derivative at 79 °C. A DSC study of apo-SOD as a function of added Zn^{2+} revealed that binding of the first two zinc ions per dimer produced most of the zinc-induced thermal stabilization of the SOD dimer. Further addition of Zn^{2+} caused the melting transition to sharpen, indicating an increase in the cooperativity of the transition. It also caused the T_m to shift to slightly higher values, but the enthalpy of the denaturation process was not significantly increased. These results suggest that zinc plays a significant role in stabilizing the structure of the protein dimer.

Binding of phosphate to bovine Cu,Zn-SOD was investigated using ^{31}P NMR. Addition of 0.4 mM native SOD to a 4 mM phosphate solution caused a 20-fold increase in the phosphate resonance linewidth relative to a solution of free inorganic phosphate. Line broadening was significantly less when derivatives of SOD chemically modified at arginine or lysine were used. The pH-dependence of the phosphate resonance linewidth indicates that HPO_4^{2-} interacts more strongly with the protein than does $H_2PO_4^{-}$. Binding of ATP to the protein was also observed using the same technique.

Introduction

Copper-zinc superoxide dismutase (Cu,Zn-SOD) was first isolated from ox blood in 1938 by Mann and Keilin (1). Because this blue-green protein had no apparent enzymatic activity, it was at that time named erythrocuprein (or hemocuprein) after its source and content of copper. During the following three decades, similar proteins were isolated from a variety of other tissues. Until 1969, no enzymatic activity was found for the cupreins and thus they were assumed to be copper storage proteins. In 1969, McCord and Fridovich discovered an enzyme with superoxide dismutase (SOD) activity and showed it to be identical with erythrocuprein (2,3). Shortly thereafter, Carrico and Deutsch showed that erythrocuprein contained zinc as well as copper (4). In addition to the copper- and zinc-containing SOD present in the cytosol of eucaryotic cells, there are two other classes of SOD's. These proteins contain iron or manganese instead of copper and zinc and are found in procaryotes and mitochondria of eucaryotic cells respectively (5). All of these proteins were found to catalyze the disproportionation of superoxide,

$$2\,O_2^- + 2\,H^+ \rightleftharpoons O_2 + H_2O_2$$

and it was therefore proposed that they were part of a defense mechanism to protect aerobic organisms from dioxygen toxicity (6-8). Although there is no doubt that the SOD's catalyze the disproportionation of superoxide anion, there exists at present a sometimes heated disagreement about the true primary physiological function of these proteins, and the proposal that Cu,Zn-SOD may be involved in metal ion metabolism has resurfaced (9,10).

Bovine erythrocyte Cu,Zn-SOD has a molecular weight of 31,200 and consists of two identical subunits (for reviews, see ref. 5-8, 11-14). In the resting enzyme, each subunit contains one copper and one zinc ion, both in the 2+ oxidation state. A great deal of structural information is available since both its amino acid sequence (15) and x-ray crystal structure at 2 Å resolution (16) are known. The copper(II) ion is found to be coordinated to four imidazole nitrogens from histidines 44, 46, 61, and 118 in a distorted square pyramidal structure with water as the fifth ligand. The zinc ion is coordinated to imidazoles from histidines 61, 69, and 78 and the carboxylate group from aspartate 81 in an approximately tetrahedral geometry. The imidazole ring of histidine 61 is deprotonated and that ligand acts as a bridge between the two metal ions in each subunit.

Pulse radiolysis studies (17) have demonstrated that the mechanism of catalysis involves alternate reduction and oxidation at the copper site during the catalytic cycle.

$$Cu(II) + O_2^- \rightleftharpoons Cu(I) + O_2$$
$$Cu(I) + O_2^- + 2\,H^+ \rightleftharpoons Cu(II) + H_2O_2$$

The role (if any) of the zinc ion in the mechanism of catalysis is not known, especially since removal of the zinc ion under conditions such that the copper ion remains in the copper site has only a small effect on the SOD activity (18). Alternatively, it has been proposed that the primary role of zinc in the protein may be structural rather than mechanistic (19-21).

X-ray crystallographic studies of bovine Cu, Zn-SOD indicate that the positively charged side chains of Arg-141, Lys-120, and Lys-134 are located in the vicinity of the active site 5, 12, and 13 Å, respectively, away from the copper(II) ion (16, 22). It has been proposed that these residues are important in providing electrostatic guidance to the anionic substrate since chemical modification of Arg-141 by phenylglyoxal or of Lys-120 and Lys-134 by acetic anhydride, succinic anhydride, or cyanate results in decreased SOD activity (23-26). The importance of these residues in the reaction mechanism of bovine Cu,Zn-SOD is apparent from the dependence of SOD activity on ionic strength (24,26,27). The isoelectric point of this protein is 4.8 (28) and, therefore, at neutral pH, bovine Cu,Zn-SOD is negatively charged. Consequently, one might predict that the reactivity of the protein with a negatively charged substrate such as superoxide would be enhanced by an increase in ionic strength. In fact, precisely the opposite is observed, and it is therefore believed that the positively charged side chains of Arg-141, Lys-120, and Lys-134 play an important role in the interaction of the protein with superoxide and that the lower SOD activity at high ionic strength is due to the partial neutralization of these charges by interactions with anions.

In addition to the generalized effect of ionic strength, several specific effects of phosphate ion on the properties of Cu,Zn-SOD have been noted. Rotilio et al. (29) noted that phosphate present at concentrations greater than 0.05 M interfered with cyanide binding to the protein. They also observed substantially reduced SOD activity under the same conditions (30). Calabrese et al. (31) found that the nature of Co(II) binding to the apoprotein was different in the presence of phosphate than in its absence, and Strothkamp and Lippard (32) observed that the imidazolate bridge linking the two subunits in the four-copper derivative of SOD was broken in the presence of high concentrations of phosphate.

The inhibitory effect of phosphate on the SOD activity of bovine Cu,Zn-SOD has generally been assumed to be caused by the increase in ionic strength resulting from the addition of phosphate salts to the solutions (24,33). However, studies of the effects of variable amounts of phosphate on the anion binding properties and SOD activity of solutions of Cu,Zn-SOD under conditions of constant ionic strength demonstrated that phosphate had a specific effect in addition to the generalized ionic strength effect (27). The SOD activity and anion binding affinities of Cu,Zn-SOD that had been chemically modified at Arg-141 by the reaction of phenylglyoxal were much less affected by the presence of phosphate, leading to the proposal (27) that Arg-141 was the site of the interaction of phosphate with the protein.

Studies of structure-function relationships in bovine Cu,Zn-SOD have tended to focus on the role of the copper ion. While there is no question that the copper ion is crucial to the SOD activity, two other aspects of the active site region are particularly intriguing. These are the zinc ion and the essential arginyl residue, Arg-141. In this manuscript, we describe results of two studies, the first one of which used differential scanning calorimetry to investigate the role of zinc in stabilizing Cu,Zn-SOD and the second one ^{31}P NMR to investigate the binding of phosphate to Cu,Zn-SOD.

Materials and Methods

Bovine liver Cu,Zn-SOD was obtained as a lyophilized powder from Diagnostic Data, Inc. (Mountain View, CA). Protein concentrations of native bovine SOD were determined by Lowry assay, by weight of lyophilized powder, or spectrophotometrically, using $\epsilon_{258nm} = 10{,}300$ M^{-1}cm^{-1}. Apo-SOD was prepared as described previously (34), and concentrations were determined by the Lowry assay (35) using a known native bovine SOD solution for the protein standard. The zinc-containing derivatives were prepared by the direct addition of a 1.53 mM Zn(NO$_3$)$_2$ solution (100 mM acetate, pH 5.5) to an acetate buffered apo-SOD solution, pH 5.5. Zinc concentrations were checked using a Perkin Elmer 603 Atomic Absorption spectrometer. Bovine Cu,Zn-SOD was chemically modified at Arg-141 with phenylglyoxal using the method of Malinowski and Fridovich (23). Succinylation of lysine residues of bovine Cu,Zn-SOD was carried out according to Marmocchi et al. (25). The purified arginine- and lysine-modified proteins were dialyzed extensively against distilled water and lyophilized. Residual SOD activities of the arginine- and lysine-modified proteins were approximately 20 and 15% of that of the native protein. Residual activity of the chemically modified proteins was shown previously to be due to the modified proteins and not to native protein that had escaped chemical modification (24,25,27). Native and arginine modified proteins were reduced by addition of sufficient sodium dithionite to bleach the color of the protein. Water used for making all buffer and other solutions was triply deionized using a Barnstead Nanopure water system.

Calorimetry. Calorimetric measurements were made on a Microcal MC-1 Differential Scanning Calorimeter (Amherst, MA) equipped with two removable hasteloy cells. The temperature was usually increased from about 15 to 105 °C at a heating rate of 50 °C per hour.

A DSC records the differential heat capacity between the sample and reference cells as the temperature is raised. The area under the transition curve, normalized for protein concentration, is proportional to the enthalpy of denaturation, ΔH_d, and the peak maximum is the melting temperature, T_m. The peak areas were determined using a Gelman Instrument Company (model 399231) Compensating Polar Planimeter.

NMR. ^{31}P NMR measurements were made at 81.02 MHz on a Bruker WP200 NMR spectrometer at the ambient probe temperature. The samples were contained in 10-mm NMR spinning tubes and a concentric capillary, centered in each NMR tube, containing 85% phosphoric acid was used as an external reference. The pH of each solution was measured in the NMR tube with a semi-micro Polymark combination electrode. NaOH and HCl solutions were used for pH adjustments. pH values quoted are not corrected for the deuterium isotope effect. ^{31}P NMR spectra were measured with 2000 Hz spectral width using 4K data points. Prior to Fourier transformation, exponential filtering was applied to the FID to enhance signal-to-noise ratio and the resultant line broadening (1Hz) was allowed for when measuring linewidths.

Calorimetric Studies of Zn Binding

Native bovine Cu,Zn-superoxide dismutase is a relatively stable protein that does not begin to denature until at least 80 °C (36). The apoprotein, on the other hand, is significantly less stable, unfolding with a T_m of 57 °C. Moreover, we found the zinc-free SOD derivative, i.e. the derivative in which only Cu^{2+} is coordinated to the native copper sites and in which the native zinc sites are unoccupied, to be destabilized by at least 25 °C relative to the native protein (36) suggesting that Zn^{2+} plays an important structural role in the overall stabilization of the protein structure. We have, therefore, undertaken a detailed study of the effect of Zn^{2+} binding to apo-SOD using differential scanning calorimetry to assess the thermally induced unfolding of apo-SOD and the zinc-containing derivatives.

We have observed that the SOD derivative in which all four metal binding sites are occupied by Zn^{2+} has a very sharp DSC profile characterized by a T_m of 79 °C. On the other hand, the stability of the Zn_2-SOD (i.e. the native copper sites are unoccupied) is not appreciably destabilized, $T_m = 72$ °C, compared to Zn_4-SOD, demonstrating that zinc bound at the native zinc sites, as opposed to the native copper sites, induces the major structural changes and provides most of the thermal stability.

The most significant observations concerning the stability that Zn^{2+}-binding confers to apo-SOD comes from the titration of apo-SOD with Zn^{2+} at ratios of Zn/protein-dimer between 0 and 2. At two equivalents of added Zn per dimer, the DSC profile shows a single transition with a T_m of 72 °C, whereas at a ratio of 1.0 Zn/dimer, two transitions are observed, one at 57 °C (apo-SOD) and the other at 72 °C (Zn_2SOD). These results suggest that the occupation by zinc of the first two binding sites on apo-SOD is accomplished in a cooperative, pairwise manner. If the binding of the first two zinc ions per dimer of SOD were instead statistical, three separate transitions, corresponding to the apo-SOD, the single-zinc derivative, and Zn_2-SOD, should have been observed during the titration. In addition, the enthalpy of denaturation, ΔH_d, for the zinc derivatives of SOD reached a maximum when the ratio of zinc ions to protein dimer was two. The addition of two more equivalents of zinc caused the single peak to sharpen while at the same time moving to a slightly higher temperature, the T_m increasing from 72 to 79 °C. However, ΔH_d did not change. When the ratio of zinc ion to protein dimer exceeded four, no appreciable change in either T_m or ΔH_d was noted, suggesting that excess Zn^{2+} does not interact with the protein in a significant fashion after the metal binding sites are filled. Other possible explanations of the observation of only two peaks during the zinc titration are (1) that the protein dimer is behaving as though it were two independent monomers during the denaturation process and (2) that the thermal stability of the one- and two-zinc derivatives are identical. Neither of these explanations seems likely to us in light of the known very strong association between the two subunits of the dimeric protein.

Cass et al. (20) and Lippard et al. (19) have reported that the NMR spectrum of apo-SOD after addition of one equivalent of Zn^{2+} per protein dimer is a superposition of the spectrum of apo-SOD and that of the two zinc derivative. This result suggests that the metal binding region of an apoprotein subunit is not substantially perturbed when zinc is bound to the other subunit. Our DSC result, that the first two zinc ions are cooperatively bound by the protein dimer, does not contradict these NMR observations since cooperative binding of zinc ions by SOD would give identical NMR results, i.e. that the addition of one zinc ion per protein dimer yields an NMR spectrum which is the superposition of that of apo-SOD and that of Zn_2-SOD.

Although we cannot at this time define the molecular origin of the cooperative binding of the first two zinc ions by the apo-SOD dimer, it does seem clear that the binding of the first zinc must cause changes in the structure of the subunit to which it is bound that are communicated to the other subunit, presumably by changes at the subunit interface.

NMR Studies

The binding of phosphate anion to bovine Cu,Zn-SOD was followed by changes in the linewidth of the phosphate resonance as measured by ^{31}P NMR. Table I lists the linewidth at half-height of the phosphate resonance in the presence and absence of native or chemically modified protein solutions. Addition of 0.4 mM native bovine Cu,Zn-SOD to a 4 mM phosphate solution caused a twenty-fold increase in linewidth relative to a solution of free inorganic phosphate. Much less line broadening was observed with sample solutions containing phosphate and arginine- or lysine-modified proteins. We attribute all of the line broadening observed to the effect of the paramagnetic Cu(II) ion in the protein since no line broadening was observed in sample solutions containing phosphate and fully reduced, i.e. Cu(I)-containing protein. Studies of the amount of line broadening in the presence of the native protein as a function of pH showed that the linewidth reached a maximum at approximately pH 6.5 suggesting that it is HPO_4^{2-} rather than $H_2PO_4^-$ that has the higher affinity for the protein. Similar studies using ATP showed that the phosphate resonances of that species were likewise broadened in the presence of Cu,Zn-SOD but not in the presence of the arginine-modified protein.

Table I

Linewidths of the [31]P Resonance of Phosphate in the Presence
and Absence of Native of Chemically Modified SOD[a,b]

	$_{1/2}$(Hz)
Phosphate	5.0
Phosphate + reduced native SOD	5.0
Phosphate + reduced Arg-modified SOD	5.0
Phosphate + native SOD	107
Phosphate + Arg-modified SOD	27
Phosphate + Lys-modified SOD	28
Phosphate + Cu^{2+}	no NMR signal

[a] $\Delta\nu_{1/2}$ readings are the average of measurements taken in at least three separate sample solutions. The uncertainty in these readings is estimated to be ± 5%.

[b] Reagent concentrations were $[K_2HPO_4]$ = 4 mM, [SOD] = 0.4 mM, $[Cu^{2+}]$ = 0.8 mM. Note that the concentration of Cu^{2+} in 0.4 mM SOD is 0.8 mM since the protein is dimeric.

[c] $\Delta\nu_{1/2}$ measured at pH 8.0 where the linewidth of phosphate is broadest. For all other samples, $\Delta\nu_{1/2}$ was measured at approximately pH 6.3.

The functional significance of the binding of phosphate and adenylates to bovine Cu,Zn-SOD is not immediately apparent to us. Although it is clear from our earlier work (27) that phosphate at concentrations typically present in the cell will cause inhibition of the SOD activity of this protein, it is also possible that phosphate and adenylates may play a role in some as yet unknown physiological function of this protein. Hopefully, future studies will clarify the role of phosphate in the function of this protein.

Acknowledgement

Financial support from the U.S. Public Health Services in the form of a grant to J.S.V. (GM28222) and an N.I.H. Postdoctoral Fellowship to A.B. and fellowship support for D.M.d.F. from the Calouste Gulbenkian Foundation and INIC/Invotan (Portugal) are gratefully acknowledged.

References and Footnotes

1. T. Mann and D. Keilin, *Proc. Roy. Soc. Ser., B. Biol. Sci. 126*, 303 (1938).
2. J.M. McCord and I. Fridovich, *J. Biol. Chem. 243*, 5753 (1968).
3. J.M. McCord and I. Fridovich, *J. Biol. Chem. 244*, 6049 (1969).
4. R.J. Carrico and H.F. Deutsch, *J. Biol. Chem. 245*, 723 (1970)
5. I. Fridovich, *Annu. Rev. Biochem. 44*, 147 (1975).
6. I. Fridovich, *Adv. Enzymol. 41*, 35 (1974).
7. I. Fridovich, *Science 201*, 875 (1978).
8. I. Fridovich, *Adv. Inorg. Biochem. 1*, 67 (1979).
9. J.A. Fee, *Trends in Biochemical Sciences 7*, 84-86 (1982).
10. *Chemical and Engineering News*, pp. 20-26 (April 9, 1984).
11. B.G. Malstrom, L.E. Andreasson and B. Reinhammar in *Enzymes, 3rd ed. Vol. 12*, p. 507 (1975).
12. I. Fridovich, *Acc. Chem. Res. 5*, 321 (1972).
13. J.S. Valentine and M.W. Pantoliano in *Copper Proteins*, Ed., T.G. Spiro, Wiley, New York, pp. 291-358 (1981).
14. K.G. Strothkamp and S.J. Lippard, *Acc. Chem. Res. 15*, 318 (1982).
15. H.M. Steinman, V.R. Naik, J.L. Abernathy and R.L. Hill, *J. Biol. Chem. 249*, 7326 (1974).
16. J.A. Tainer, E.D. Getzoff, K.M. Beem, J.S. Richardson and D.C. Richardson, *J. Mol. Biol. 160*, 181 (1982).
17. D. Klug-Roth, I. Fridovich and J. Rabani, *J. Amer. Chem.Soc.95*, 2786 (1973).
18. M.W. Pantoliano, J.S. Valentine, A.R. Burger, and S.J. Lippard, *J. Inorg. Biochem. 17*, 325 (1982).
19. S.J. Lippard, A.R. Burger, K. Uqurbil, M.W. Pantoliano and J.S. Valentine, *Biochemistry 16*, 1136 (1977).
20. A.E.G. Cass, H.A.O. Hill, J.V. Bannister and W.H. Bannister, *Biochem. J. 177*, 477 (1979).
21. A.E.G. Cass, H.A.O. Hill, J.V. Bannister and W.H. Bannister, *Biochem. J. 183*, 127 (1979).
22. T.A. Tainer, E.D. Getzoff, J.S. Richardson and D.C. Richardson, *Nature 306*, 284 (1983).
23. D.P. Malinowski and I. Fridovich, *Biochemistry 18*, 5909 (1979).
24. A. Cudd and I. Fridovich, *J. Biol. Chem. 257*, 11443 (1982).
25. F. Marmocchi, I. Mavelli, A. Rigo, R. Stevanato, F. Bossa and G. Rotilio, *Biochemistry 21*, 2853 (1982).
26. D. Cocco, L. Rossi, D. Barra, F. Bossa and G. Rotilio, *FEBS Lett. 150*, 303 (1982).
27. D. Mota de Freitas and J.S. Valentine, *Biochemistry 23*, 2079 (1984).
28. F. Marmocchi, E. Argese, A. Rigo, I. Mavelli, L. Rossi and G. Rotilio, *Mol. Cel. Biochemistry 51*, 161 (1983).
29. G. Rotilio. L. Morpurgo, C. Giovagnoli, L. Calabrese and B. Mondovi, *Biochemistry 11*, 2187 (1972).
30. A. Rigo, P. Viglino, G. Rotilio and R. Tomat, *FEBS Lett. 50*, 86 (1975).

31. L. Calabrese, D. Cocco and A. Desidori, *FEBS Lett. 106,* 142 (1979).
32. K.G. Strothkamp and S.J. Lippard, *Biochemistry 20,* 7488 (1981).
33. M.E. McAdam, *Biochem. J. 161,* 697 (1977).
34. J.S. Valentine, M.W. Pantoliano, P.J. McDonnell, A.R. Burger, and S.J. Lippard, *Proc. Natl. Acad. Sci. U.S.A. 76,* 4245 (1979).
35. O.H. Lowry, N.J. Rosebrough, A.L. Farr and R.J. Randall, *J. Biol. Chem. 193,* 265-275 (1951).
36. A. Butler and J.S. Valentine, unpublished results.

Biological & Inorganic Copper Chemistry,
'SBN 0-940030-11-X, Eds., K. D. Karlin & J. Zubieta, Adenine Press, ©Adenine Press, 1985

Hemocyanin Cooperativity:
A Copper Coordination Chemistry Perspective

Christopher A. Reed
Department of Chemistry
University of Southern California
Los Angeles, California 90089-1062

Abstract

The mechanism of cooperativity of oxygen binding to hemocyanin is unknown. And it differs from hemoglobin in a very significant way: carbon monoxide binding to hemocyanin is non-cooperative. This identifies the formal oxidation state change at copper upon oxygen binding as the instigator of cooperativity. Two major structural and electronic changes accompanying the oxidative addition of oxygen to the dicopper(I) deoxy state are identified. These are the angular movement of the dominant histidine ligands and the production of large dipoles within the Cu_2O_2 moiety. It is suggested that these features are the basis of the cooperativity mechanism. The possibility of distal histidine at the oxygen binding site is also discussed.

Introduction

Cooperativity of oxygen binding to aggregated hemocyanins is well documented (1). There is a natural tendency to view this phenomenon in a similar way to the intensively studied cooperativity of ligand binding in hemoglobins. While this approach is fundamentally sound in dealing phenomenologically with the thermodynamic and kinetic aspects it may obscure important differences when considering a molecular mechanism. For example, it is little appreciated that the non-cooperativity of carbon monoxide binding to hemocyanin (2) is in marked contrast to hemoglobin where both O_2 and CO binding are cooperative. In this paper we discuss the active site structure of hemocyanin with a view to identifying those features of its copper coordination chemistry which might induce a cooperative interaction when binding O_2. Because of the growing confidence in the molecular level description of the active site from recent chemical, spectroscopic (3,4) and model compound (5) studies the time is approaching when such a discussion can be meaningful and stimulating to the field. The solution to the Xray crystal structure of hemocyanin has recently progressed from shape resolution (5 Å) (6) to polypeptide chain recognition (3.2 Å) (7) and three histidine ligands per copper have been identified with reasonable certainty. Moreover, the first experiments which prove that deoxygenation of one site can cause structural changes at another are beginning to appear (8). It is anticipated that some of the ideas and concepts of copper coordination chemistry generated at this time will eventually be incorporated into a detailed molecular mechanism for oxygen cooperativity in hemocyanin.

Hemocyanin Cooperativity

In aggregated states, hemocyanins can show marked cooperativity of oxygen binding (1). Hill coefficients as high as 9 have been reported but usually they are 2-4. Hexamers of the basic 50,000-75,000 MW subunit are common particularly in arthropods but much higher oligomers, sometimes containing varying amounts of different subunits (α, β, etc.) are also quite common. High cooperativity appears always to be associated with the presence of divalent cations (Ca^{2+}, Mg^{2+}, etc.) called heterotropic effectors. Bohr effects (pH effects) on oxygen cooperativity can be positive or negative but tend to maximize near neutral pH.

While the degree of oligomerization may change during oxygenation and deoxygenation an explanation of cooperativity based solely upon association and dissociation is inadequate. Conformationally distinct low and high affinity forms are assumed to exist in accord with the classical two-state allosteric theory of Monod, Wyman and Changeux (9). By analogy to hemoglobin the low affinity state is labelled T (tense) and the high affinity state R (relaxed). Since the physiological purpose of cooperativity must be to facilitate off-loading of O_2 at locations of low O_2 tension it is preferable to think in terms of mechanisms which reduce O_2 affinity in the T state relative to the R. This approach makes further sense when viewed in the light of kinetic data (1,10). 'On' rates for O_2 binding vary rather little. Differing O_2 affinities are, in fact, largely the result of varying 'off' rates (2-4000 sec^{-1}). Whatever conformational changes accompany the R to T transition, they lower the O_2 affinity by destabilizing the oxygen adduct. It is probably fair to assume that this is achieved in the T state by protein conformational constraints at the active site which favor the deoxy copper(I) structure over the oxy copper(II) structure. The transmission of structural effects from one active site to another is an impressive feat of trans-protein communication because the copper centers are some 50 Å apart (7). The comparable distance in hemoglobin is about 25 Å (11). As we shall see it could be argued that the active site structural and electronic changes between the oxy and deoxy forms of hemocyanin are, at least in principle, greater than those of hemoglobin. This difference between copper and iron coordination chemistry may account for the more extensive transmission of cooperative effects in hemocyanins compared to hemoglobins. It is also true, however, that while distance transmission is greater in hemocyanin the free energy change per active site (0.9-2.5 kcal·mole^{-1}) (12) is only about half that of hemoglobin (3-4 kcal·mole^{-1}). Comparable Hill coefficients for both proteins are seen then to arise from the higher degree of oligomerization in hemocyanin.

Although heterotropic effectors (H^+, Ca^{2+}, etc.) have been shown to have some effect on CO affinities (13) there is no homotropic cooperativity with this ligand (12). It is likely, therefore, that CO ligation is unable to effect the T to R state structural change. The chemical basis of the ligation differences between CO and O_2 is clearly a primary clue in unravelling the mechanism of cooperativity.

Before any molecular level description of cooperativity can be realized the structures of the deoxy (Hc) and oxy (HcO_2) active sites must be known in considerable detail. Indeed, knowing the active site structures is the minimal structural information needed since a full description would require a rather precise knowledge of the protein conformational changes attendant to the R to T switch. At this point in time the structural parameters of the oxy active site are known with a fair degree of certainty, enough to propose a working model. Less well known are the structures of the deoxy site and the carbonmonoxy site. What follows is a summary of the key indicators of active site structure that are presently available. The intention of this exercise is to deduce plausible structures for the three operative states of hemocyanin, HcO_2, Hc and HcCO, and to indicate the boundaries of uncertainty. In ultimately choosing a particular working model for the active site there are bound to be inaccuracies which will have to be corrected as more refined structures become available. The present working model is intended only to illustrate the operation of certain chemical principles of copper chemistry that hemocyanin might be exploiting in triggering the cooperative alteration of O_2 affinities.

The Oxy Site

The most plausible structure for the active site of HcO_2 is illustrated in Figure 1. Peroxidic bound dioxygen (ie formally O_2^{2-}) is required by the low νO-O stretching frequency (~ 745 cm^{-1} for $^{16}O_2$) and is consistent with the magnitude of the isotopic shift ($\Delta = -40$ cm^{-1} for $^{18}O_2$) (14,15). The lack of measurable splitting of νO-O in the mixed isotope $^{16}O^{18}O$ adduct suggests a symmetrical, 1,2-bridged mode of binding (16). Planarity of the CuO_2Cu unit is a debatable requirement (16,17) but geometrical

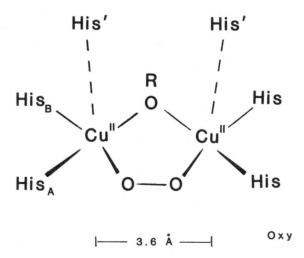

Figure 1. Model for the oxy active site of hemocyanin.

considerations, which assume an O-O bond length in the range 1.45-1.50 Å and Cu-O bond lengths of 1.95 Å, militate against severe puckering of the bridge.

Diamagnetism (18) and Cu...Cu distance considerations (~3.6 Å) (4) demand an additional single atom bridging ligand which is most probably an anionic oxygen donor, RO^-. This ligand is frequently referred to as the endogenous bridge. The only realistic candidates are hydroxide, alkoxide from serine or threonine, and phenoxide from tyrosine. All three ligands are known to be good mediators of antiferromagnetic coupling particularly when the Cu-O-Cu angle is about 135° (19-23). However, none is a clear favorite at this time. Hydroxide would be a little surprising since hydrophobicity is usually associated with unreactive oxygen adducts and HO^- may be at odds with pKa indications (24). Alkoxide ligation is to our knowledge unproven as a ligand in any metalloprotein although spontaneous formation of an alkoxide bridge from an alcohol can be quite facile in model complexes (5,23). Phenoxide ligation would seem the most accessible considering the comparitively low pKa of tyrosine but its spectroscopic identification (17) remains tentative. The preliminary interpretation of the Xray structure of Hc finds no evidence for a bridging ligand having major electron density (7). However, it must be pointed out that this Xray structure is presumed to be that of the deoxy form not the oxy. Since all three candidates find ample precedent in the copper(II) coordination chemistry literature it is unlikely that a model compound approach will be helpful in eliminating any of these possibilities.

Two histidine ligands make up what electronic spectroscopy (17) and magnetic coupling arguments (5) require to be an approximately tetragonal stereochemistry around each copper atom. Approximate equivalence of the copper atoms is indicated by the relative simplicity of the spectroscopy of HcO_2 and various methemocyanin derivatives. EXAFS data have been interpreted in terms of two histidines per copper (4,25) but the almost certain proximity of a third (7) and the predilection of Cu(II) for five-coordination encourages us to place a fifth ligand, His', in an apical site. The dashed line to His' in Figure 1 is used to indicate the uncertainty of this assignment as well as the predictably long Cu-N bond if this histidine is present. Weakly bonded apical ligands are the rule rather than the exception in tetragonal copper(II) complexes and the most recent interpretation of the long Cu-S bond to methionine in plastocyanin invokes precisely this effect (25). We also note that EXAFS experiments fail to detect the presence of this methionine (27). It can be expected that the greater the tetragonality of the four basal ligands the longer the apical bond. A distance of up to 2.9 Å should still be considered a bond to His' rather than a truely distal, non-bonding interaction. We will refer to the other two strongly bonding histidines as the dominant histidine ligands.

Model complexes for oxyhemocyanin remain poorly characterized structurally. However, since methemocyanin azide, $metHcN_3$, is structurally almost indistinguishable from oxyhemocyanin (4) and since the criteria for similarity are fairly exacting, a model compound approach to $metHcN_3$ has proved to be quite informative with regard to HcO_2. The essential structural features of diamagnetism, a 3.6 Å Cu...Cu

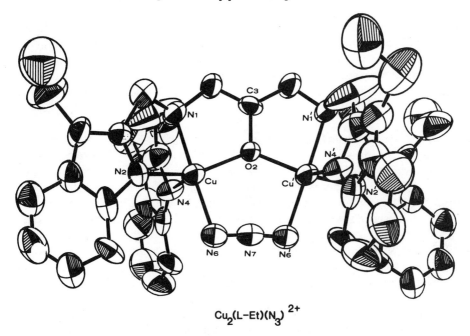

$$Cu_2(L-Et)(N_3)^{2+}$$

Figure 2. Model complex $[Cu_2(L-Et)(N_3)]^{2+}$ for methemocyanin azide. The donor atoms N1, N2, O2 and N6 make up the tetragonal plane. Donor atom N4 is apical. (Reprinted with permission from The Journal of the American Chemical Society, 106, 4770. Copyright (1984) American Chemical Society).

separation, approximate tetragonal stereochemistry, imidazole ligation, an RO^- bridging ligand and an exogenous bridging ligand are all reproduced in the azide complex $[Cu_2(L-Et)(N_3)]^{2+}$ (Fig. 2) (5). Replacing azide in this complex with other bridging ligands (acetate, nitrite, pyrazolate, etc.) does not lead to diamagnetic complexes. Xray structural analysis of the acetate complex reveals a trigonal bipyramidal stereochemistry unlike the azide complex. These contrasting structures of azide and acetate complex suggest that a fundamentally tetragonal stereochemistry must prevail around each copper atom in order to attain diamagnetism. Moreover, the bridging ligands (O_2^{2-} and RO^- in HcO_2) almost certainly make up two of the four basal (equatorial) ligands. The distortions of the copper stereochemistry from ideal tetragonality can probably be moderately large since in the azide model complex the apical (axial) ligand has angles of 114, 99, 97 and 83° to the basal ligands and the two pairs of trans basal ligands have N-Cu-N and N-Cu-O angles of 178 and 144° respectively. These parameters are, however, collectively quite distinct from those of a trigonal bipyramid, the other common idealized geometry of five-coordinate copper(II). In HcO_2 the basal $Cu-N_{His}$ bond lengths are close to 2.00 Å and the Cu-O bond lengths are probably close to 1.95 Å (4). The apical $Cu-N_{His}$ distance is likely to be long (2.5-2.9 Å) since it is not clearly observed in EXAFS experiments.

The Deoxy Site

Preliminary indications from the Xray structure of Hc are that the deoxy site contains three histidine ligands per copper (7). Only two are seen with certainty in EXAFS measurements (4,28) but the presence of additional ligands might pass undetected in this technique. Also, it can be argued that a third ligand, either RO⁻ or histidine at a greater distance, would rationalize the longer average Cu-N bond length (1.95 Å) (4) in Hc compared to cationic bis(imidazole) copper(I) complexes (1.87-1.92 Å) (29).

With unconstrained ligands the stereochemistries of copper(I) complexes are quite predictable. Having a filled shell d^{10} configuration its geometric preferences are dictated largely by the number of available ligands and a minimization of inter-ligand repulsions. In other words, the sterically most desirable geometry is usually adopted. Ideally, two-coordinate complexes are linear, and indeed, bis-imidazole complexes do show a predilection for linearity (30). However, a third more weakly bound ligand which makes up a distorted T-shaped geometry is beginning to appear typical of partially constrained ligand systems (29,31). Ideally, three coordination in copper(I) is trigonal but if one ligand binds more weakly than the other two the dominant pair will tend towards linearity in trans sites.

From the most recent interpretation of the EXAFS data on Hc a Cu...Cu separation of 3.43-3.48 Å has been estimated (4). There is some uncertainty about this distance (4,32) but it is very reasonable.

From a reactivity point of view, the copper(I) centers must have vacant coordination sites in order to be kinetically competent. Since the 'on' rates for O_2 binding approach the diffusion controlled limit the coordination number must be two or three but not four.

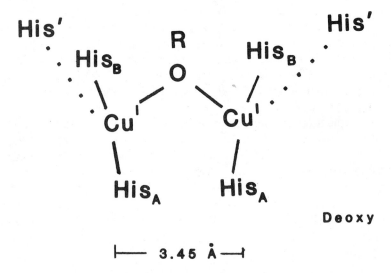

Figure 3. Model for the deoxy active site of hemocyanin.

With the above considerations in mind we presently adopt the structure depicted in Figure 3 as a working model for the deoxy active site. The fundamental assumption is that "pure" two coordination is unlikely. We choose RO^- ligation since the partial charge compensation on $[Cu(I)]^+$ should allow lengthening of the Cu-N bonds from the 1.90 Å found in two-coordinate model complexes (30) to the 1.95 Å estimated from EXAFS (4). A stereochemistry somewhere between trigonal and T-shaped is the likely compromise resulting from an additional, more weakly binding ligand. There is no absolutely compelling reason to adopt a symmetrical structure with respect to equivalence of the two copper atoms although we do so for simplicity. One could equally well propose one two-coordinate and one three-coordinate copper atom. EXAFS data, which frequently lead to reliable average bond distances, are less reliable in determining the number of ligands. A shared O atom between the metal centers could possibly go undetected. Also, the adopted geometry in Figure 3 does not have all five donor atoms coplanar. Rather, there is a torsion at Cu which avoids serious steric congestion of the two histidines labelled His_A. A third histidine, His', is apparently required at the active site by the single crystal study on Hc (7) although, until proven otherwise, we prefer to make it essentially non-bonding or 'distal'. In any event, a very long bond to His' is indicated by its apparent absence in the copper EXAFS (4,32). The apparent conflict in the number of histidine ligands between the single crystal Xray studies and the EXAFS studies is seen to raise the intriguing prospect that, like hemoglobin, hemocyanin has both proximal and distal histidines at the active site.

The Carbonmonoxy Site

Deoxyhemocyanin binds a single terminal CO ($\nu CO \sim 2050$ cm^{-1}) (33) indicating that the two copper atoms become quite different in HcCO. The source of the stoichiometric control could be steric or electronic (or both). One appealing electronic explanation is based on the observation that three-coordinate Cu(I) complexes bind CO much more strongly than do two-coordinate complexes (34). Conversion of the deoxy structure to a four-coordinate carbonyl complex at one copper center and a two-coordinate complex at the other follows naturally from the proposed deoxy structures as shown in Figure 4. An approximately tetrahedral stereochemistry

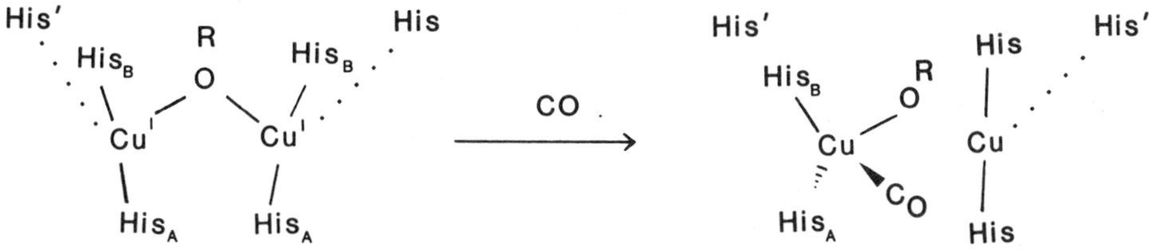

Figure 4. Active site model for CO binding to hemocyanin.

is expected at the four-coordinate center while a nearly linear stereochemistry is most reasonable at the other. The distal His' at the low coordinate center is presumed to remain distal because of protein constraints and steric destabilization of the pseudo tetrahedral geometry that would be required if it, and a second CO molecule, were to bind.

Cooperativity Mechanisms

A fundamental assumption made for the purpose of the following discussion is that the T conformation lowers the O_2 affinity via protein constraints upon the active site which destabilize the copper(II) oxy structure relative to the copper(I) deoxy structure. Another way of looking at this is to view the oxygenated active site in the T state protein as lying along the active site reaction coordinate between the deoxy structure and the fully relaxed oxygenated structure found in the R state protein. It becomes convenient, then, to limit the discussion of a cooperativity mechanism to these three states realizing that all the arguments can be applied in reverse to the two deoxy structures should one choose to focus on R state destabilization of the deoxy state rather than T state destabilization of the oxy active site. So, in discussing a cooperativity mechanism we will look for protein constraints that destabilize the oxy active site while at the same time stabilizing the deoxy active site.

We note at this point that the kinetics of O_2 uptake can be complex (10). With the larger oligomers (eg Helix pomatia) this can be interpreted in terms of initially rapid O_2 binding followed by a slow protein conformation change (10). This is consistent with the idea that slow T$\rightleftharpoons$R state conformation changes occur in response to rapid active site events.

But at present, the best clue to what is important in cooperative O_2 binding is the non-cooperativity of CO binding. Thus, we will focus upon structural and electronic features of the active site that will respond differently to CO and O_2. The following

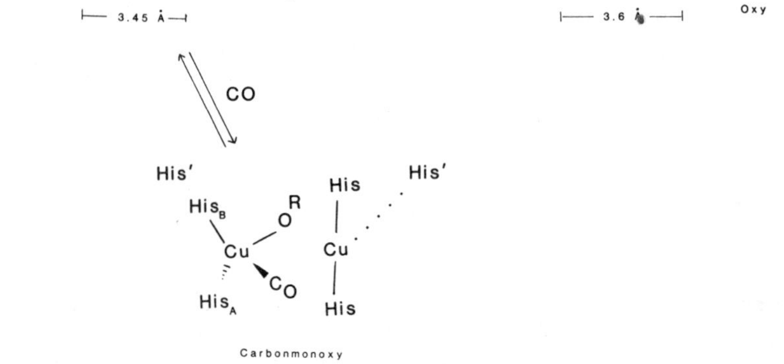

Figure 5. Active site models for CO and O_2 binding to hemocyanin.

discussion uses the active site structures depicted in Figure 5 as a reaction framework. The earlier mentioned caveats remind us that we are searching for principles that may be operating and that certain details of the structures should be taken con granulo salis.

Whatever the precise structures of the oxy and deoxy forms of hemocyanin are it is clear that a large structural reorganization of the active site must occur upon oxygenation or deoxygenation. As outlined earlier, this derives from the markedly different structural preferences of copper(I) and copper(II) in their coordination chemistry. The low coordination number preference of the d^{10} copper(I) ion differs greatly from the d^9 copper(II) ion where five-coordination is common and tetragonality leads to energetically favorable d orbital splittings (29). Since oxygen binding involves a copper(I) to copper(II) oxidation state change the stereochemical and electronic consequences of this redox change must provide the driving force for protein propagated cooperativity. We shall discuss, in turn, the various features which might play a key role in energizing this long range protein constraint of one active site upon another.

(a) Dominant histidine orientation

The fundamental tetragonality of copper(II) when contrasted with the drive of copper(I) towards linearity with two imidazole ligands suggests that a large angular change will occur at His_A-Cu-His_B upon oxygenation (Fig. 5). In theory, the change could be as great as $90°$ but in reality it probably approaches only half this amount because of the various distortions to ideal stereochemistry previously discussed. Nevertheless, it is clear that the redox change at copper can coerce a potentially large protein conformation change via histidine reorientation. It is equally clear that if the T state conformation constrains the His_A-Cu-His_B angle to a more obtuse angle than the R state this will lower the O_2 affinity by preferential stabilization of the deoxy active site. We note that in the CO adduct the His_A-Cu-His_B angle must approach a value of $109°$ as demanded by tetrahedrality of the four-coordinate copper(I) center. Not only is the angular change between the deoxy and carbon-monoxy forms smaller than between the deoxy and oxy forms but the change occurs at only one of the two copper centers. Clearly there is much less driving force for the T to R switch in CO binding and a cooperativity mechanism for O_2 binding triggered by angular movement of the dominant histidine ligands is thus consistent with the non-cooperativity of CO binding.

(b) Copper-copper separation

Previous discussions of a cooperativity mechanism for hemocyanin have focused on changes in the Cu...Cu separation as a possible factor in triggering a protein conformational change (2,3,12,35). While it is true that a large change in this distance could cause substantial movement of all of the ligands and thereby propagate a protein conformational change, the most recent interpretation of the EXAFS results places the change at only ~0.2 Å (4). It seems likely, therefore, that the orientation of the ligands as dictated by the oxidation level change is a more important consideration than simply the Cu...Cu distance.

(c) Endogenous bridge

Our adopted structural model makes the bridging ligand, RO^-, a central component of the oxygen binding process but concedes to it rather little change in orientation between oxy and deoxy states. Other deoxy structures, for example with RO^- protonated as ROH and non-ligating, or, with RO^- bound to only a single copper center (4), would provide the opportunity for a much greater role for the bridging ligand in propagating a protein conformational change. There are, in fact, experiments which indicate a significant change in both the orientation and the binding properties of the endogenous bridge upon oxygenation/deoxygenation. Using some EPR active half-met sites as a spectral probe dispersed throughout otherwise normally operating protein, Solomon and coworkers (8) have shown that deoxygenation at the normal sites produces two measurable effects at the half-met sites. Firstly, there is a decrease in affinity for a second exogenous ligand (eg. azide) suggesting that the endogenous bridging ligand may have become a more competitive binder, or, at least, a steric inhibitor for excess exogenous ligand. Secondly, the half-met EPR signal changes in a manner indicative of more delocalization of the unpaired electron over both copper atoms. It is assumed that the oxygenated protein is in the R state and the deoxygenated protein is in the T configuration so that the changes at the half-met site reflect the R to T state constraints upon the active site. This clever experiment provides the first experimental evidence that oxygenation/deoxygenation at one site can indeed propagate a structural change at another site some 50 Å distant. The results are, however, difficult to interpret in detail. The decreased affinity of the half-met site for a second exogenous ligand is consistent with a T state constraint which makes the copper(I) site less amenable to copper(II)-like chemistry. But the greater delocalization of the EPR signal onto both copper atoms is problematical. The interpretation that better tetragonality must exist in the T state half-met site (8) is apparently in conflict with the hypothesis that the T state enforces a more copper(I)-like ligand orientation upon the active site. Nevertheless, since the EPR signal is likely to be rather sensitive to small changes in ligand orientation, particularly the Cu-OR-Cu angle, a detailed discussion is not yet possible. Model compounds which reproduce the unique EPR spectra could, however, be quite useful in understanding how best to interpret these results.

(d) The "distal" histidines

At least as portrayed in our working model, the weakly bonding or distal histidines, His', if present, are assumed to play a secondary role in propagating a cooperative interaction simply because the energetics of their interaction with the active site are small compared to those of the dominant ligands. If however, their role is to H-bond to coordinated dioxygen, as occurs in oxyhemoglobin, then their orientation will be quite specific and they could play a significant role in triggering a protein conformation switch.

(e) Oxygen

The role of oxygen as an exogenous bridging ligand is probably crucial to the mechanism of cooperativity. But this role may not be in a stereochemical capacity as has been implicit for the ligand reorientations discussed in the preceding sections. While O_2 must have a clamping role (12) in fixing the positions of the two copper(II) ions the redistribution of charge may be more important. The redox reaction of O_2 to O_2^{2-} and Cu(I) to Cu(II) must produce very substantial dipoles in the $Cu-O_2-Cu$ moiety to which the surrounding protein must respond. These dipoles are indicated by the arrows in Figure 6. As mentioned in the previous section, one response of the protein to those dipoles might be to orient a distal histidine, His', to H-bond to coordinated peroxide. However, any dipolar protein moiety in the near vicinity will be affected by the presence or absence of this dipole and there is probably ample energy in this effect alone to cause the R to T conformational change. Of course, protein constraints in the T state that restrain the affected protein dipoles from stabilizing the $Cu-O_2-Cu$ unit will lower the O_2 affinity.

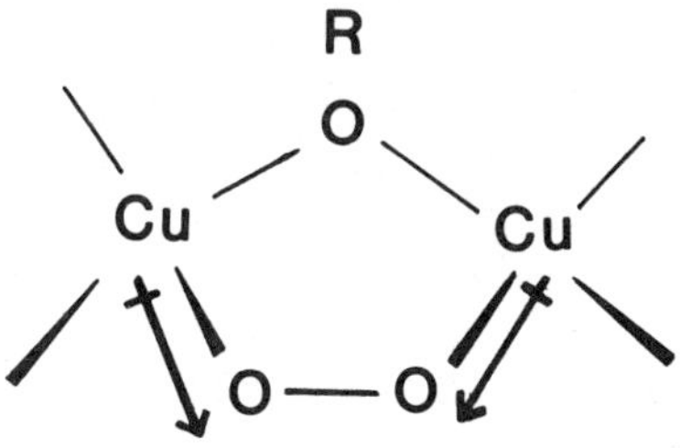

Figure 6. Dipole formation at the active site of HcO_2.

Clearly the non-cooperativity of CO binding is consistent with the lack of significant dipole formation in the Cu-CO moiety.

Conclusions

There are two fundamental questions about a molecular mechanism of cooperativity. How does deoxygenation at one site trigger a conformational change which lowers the O_2 affinity at another site? And by what chemical mechanism is the O_2 affinity of the T state lowered relative to the R state?

Regarding the first question, cooperativity probably has its origins in both the stereochemical and electrostatic effects that accompany the oxidation state change at the active site. The stereochemical effects arise from the differing coordination stereochemistry requirements of copper(I) and copper(II). The greatest of these effects may be the angular orientation of the dominant histidine ligands although there is clearly some role for the endogenous bridge also. The electrostatic effects arise primarily from the presence or absence of large Cu-O electric dipoles but will be augmented by many subtle charge redistributions occurring at the active site upon oxygenation and deoxygenation. The non-cooperativity of CO binding allows us to single out these effects as those most likely to be operative. Transmission of these effects via stereochemical and electrostatic coercion to neighboring active sites can provide a mechanism for long distance communication throughout the protein. The possibility of distal histidine involvement with bound dioxygen is but one suggestion of how an electrostatic effect might be converted into a stereochemical effect or be propagated via other dipole reorientations to neighboring residues. The cumulative effect must be to impose constraints upon a neighboring active site such that its affinity is altered. Incidentally, H-bonding to coordinated peroxide might help explain the exceptionally low νO-O stretching frequency.

Addressing the second question, we must accept that any protein constraints upon the active site in the T state which lead to a destabilization of the O_2 adduct and/or a stabilization of the copper(I) form (relative to the R state) will lower the O_2 affinity. Likely effects include protein constraints which maintain large obtuse His-Cu-His angles for the dominant histidine ligands, those which impose strain upon the endogenous RO^- ligand such that it cannot adopt an optimal location for bridging two tetragonal copper(II) atoms, those which restrain protein dipoles from optimally stabilizing the CuO_2Cu moiety, and those which sterically block the O_2 binding site or block the movement of the other ligands to their optimal locations. It may eventually be possible to illustrate the operation of some of these effects in model compounds but not until high resolution Xray structures of both T and R state forms of the protein are available will it be possible to decide on the relative importance of these various factors. In hemoglobin, it is generally agreed that tethering and tilting of the proximal histidine ligand in the T state (which restrains its movement along with the iron atom towards the porphyrin plane in the oxy state) is one of the most important factors in lowering of the T state O_2 affinity. Partial steric blocking of the O_2 binding site also seems to be important (36).

In comparing the cooperativity in hemoglobin and hemocyanin there are both similarities and differences. The most dramatic difference is in CO ligation. The stereochemical consequences of CO and O_2 ligation are quite similar in hemoglobin and both are cooperative. This supports a stereochemical mechanism. The stereochemical and electronic consequences of CO and O_2 ligation to hemocyanin, however, are very different and lead to the probability of both stereochemical and electrostatic instigation of cooperativity with O_2. It is impressive to see how much detailed iron porphyrin chemistry has been incorporated into the understanding of the mechanism of hemoglobin cooperativity (37). Since there must be interesting differences between the two proteins, and perhaps some unexpected surprises, we hope the present discussion will hasten the time when the same can be said about copper coordination chemistry vis-a-vis hemocyanin cooperativity.

References and Footnotes

1. (a) K.E. Van Holde and K.I. Miller, *Q. Rev. Biophys. 15*, 1, (1982); (b) *Invertebrate Oxygen-Binding Proteins*, Ed. J. Lamy and J. Lamy, Dekker, New York, 1981.

2. M. Brunori, L. Zolla, H.A. Kuiper, and A.F. Agro, *J. Mol. Biol. 153,* 1111 (1981).
3. E.I. Solomon in *Copper Proteins,* Ed., T.G. Spiro, Wiley-Interscience, New York, 1981, p.41.
4. (a) T.G. Spiro, G.L. Wollery, J.M. Brown, L. Powers, M.E. Winkler, and E.I. Solomon in *Copper Coordination Chemistry: Biochemical and Inorganic Perspectives,* Ed., K.D. Karlin and J. Zubieta, New York, 1983, p23; (b) G.L. Woolery, L. Powers, M. Winkler, E.I. Solomon, and T.G. Spiro, *J. Am. Chem. Soc. 106,* 86 (1984).
5. (a) V. McKee, J.V. Dagdigian, R. Bau and C.A. Reed, *J. Am. Chem. Soc. 103,* 7000 (1981); (b) V. McKee, M. Zvagulis, J.V. Dagdigian, M.G. Patch and C.A. Reed, *J. Am. Chem. Soc. 106,* 4765 (1984).
6. E.J.M. van Schaick, W.G. Schutter, W.P.J. Gaykema, A.M.H. Schepman and W.G.J. Hol, *J. Mol. Biol. 158,* 457 (1982).
7. W.P.J. Gaykema, W.G.J. Hol, J. M. Vereijken, N.M. Soeter, H.J. Bak and J.J. Beintama, *Nature 309,* 23 (1984).
8. Y.T. Hwang and E.I. Solomon, *Proc. Natl. Acad. Sci. USA 79,* 2564 (1982).
9. A. Colosimo, M. Brunon and J. Wyman in *Structure and Function of Haemocyanin,* Ed. J.V. Bannister, Springer-Verlag, Berlin, 1977, p.189.
10. M. Brunori, H.A. Kuiper, E. Antonini, C. Bonaventura and J. Bonaventura in ref. 1(b) p.693.
11. M.F. Perutz, *Annu. Rev. Biochem. 48,* 327 (1979).
12. M. Brunori, B. Giardina and H.A. Kuiper, *Inorg. Biochem.,* Specialist Periodical Reports, Royal Society of Chemistry *3,* 126 (1981).
13. C. Bonaventura, B. Sullivan, J. Bonaventura and S. Bourne, *Biochemistry 13,* 4784 (1974).
14. T.B. Freedman, J.S. Loehr and T.M. Loehr, *J. Am. Chem. Soc. 98,* 2809 (1976).
15. J.A. Larrabee and T.G. Spiro, *J. Am. Chem. Soc. 102,* 4217 (1980).
16. T.J. Thamann, J.S. Loehr and T.M. Loehr, *J. Am. Chem. Soc. 99,* 4187 (1977).
17. N.C. Eickman, R.S. Himmelwright and E.I. Solomon, *Proc. Natl. Acad. Sci. USA 76,* 2094 (1979).
18. D.M. Dooley, R.A. Scott, J. Ellinghaus, E.I. Solomon and H.B. Gray, *Proc. Natl. Acad. Sci. USA 75,* 3019 (1978).
19. M.S. Haddad, W.R. Wilson, D.J. Hodgson and D.N. Henrickson, *J. Am. Chem. Soc. 103,* 384 (1981).
20. P.L. Burk, J.A. Osborn and M.T. Youinou, *J. Am. Chem. Soc. 103,* 1273 (1981).
21. P.K. Coughlin and S.J. Lippard, *J. Am. Chem. Soc. 103,* 3228 (1981).
22. M.G.B. Drew, J. Nelson, F. Esho, V. McKee and S.J. Nelson, *J. Chem. Soc., Dalton Trans.* 1837-1843, (1982).
23. V. McKee and J. Smith, *J. Chem. Soc. Chem. Commun.* 1465 (1983).
24. D.E. Wilcox, J.R. Long and E.I. Solomon, *J. Am. Chem. Soc. 106,* 2186 (1984).
25. M.S. Co, K.O. Hodgson, T.K. Eccles and R. Lontie, *J. Am. Chem. Soc. 103,* 984,(1981).
26. K.W. Penfield, R.R. Gay, R.S. Himmelwright, N.C. Eickman, V.A. Norris, H.C. Freeman and E.I. Solomon, *J. Am. Chem. Soc. 103,* 4382 (1981).
27. R.A. Scott, J.E. Hahn, S. Doniach, H.C. Freeman and K.O. Hodgson, *J. Am. Chem. Soc. 104,* 5364 (1982).
28. M.S. Co, R.A. Scott and K.O. Hodgson, *J. Am. Chem. Soc. 103,* 986 (1983).
29. J.V. Dagdigian, V. McKee and C.A. Reed, *Inorg. Chem. 21,* 1332 (1982) and references therein.
30. (a) P.J.M.W.L. Birker and J. Reedijk in *"Copper Coordination Chemistry: Biochemical and Inorganic Perspectives"* Ed. K.D. Karlin and J. Zubieta, Adenine, New York, 1983, p409; (b) T.N. Sorrell and D.L. Jameson, *J. Am. Chem. Soc. 105,* 6013 (1983).
31. (a) T.N. Sorrell, M.R. Malachowski and D.L. Jameson, *Inorg. Chem. 21,* 3250 (1982); (b) T.N. Sorrell and M.R. Malachowski,*Inorg. Chem. 22,* 1883 (1983).
32. M.S. Co and K.O. Hodgson, *J. Am. Chem. Soc. 103,* 3200 (1981).
33. (a) L.Y. Fager and J.O. Alben, *Biochemistry 11,* 4786 (1972); (b) M. Munakata, S. Kitagawa and K. Goto, *Inorg. Biochem. 16,* 319 (1982).
34. T.N. Sorrell and D.L. Jameson, *J. Am. Chem. Soc. 104,* 2053 (1982).
35. C. Bonaventura, J. Bonaventura and M. Brouwer in ref. 1(b) p.677.
36. J. Baldwin and C.J. Chothia, *J. Mol. Biol. 129,* 175 (1979).
37. W.R. Scheidt and C.A. Reed, *Chem. Rev. 81,* 543 (1981).

Biological & Inorganic Copper Chemistry,
ISBN 0-940030-11-X, Eds., K. D. Karlin & J. Zubieta, Adenine Press, ©Adenine Press, 1985

Characteristics of the Rate-Determining Step(s) of the Reaction Catalyzed by Galactose Oxidase and a Model Complex, Cu(II)-Tetrapyridine

James J. Driscoll and Daniel J. Kosman
Department of Biochemistry
SUNY at Buffalo
Buffalo, New York 14214

Abstract

The oxidation of α-ketoalcohols by O_2 catalyzed by galactose oxidase (GO) and Cu(II)-tetrapyridine was investigated using classical mechanistic organic protocols. The physico-chemical similarity of the Cu sites in enzyme and complex was indicated by spin Hamiltonian and $E^{\circ\prime}$ values. Catalytic similarities include: Michaelis-Menten kinetics; observed primary kinetic and solvent isotope effects; substitutent ρ values; apparent base-catalysis; and proton inventory. Data are consistent with, but do not prove, a reaction mechanism involving consecutive one-electron transfer steps. Activation parameters indicate a substantial difference in $\Delta S^{\dagger}$. This could be associated with some combination of solvent and Cu complex reorganization.

Introduction

Galactose oxidase (EC 1.1.3.9, GO) is a 68 kilodalton single chain protein isolated from the extracellular medium of the fungus Dactylium dendroides (1). GO is a mono-nuclear, Cu(II) protein of the non-blue (type 2) classification which catalyzes the oxidation of an alcohol by molecular oxygen yielding the corresponding aldehyde and hydrogen peroxide. The simplest copper oxidase known, GO is the enzyme most amenable to studies examining the mechanism of action of copper-containing oxidases.

The kinetic mechanism of GO is ordered, bisubstrate sequential with the alcohol substrate binding first. One-electron oxidants may substitute for O_2 in the reaction mechanism (2). The velocity is first-order in these species, indicating the involvement of an initial rate-limiting one-electron transfer. Wiberg and Nigh (3) have proposed a similar initial one-electron transfer in the reduction of Cu(II)-tetrapyridine by α-hydroxyacetophenone and para-substituted congeners. Since α-ketoalcohols are excellent GO substrates, we have undertaken a detailed comparison and analysis of the reaction catalyzed by the enzyme GO and the simple complex Cu(II)-Pyr$_4$.

Experimental Section

Materials

Galactose oxidase was isolated from the fungal cultures of D. dendroides according to the method of Tressel and Kosman (4). Protein concentration was determined by absorbance at 280 nm, using $E_{1cm}^{1\%} = 15.4$ (4). Cu(II)-Pyr$_4$ was prepared by addition of a sixteen-fold molar excess of pyridine, added with stirring, to stoichiometric amounts of copper perchlorate in 20% DMF (v/v). Solutions were then adjusted to the desired pH with 1N HCl or 1N NaOH. Monohydroxyacetone (acetol) was purchased from Aldrich Chemical and redistilled in vacuo prior to use. α-Hydroxyacetophenone and derivatives were prepared as described (3).

Methods

Initial velocity measurements were made under air (0.24 mM O$_2$) except where otherwise noted. A biological oxygen monitor, equipped with a Clarke-type electrode (YSI) was used to record the amount of O$_2$ uptake upon injection of substrate. The output of the oxygen monitor was recorded on a strip chart recorder, temperature being maintained by a circulating water bath. Kinetic data were handled by computer fitting to standard hyperbolic programs; PENNZYME and POLYFIT were used for the pH and proton inventory data respectively.

Results

Table I summarizes a variety of physicochemical characteristics for both the enzyme and complex. The similarity between GO and Cu(II)-Pyr$_4$ is apparent. The two Cu(II) sites do differ, however, in that GO has an H$_2$O-occupied equatorial coordination site, and a much more intense visible absorption spectrum (1). Cu(II)-Pyr$_4$ is an N$_4$ complex, as indicated by well-defined ^{14}N shfs (cf. Table I), and has an $\epsilon = 15$ M^{-1}cm^{-1} at 780 nm.

Table I

Spin Hamiltonian Parameters and Cu(II)/Cu(I) E$^{o\prime}$ Values for Galactose Oxidase and Cu(II)-pyr$_4$

	Galactose Oxidase[a]	Cu(II)-pyr$_4$
$g_\parallel$	2.227	2.279
$A_\parallel^{Cu}$ (G)	175	191
$A_\parallel^{N}$ (G)	14.5(2)[b]	11.8(4)[b]
$g_\perp$	2.051	2.036
$A_\perp^{Cu}$ (G)	0	0
$E^{o\prime}$	+300 mV[c]	+343mV[d]

[a]Spin Hamiltonian parameters for galactose oxidase from Reference 5.

[b]Number of (equivalent) ^{14}N nuclei. In galactose oxidase, these are assigned to imidazole.

[c]From Reference 6.

[d]Determined using a PAR Model 173 potentiostat with dichlorophenolindophenol as mediator. A thin cell/pulse technique was employed as described by Su et al. (7). Values versus NHE in 50% (v/v) DMF, pH = 7.0, 0.02 M Na acetate.

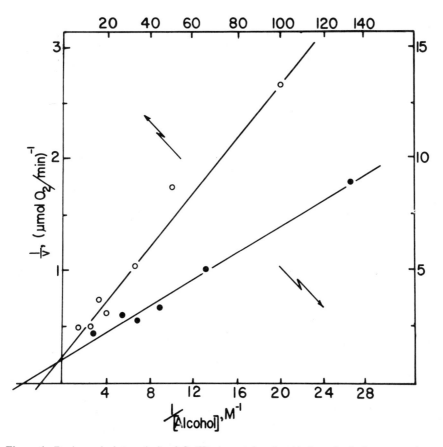

Figure 1. Reciprocal plot analysis of Cu(II)-pyr₄-catalyzed oxidation of α-hydroxyacetophenone (O) and acetol (●). Conditions: [Cu(II)-pyr₄] = 0.014 M in pH = 7.0, 0.02 M Na acetate prepared in 50% (v/v) DMF at 25° C; [O₂] = 1.3 mM. Data points are averages of 3-5 determinations; line is best fit to standard hyperbolic function.

α-Ketoalcohols serve as excellent substrates for GO; their oxidation by O_2 is effectively catalyzed by Cu(II)-Pyr₄ also. The turnover reaction catalyzed by the complex is saturable, as indicated by the data in Figure 1. A comparison of the kinetic constants for GO- and Cu(II)-Pyr₄-catalyzed reactions is given in Table II. Aldehyde was product, as indicated by TLC analysis of reaction mixtures. In the Cu(II)-Pyr₄ reaction, the expected H_2O_2 product could not be detected due to either the catalatic activity of Cu(II)-Pyr₄ or H_2O_2-dependent turnover of alcohol. Both of these possibilities have been well-documented (8,9). Although the GO-catalyzed oxidation of acetol is 10^5-fold faster than that for Cu(II)-Pyr₄, the enzymic enthalpy of activation is actually more unfavorable (Table III). The difference in $\Delta G^{\ddagger}$ is due predominantly to a substantially less negative $\Delta S^{\ddagger}$.

An observed primary kinetic isotope effect (KIE) on V/K, ^{D}(V/K), was determined using $\alpha,\alpha[^2H_2]$-HAP. How this value compares to the intrinsic KIE for either reaction is unknown. However, the values suggest a comparable transition state for the C-H

Table II

Kinetic Constants for Galactose Oxidase and Cu(II)-pyr$_4$-catalyzed Turnover Reactions

	α-Hydroxyacetophenone	Acetol
Galactose Oxidase		
k_{cat} (s^{-1})[a]	——[b]	402
K_m (M)[a]	——[b]	1.4
k_{cat}/K_m (M^{-1}s^{-1})[a]	8.2	290
^{D}(V/Km)[a,c]	3.0	
ρ[a,d]	0.8	
k_{H_2O}/k_{D_2O}[e]		1.41
Cu(II)-pyr$_4$[f]		
k_{cat} (s^{-1})[a]	5.5×10^{-6}	5.4×10^{-4}
K_m (M)[a]	0.1	0.3
k_{cat}/K_m (M^{-1}s^{-1})[a]	5.5×10^{-5}	1.8×10^{-3}
^{D}(V/Km)[a,c]	3.8	
ρ[a,d]	0.6	
k_{H_2O}/k_{D_2O}[e]		1.34

[a]Values determined in 50% (v/v) DMF; galactose oxidase data from pH = 7.0, 0.1 M phosphate, Cu(II)-pyr$_4$ data from pH = 7.0, 0.02 M Na acetate at 25°C using O$_2$-electrode.
[b]Galactose oxidase data indicate $K_m > 1$ M.
[c]Observed primary KIE on V/K$_m$ determined for $\alpha,\alpha[^2H_2]$-α-hydroxyacetophenone using k_{cat}/K$_m$ at 1.3 mM O$_2$.
[d]Determined for para-substituted α-hydroxyacetophenones; data fit to log k_{cat}/K$_m$ = $\rho\sigma_p$.
[e]Determined in pL 7.0, 0.02 M Na acetate with 20% (v/v) DMF and 0.24 mM O$_2$.
[f]Turnover was first-order in Cu(II)-pyr$_4$ over the concentration range studied 5-30 mM.

cleavage for enzyme and complex, although real differences could be masked by contributions of other steps to ^{D}(V/K) and/or different contributions from secondary KIE. These would be relatively small however.

Similarity in ρ for the oxidation of para-substituted HAP congeners was noted for enzyme and complex also. Log kcat/Km data were used since for some derivatives, solubility precluded reliable determination of Vmax. However, the Km values for those whose solubility was not limiting, exhibited no systematic dependence on substituent constant(s).

The reaction catalyzed by Cu(II)-Pyr$_4$ was first-order in complex. In addition, turnover of substrate was dependent on the mole ratio of pyr:Cu, increasing as this

Table III

Activation Parameters for the Oxidation of Acetol Catalyzed by Galactose Oxidase and Cu(II)-Pyr$_4$[a]

	k_{cat}(s^{-1})	$\Delta G^\dagger$(Kcal/mol)	$\Delta H^\dagger$(Kcal/mol)	$\Delta S^\dagger$(e.u.)
Galactose oxidase	6.3	16.3	12.8	−11.7
Cu(II)-Pyr$_4$	9.5×10^{-5}	22.9	7.8	−49.1

[a]Values determined at 25°C from data obtained in pH 6.0, 0.02 M Na acetate with 20% (v/v) DMF and 0.24 mM O$_2$.

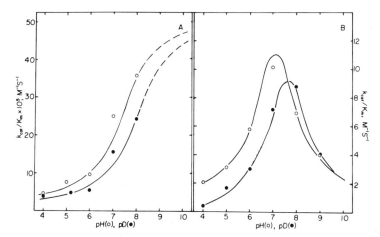

Figure 2. k_{cat}/K_m as a function of pL for the oxidation of acetol at 0.24 mM O$_2$ catalyzed by Cu(II)-pyr$_4$ (A) and galactose oxidase (B). Experimental points are averages of these determinations, curves are theoretical fits to standard mono-(A) and diprotic (B) rate expressions. Note that these fits are not yet significant at a 95% confidence level.

ratio was increased from 4 (essentially no "free" pyr) to 16 (corresponding to 240 mM "free" pyr). A decrease in rate was observed at higher mole ratios, due to the formation of five- and six-coordinate Cu(II) complexes, as indicated by visible absorbance (data not shown). Wiberg and Nigh have reported similar results (3). These data indicate that a single Cu(II) is involved in the rate-determining process and that free pyridine may serve as a general base catalyst.

The bell-shaped pH dependence of the GO reaction with β-O-methyl-galactopyrano-side has been reported (10). Preliminary data indicate a similar pH dependence for the oxidation of acetol (Figure 2B). The pD dependence exhibited a standard 0.5 pH unit shift in the pKa of a catalytic conjugate base group; the group pKa catalytic in the undissociated state did not appear to shift markedly in D$_2$O (Figure 2B). The pL dependence of the Cu(II)-Pyr$_4$ catalysis likewise exhibited a pKa shift of 0.5 pH units. However, the ionization responsible for the dependence observed remains uncertain.

The solvent kinetic isotope effect (KSIE) was investigated further via a proton inventory (Figure 3). At pL = 7.0, the KSIE for GO was 1.41; that for Cu(II)-Pyr$_4$ was 1.34, indicating the existence of a solvent-derived proton in both reactions. These effects were first-order in D$_2$O, indicating that a single "site" was involved in the solvent proton-dependent step.

Discussion

Structurally and chemically, the similarities between the Cu sites in GO and Cu(II)-Pyr$_4$ are striking. In particular, the E$^{\circ\prime}$ values, the values for ^{D}(V/K) and ρ, the apparent general base-catalyzed nature of the alcohol turnover, and the KSIE

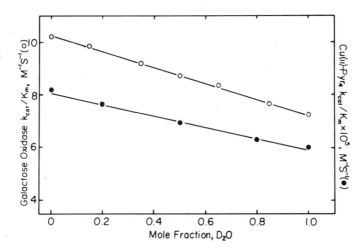

Figure 3. A proton inventory for the oxidation of acetol catalyzed by galactose oxidase (○) and Cu(II)-pyr$_4$ (●). k_{cat}/K_m determined in pH 7.0, 0.02 M Na acetate with 20% (v/v) DMF and 0.24 mM O$_2$. Values are averages of three determinations, line is best fit polynomial (n=1).

suggest a possible correspondence between the mechanisms of substrate oxidation catalyzed by these two Cu(II) centers. Although the details of the reaction mechanisms remain unclear, the data do delineate possible components of any mechanism postulated.

Alcohol oxidation appears to occur either at an axial site or outersphere, since Cu(II)-Pyr$_4$ is four-coordinate. A similar geometry for the GO-substrate Michaelis complex has been proposed (1). The reactions appear base catalyzed; the group in GO, pKa=6.3, has been identified as a histidine imidazole (10). Wiberg and Nigh have suggested that the anaerobic reduction of Cu(II)-Pyr$_4$ by HAP is base-catalyzed as well (3). The C-H bond cleavage which is base-catalyzed exhibits an observed KIE, $^D(V/K)$, which is probably less than the intrinsic value, since it was determined at [O$_2$]<K$_m$. These values of 3.0 and 3.8 may be no more than one-half the intrinsic KIE. Such a value indicates that C-H bond cleavage makes a substantial contribution to a rate-limiting step in both reactions.

The ρ values compare favorably, as well. Although the electronic effects indicated by the measured ρ values cannot be explicitly related to a particular step in either reaction, the positive value, though small, is consistent with a (partially) rate-limiting C-H bond cleavage step. The resultant negative charge density on the carbinol carbon in the transition state could be stabilized by electron-withdrawing substituents. Again, while not proving a mechanism for either reaction, the values indicate similar charge distributions in related transition states.

The pL data are too preliminary for detailed evaluation. However, the pD data for GO indicate that the pKa = 6.3 group experiences a standard 0.5 pH shift in D$_2$O. On the other hand, the pKa shift for the EH+ state (pKa = 7.5) appears to be significantly less than this value. A $\Delta pKa = 0.11$ has been reported for a catalytic conjugate acid group in liver alcohol dehydrogenase. This behavior was attributed to a Zn^{2+}-H_2O (11), although this assignment is speculative (12). Nonetheless, a Cu^{2+}-H_2O ionization is possible for GO since an H_2O molecule is known to bind equatorially to the enzymic Cu(II) (1).

The pL dependence and shift in Cu(II)-Pyr₄ catalysis is unassigned. Although pyridine is thought to act as a base catalyst, its ionization (pKa = 5.1) is not observed in these pH-rate data. It is possible that the data represent specific base catalysis above pH = 6.0. This behavior remains to be evaluated.

The activation parameters for the two reactions differ in significant ways. First, $\Delta S^{\dagger}$ for the complex-catalyzed reaction is markedly more negative. Although the reaction does proceed through a Michaelis complex, it still is very unfavorable entropically. This suggests several possibilities. First, the reaction for the complex, and not for GO, is explicitly first-order in O_2, i.e. kcat for the complex is a pseudo-first-order rate constant and that the more negative $\Delta S^{\dagger}$ reflects the bimolecularity of the O_2-dependent step. Second, the transition state for the Cu(II)-Pyr₄ reaction may involve extensive solvent reorganization and/or coordination geometry change. This certainly would be true if a Cu redox reaction occurred in a rate-determining step. Such changes would be masked in the enzymic reaction, accommodated by the active site environment. Thirdly, the reactions could be significantly different mechanistically, with the activation parameters associated with entirely different chemistry. This possibility could explain the difference in $\Delta H^{\dagger}$, in particular. On the other hand, the less positive $\Delta H^{\dagger}$ for Cu(II)-Pyr₄ could reflect compensation for the solvent or coordination changes; i.e. in the transition state increases in the solvent-complex, solvent-substrate, and solvent-solvent interactions, lowering the entropy, could make a favorable enthalpic contribution to the free energy.

These results do not explicitly relate to any possible role for Cu redox in turnover. However, comparison of the kcat/Km values for turnover of HAP and acetol by Cu(II)-Pyr₄ (Table II) with the rates of anaerobic reduction of the complex by these two substrates, 6×10^{-6} $M^{-1}S^{-1}$, and 2.8×10^{-4} $M^{-1}S^{-1}$, respectively, show that reduction per se cannot be a step in the turnover reaction catalyzed by Cu(II)-Pyr₄. Furthermore, the first-order dependence in Cu(II)-Pyr₄, and GO, suggests that an additional electron acceptor must be present in the first, rate-limiting electron transfer since, if this step only involved Cu(II)-Pyr₄, it would have to be comparable to the simple anaerobic reduction reaction. It is reasonable that the additional electron acceptor is O_2 and that the kinetic parameters being measured are for a two-step process involving both C-H bond cleavage and electron transfer to O_2. The relationship between these two events is the focus of our continuing work.

References and Footnotes

1. M.J. Ettinger and D. J. Kosman in *Copper Proteins,* Ed., T.G. Spiro, Wiley-Interscience, New York, p. 219 (1981).

2. L.D. Kwiatkowski, M. Adelman, R. Pennelly, and D. J. Kosman, *J. Inorg. Biochem. 14*, 209 (1981).
3. K.B. Wiberg and W.G. Nigh, *J. Amer. Chem. Soc. 87*, 3849 (1965).
4. P. Tressel and D.J. Kosman, *Meth. Enzymol. 89*, 163 (1982).
5. R.D. Bereman and D.J. Kosman, *J. Amer. Chem. Soc. 99*, 7322 (1977).
6. D. Melnyk and M.J. Ettinger, unpublished. See D. Melnyk, *"An Investigation of the Type 2 Cu(II) Enzyme Galactose Oxidase: Determination of the Oxidation-Reduction Potential, Identification of An Equatorial Ligand and Determination of pH Dependence of the Stereoelectronic Properties",* Ph.D. Dissertation, SUNY at Buffalo, Buffalo, New York, 14214 (1979)
7. C.H. Su and W.R. Heineman, *Anal. Chem. 53*, 594 (1981).
8. P.K. Adolf and G.A. Hamilton, *J. Amer. Chem. Soc. 93*, 3420 (1971).
9. H. Erlenmeyer, C. Flierl and H. Siegel, *J. Amer. Chem. Soc. 91*, 1065 (1969).
10. L. D. Kwiatkowski, L. Siconolfi, R. E. Weiner, R. S. Giordano, R.D. Bereman, M.J. Ettinger and D.J. Kosman, *Arch. Biochem. Biophys. 182*, 712 (1977).
11. J.P. Klinman in *Isotope Effects in Enzyme-Catalyzed Reactions,* Eds., W.W. Cleland, M.H. O'Leary, and D.B. Northrup, Univ. Park Press, Baltimore, MD., p.176 (1977).
12. K.B. Schowen and R.L. Schowen, *Meth. Enzymol. 87*, 551 (1982).

Biological & Inorganic Copper Chemistry,
ISBN 0-940030-11-X, Eds., K. D. Karlin & J. Zubieta, Adenine Press, ©Adenine Press, 1985

The Structures of Copper(II) Poly(L-Lysine) Complexes

Coleen M. Young and Frederick T. Greenaway

Department of Chemistry, Clark University,
Worcester, MA 01610

Abstract

Aqueous solutions of poly(L-lysine) containing various amounts of copper(II) at pH between 1 and 13 have been studied by EPR spectroscopy. Although previous workers have reported only two $Cu(Lys)_n$ species, the EPR spectra show that there are six different $Cu(Lys)_n$ compounds in pH-dependent equilibrium and that these species apparently correspond to progressive replacement of water ligands by amines and, at high pH, by replacement of two amines by deprotonated amide nitrogen atoms.

Introduction

Poly(L-lysine), $(Lys)_n$, when bound to copper(II), catalyzes the oxidation of 3,4-dihydroxyphenylalanine, DOPA, at high pH and has been considered a model for DOPA oxidase which is utilized in melanin production (1). The $Cu(Lys)_n$ complex behaves as an asymmetrically-selective catalyst, favoring D-DOPA over L-DOPA (2), particularly at high pH where $(Lys)_n$ exists in a helical form (3,4). $Cu(Lys)_n$ has also been reported to model the enzyme catalase (5) and catalyze the decomposition of H_2O_2 at pH between 6 and 7.

The binding of Cu(II) to $(Lys)_n$ has been previously studied by potentiometric titration (6-8), absorption spectroscopy (6-9), circular dichroism (6-9), and NMR spectroscopy (10,11). The various groups disagree in their structural assignments but agree that there are two types of Cu(II) complex which form, one at pH<8 and one at pH>8. This paper reports the results of an investigation of the $Cu(Lys)_n$ system using EPR spectroscopy.

Materials and Methods

Poly(L-lysine) hydrobromide of molecular weight 4000-15000 and 70000-150000 was purchased from Sigma Chemical Co. EPR spectra were recorded at 9.1 GHz using a Varian E-9 EPR spectrometer equipped with a nitrogen-flow dewar. The magnetic field was calibrated using a Magnion gaussmeter and the frequency was measured on a Hewlett-Packard frequency counter. The pH was adjusted by the addition of small amounts of concentrated HCl and NaOH solutions.

Previously Proposed Structures

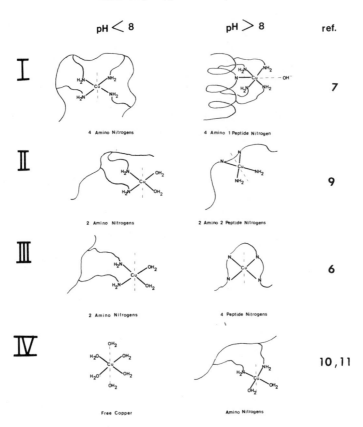

FIG. 1

Results and Discussion

EPR spectra obtained of frozen solutions of Cu(Lys)$_n$ at 120K were typical of tetragonally-elongated octahedrally coordinated Cu(II) with $g_\parallel > g_\perp$. Anisotropic spectra were also obtained for liquid solutions at 300K and although of poorer resolution due to partial motional averaging, were identifiable as arising from the same species observed in frozen solutions. Although methanol promotes α-helix formation in (Lys)$_n$, EPR spectra obtained for frozen methanol solutions of Cu(Lys)$_n$ showed few differences from the spectra of frozen aqueous solutions.

Initially an EPR study of pH-dependence was carried out at a 4:1 Lys:Cu ratio to enable comparison with previous studies. However, EPR spectra were broad and baselines were poor between pH 6 and 11 due to Cu(OH)$_2$ precipitation and, above pH 11, due to Cu(OH)$_4^{2-}$ formation. Therefore most studies were carried out at a

30:1 Lys:Cu ratio where copper hydroxide species did not form. Although Garnier and Tosi (12) observed terminus binding of $(Lys)_n$ for n = 25, our spectra showed no variation with the $(Lys)_n$ chain length which indicates that coordination of chain termini is not significant for longer chains.

EPR spectra of seven different Cu(II) species were obtained between pH 2 and 13. When solutions of $(Lys)_n$ and Cu(II) were initially prepared a pH of about 4 resulted and the broad EPR spectra indicated aggregation of Cu(II). Slowly increasing the pH did not change the spectra. It was therefore necessary to raise the pH to 13 and reduce the pH by progressive additions of acid to fully observe all species. The same species did form at lower pH but at a much slower rate, equilibrium being attained only after several days. This slow rate is probably the cause of disagreement between potentiometric data obtained by titration with acid (7) and base (6,9). Our results suggest that titration with acid leads to a more rapid attainment of equilibrium and thus more reliable results.

Values of $A_{\|}$ and $g_{\|}$ are given in Table I and plotted against one another following the method of Peisach and Blumberg (13) in Figure 2. Although we were unable to detect any nitrogn superhyperfine structure on the parallel lines, we have assigned likely ligand environments for the Cu(II) based on Figure 2 and on the widths of the parallel lines which are affected by unresolved nitrogen splitting. These assignments together with the limited number of ligand atoms in $(Lys)_n$ suggest the equilibria detailed in Figure 3.

TABLE I

EPR Parameters[a]

COMPLEX	$A_{\|}$	$g_{\|}$	$g_{\perp}$	pH	PROBABLE ENVIRONMENT (Total Copper Charge)	
A	.0129 cm^{-1}	2.388	2.090	1 – 2	4 Oxygens	(+2)
B	.0137 cm^{-1}	2.337	2.084	2 – 3	1 Nitrogen	(+2)
C[b]	.0145 cm^{-1}	2.330	2.075	3 – 5	2 Nitrogens	(+2)
D	.0153 cm^{-1}	2.304	2.063	5 – 6	3 Nitrogens	(+2)
E	.0171 cm^{-1}	2.243	2.062	6 – 8	4 Nitrogens	(+2)
F[c]	.0175 cm^{-1}	2.222	2.054	8 – 9	4 Nitrogens	(+1)
G	.0205 cm^{-1}	2.164	2.047	9 – 13	4 Nitrogens	(0)

[a] Poly(L-lysine)–Cu(II) in aqueous solution. PLL:Cu(II) in 30:1 ratio. M.W. = 4,000

[b] High M.W. (90,000) pH study did not observe this complex.

[c] High M.W. study showed $g_{\|}$ = 2.220 and $A_{\|}$ = .0188 cm^{-1}

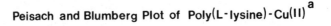

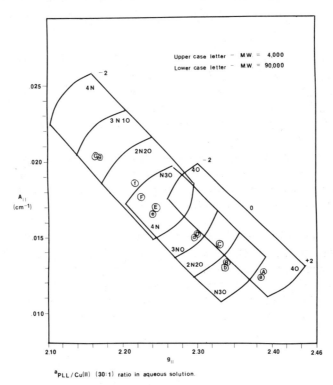

Peisach and Blumberg Plot of Poly(L-lysine)-Cu(II)[a]

[a] PLL/Cu(II) (30:1) ratio in aqueous solution.

FIG. 2

These equilibria are consistent with all previous literature data. At low pH, water molecules are progressively replaced by amine groups until at pH 6-8 the major structure has four amine nitrogen atoms in a planar arrangement about the Cu(II). Above pH 8 first one, then a second of the amines is replaced by a deprotonated amide nitrogen so that between pH 9 and 13 the major species has two amine and two amide nitrogen atoms in approximately planar coordination. The amide co-ordination confers dichroism to the copper d-d band. Although $(Lys)_n$ has α-helical structure in aqueous solution at high pH it has been found that Cu(II) destroys this structure (6) and thus early explanations of the asymmetric oxidation of DOPA (2) can not be correct. The binding of two amide nitrogen atoms of the backbone at high pH does, however, confer a high degree of organization upon the $(Lys)_n$ chain which may enable D-DOPA to bind preferentially. It would be of interest to investigate the catalytic specificity of Cu(II) $(D-Lys)_n$ or $(DL-Lys)_n$.

At neutral pH, $Cu(Lys)_n$ catalyzes the decomposition of H_2O_2 (5) and it has been suggested that the catalytic site has two replaceable ligands on the Cu(II). Our

Proposed Structures

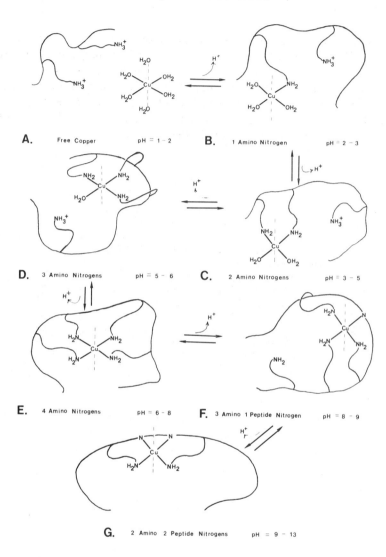

A. Free Copper   pH = 1 − 2   B. 1 Amino Nitrogen   pH = 2 − 3

D. 3 Amino Nitrogens   pH = 5 − 6   C. 2 Amino Nitrogens   pH = 3 − 5

E. 4 Amino Nitrogens   pH = 6 − 8   F. 3 Amino 1 Peptide Nitrogen   pH = 8 − 9

G. 2 Amino 2 Peptide Nitrogens   pH = 9 − 13

FIG. 3

findings are consistent with this structure. Below pH 8 the amine and water ligands are both quite labile and several complexes exist in equilibrium. The sensitivity of the species present in solution to pH, Lys:Cu ratio, and concentration observed by others are all due to the complexity of the equilibria. Although we have not measured equilibrium constants, it is clear that they are not widely separated in magnitude. This also explains the discrepancy of the NMR results (10,11) with other work since the NMR data were obtained at high Lys:Cu ratios which results in less amide coordination.

The EPR results confirm the high pH structure of two amide and two amine ligands bound to Cu(II) in a tetragonally-distorted octahedral arrangement. EPR spectra are not sensitive to the nature of the axial ligands but do show that a square pyramidal complex (8) is not formed. Other studies have claimed either four amine (7) or two amine and two water ligands (6,9) to be bound to copper between pH 6 and 8. The EPR results show that both structures are present but that it is not valid to interpret the results in terms of a single species at pH < 8.

References and Footnotes

1. M. Hatano, T. Nozawa, S. Ikeda and T. Yamamoto, *Makromol. Chem. 141,* 11 (1971).
2. T. Nozawa and M. Hatano, *Makromol. Chem. 141,* 31 (1971).
3. M. Hatano, Y. Yamamoto, I. Ito, T. Nozawa and M. Nakai, *J. Amer. Chem. Soc. 91,* 2165 (1969).
4. M. Hatano and M. Yoneyama, *J. Amer. Chem. Soc. 92,* 1392 (1970).
5. H. Sigel and G. Blauer, *Helv. Chim. Acta 51,* 1246 (1968).
6. M. Palumbo, A. Cosani, M. Terbojevich and E. Peggion, *Macromolecules 10,* 813 (1977).
7. M. Hatano, T. Nozawa, S. Ikeda and T. Yamamoto, *Makromol. Chem. 141,* 1 (1971).
8. T. Nozawa and M. Hatano, *Makromol. Chem. 141,* 21 (1971).
9. A. Garnier and L. Tosi, *Biochem. Biophys. Res. Commun. 74,* 1280 (1977).
10. N. Higuchi, K. Kakiuchi and K. Hikichi, *Macromolecules 13,* 79 (1980).
11. N. Higuchi, T. Hiraoki and K. Hikichi, *Macromolecules 13,* 81 (1980).
12. A. Garnier and L. Tosi, *Bioinorg. Chem. 8,* 493 (1978).
13. J. Peisach and W. E. Blumberg, *Arch. Biochem. Biophys. 165,* 691 (1974).

Biological & Inorganic Copper Chemistry,
ISBN 0-940030-11-X, Eds., K. D. Karlin & J. Zubieta, Adenine Press, ©Adenine Press, 1985

The Preparation and Characterization of a Mixed Metal Derivative of Laccase

M. Michelle Morie-Bebel, Janelle L. Menzie, and David R. McMillin

Department of Chemistry
Purdue University
West Lafayette, IN 47907, U.S.A.

Abstract

The preparation and characterization of a novel mixed metal derivative of *Rhus* laccase containing Hg(II) in the type-1 binding site are described. Numerous observations support this formulation. First, metal analyses show there are one mercury and three copper atoms per polypeptide chain. Protein fluorescence measurements also indicate complete metalation of all three copper binding sites. The type-2 copper is observed by EPR, and ligand hyperfine is present in the perpendicular region. The superhyperfine structure is resolved by low frequency EPR to determine the number of nitrogen ligands coordinated to copper. The integrity of the type-2 site is further demonstrated by anion binding studies done on the mercury derivative which are virtually identical with those done on the native protein. The difference spectrum at 330 nm ($\Delta\epsilon_{330} = 2800 \pm 300$) indicates the type-3 copper is present. Thiol titrations of the apoprotein exhibit only one accessible thiol ligand. This group is blocked in the mixed metal derivative, consistent with mercury binding at the type 1 site.

Introduction

Laccase, a water-soluble blue copper protein obtained from the oriental lacquer tree, *Rhus vernicifera,* has been intensively studied by many researchers. Its main function is to mediate the reduction of molecular oxygen to water (1). The protein contains four copper atoms, which are found in three distinct coordination sites (2). The type-1 site, which gives the protein its characteristic blue color, has a visible absorbance at 614 nm, and exhibits an EPR spectrum that has an unusually small hyperfine splitting in the low field region. Its structure can be inferred from plastocyanin (3,4) and azurin (5,6), two small blue copper proteins that contain only the type-1 copper center with the same coordination geometry and donor set (two histidine nitrogens, one cysteine sulfur, and one methionine sufur) (3). A similar coordination environment is probably present in the type-1 site of all blue copper proteins (7); thus, the type-1 site in laccase can be represented as in Figure 1. Stellacyanin, another blue copper protein, lacks methionine and may bind a cystine sulfur in its stead (8).

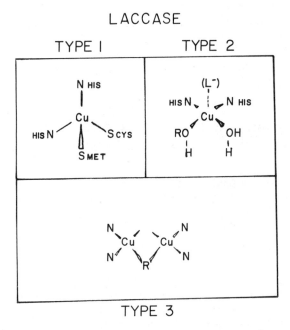

Figure 1. Proposed structures for the copper sites of laccase. See text for references.

The type-2 copper has no intense optical absorbance, but exhibits an EPR signal characteristic of a tetragonal coordination environment. Little is known about the nature and the geometry of this site. NMR relaxation studies using ^{17}O-enriched water have suggested the presence of an H_2O ligand in this site (9). EPR studies of cyanide-treated fungal laccase (10,11), and type-1 depleted ceruloplasmin (12) indicate the presence of three or four nitrogen ligands. Based on these studies, Pecht has proposed a structure for the type-2 site (9), also depicted in Figure 1. Anions, such as CN^- and F^- bind to this site, producing characteristic changes in the EPR spectrum of the protein (13).

The two EPR-undetectable copper atoms found in the type-3 site are proposed to exist as an anti-ferromagnetically coupled pair of copper(II) ions (2,14). This dimeric site is where oxygen interacts with the protein, and is responsible for an optical absorbance around 330 nm (2). Studies of the active site of oxyhemocyanin (15) and anion derivatives of type-2 depleted laccase (16) have led to the structural model depicted in Figure 1. EXAFS studies on type-2 depleted laccase indicate there are no sulfur ligands in the type-3 site (17); thus the only ligating thiol group occurs in the type-1 site.

One of the major difficulties in studying laccase is the fact that important spectral features overlap, making it difficult to identify the intrinsic signals of each site. One important modification of the protein, removal of the type-2 site to form the type-2 depleted protein (18,19), afforded new avenues of study for the type-1 and -3 sites.

Metal replacement studies, whereby Co(II) was used in place of copper have also proved useful in the interpretation of spectral features (20). The preparation of mixed-metal derivatives is another potentially useful approach; the derivative containing mercury in the type-1 site will be described herein.

Materials and Methods

The acetone powder from the Chinese lacquer tree *Rhus vernicifera* was obtained from Saito and Co., Ltd. Osaka, Japan, and extracted according to the method of Reinhammar (21) with some modifications. All chemicals were reagent grade and were used as obtained. Deoxygenated buffer solutions were obtained by purging with N_2 which had been passed through a scrubbing solution containing vanadous ion over zinc amalgam or passed through a column containing catalyst R3-11 (Chemlog #18-3000-00) to remove oxygen. Buffers were prepared from deionized water and passed through a Chelex-100 column to remove any trace metal contaminants. The UV-visible spectra were obtained on a Cary-17D spectrophotometer, while the fluorescence measurements were performed on a Perkin-Elmer MPF-44B spectrofluorimeter. The pH was measured at room temperature on either an Orion model 601A digital ionanalyzer or a Radiometer PHM64 pH meter. EPR measurements were carried out on a Varian E-109 spectrometer. Elution profiles were monitored at 280 nm with a Pharmacia UV-1 column monitor, and fractions collected with a Gilson FC-80K microfractionator.

The mercury derivative was prepared from apolaccase made by a modification of the previous method (22). The apoprotein was first dialyzed against 0.5M NaOAc pH 5.5 buffer, after which 1.5-2.0 site equivalents of Hg(II) were added. After 30-45 minutes, 4.0 site equivalents of Cu(I) were slowly introduced using a syringe pump. The protein was allowed to equilibrate for several hours, then excess metal ions were removed by dialysis against 0.02 M phosphate pH 7 buffer. Subsequent column chromatography on a CM-C50 sephadex column gave two fractions. The first fraction contained partially metalated protein. The second fraction was eluted with 0.2 M phosphate pH 7 buffer, and contained the desired product in about 70-80% yield. Finally, the sample was dialyzed against 0.1 M phosphate pH 6 buffer for subsequent analysis.

Results and Discussion

Analyses of various preps are given in Table I, and metal/protein ratios are consistant with uptake at all three metal sites. In the best runs the protein fluorescence, found to be a sensitive indicator of the degree of metalation of the protein (22), is almost identical for native and the mercury derivative (Figure 2), further demonstrating that the mercury derivative contains metal in all three binding sites. Spectral studies reveal how the metals are distributed.

EPR studies show that the type-2 site contains copper. The characteristic type-2 signal is present in the mercury protein (Figure 3). The EPR parameters agree with

Table I
Cu and Hg Analysis of Various Preparations

Sample	N_{Cu}^a	N_{Hg}^a	A_{280}/A_{333}^b	A_{280}/A_{614}^b
native	4.0	—	19.9	20.6
recon[c]	3.9	—	18.3	21.0
HgCu₃	3.0	1.0	20.3	—
HgCu₃	2.9	.97	18.1	—

[a]metal to protein rations; total protein was determined by a modification of the biuret method using native laccase as a standard.
[b]Absorbance ratios.
[c]reconstituted Cu_4 laccase.

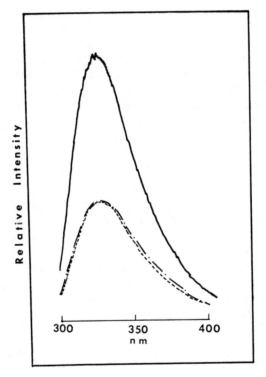

Figure 2. Room temperature fluorescence spectra of native laccase (------) and the mercury derivative (------) at pH 7; the spectrum of apolaccase (——) was run at pH 5.5. A_{280} for all samples was 0.87 + .02; excitation wavelength was 295 nm.

those of the Japanese protein (23), and the spectrum closely parallels the type-2 signal seen in partially reduced fungal laccase (10). The presence of a narrow hyperfine splitting in the perpendicular region suggests the presence of nitrogen ligands in the type-2 site. Low frequency EPR experiments provide valuable additional information. The nitrogen superhyperfine structure due to the nitrogen ligands is clearly resolved in the S-band spectrum when the protein is in a D_2O buffer (less clearly when in an H_2O buffer) consistent with the presence of a water ligand in this site (24). Computer simulations of the parallel region at 2.39 GHz suggest the presence of three nitrogen ligands (24). Further evidence that the type-2 site in the mercury derivative is similar to the native site is found by anion binding studies, where F^- binds to the type-2 site in an identical fashion to native. In the presence of excess fluoride, the Q-band spectrum clearly reveals ^{19}F superhyperfine splitting indicative of two approximately equivalent F^- ligands bound in an equatorial fashion (25).

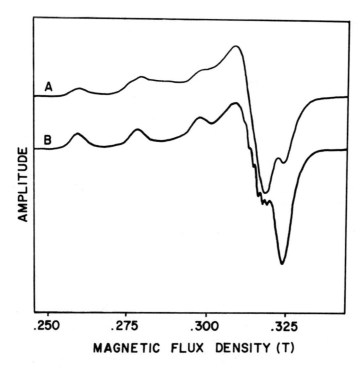

Figure 3. EPR spectra of native laccase (A) and the mercury derivative (B). Spectrum A was recorded at $-150°C$ with a modulation amplitude of 1.0 mT, a power of 40 mW, and a frequency of 9.080 GHz. Spectrum B was obtained under the same conditions, except the gain was increased by a factor of 2.5, and the modulation amplitude was increased to 1.25 mT. Both samples were remetalated with isotopically pure [65]Cu. The buffer is 0.1 M pH 6 phosphate.

The ratio of absorbances between aromatic side chains and the type-3 site (A_{280}/A_{333}) gives some indication of the amount of copper that is bound to that site. As seen in Table I, the ratio accords well with that of the native enzyme. Further, when the spectrum of reduced laccase was subtracted from that of the mercury derivative, an observed $\Delta\epsilon = 2800 \pm 300\ M^{-1}cm^{-1}$ was obtained, in excellent agreement with the reported value of $2800\ M^{-1}cm^{-1}$ for the difference spectrum between oxidized and reduced laccase (23).

If the three site equivalents of copper are bound at the type-2 and type-3 sites, the mercury must be found in the type-1 site. Indeed, mercury has a very high affinity for the type-1 site (26), as would be expected in view of the pseudotetrahedral coordination geometry and the presence of a thiolate ligand (4,5). The absence of the intense charge transfer absorption of the blue copper chromophore shows that copper is not bound at the type-1 site. Further, thiol titrations show that apolaccase has only one accessible thiol group and that this group is blocked in the native enzyme, the fully metalated mercury derivative, and the partially metalated protein, formed by the addition of one site equivalent of mercury to apolaccase. Finally, the binding of mercury is competitive with that of copper in the type 1 site in as much as the characteristic spectroscopic signatures of type-1 copper become increasingly evident in the remetalated protein as the ratio of Hg(II) to protein is decreased in preparing samples.

Future studies planned for this derivative, including EXAFS studies, visible absorbance and kinetic studies, should provide useful structural and mechanistic information about the protein.

Acknowledgement

This research was supported by NIH Grant GM 22764. The purchase of the EPR spectrometer was supported in part by Grant PCM 75-19127 from the National Science Foundation.

References and Footnotes

1. L. Andréasson, R. Branden, and B. Reinhammar, *Biochim. Biophys. Acta 438,* 370 (1976).
2. R. Malkin and B.G. Malmström, *Adv. Enzymol. Relat. Areas. Mol. Biol. 33,* 177 (1970).
3. H.C. Freeman in *Coordination Chemistry: Proceedings of the Twenty-first International Conference on Coordination Chem.,* Ed., J.P. Laurent, Pergamon, New York, *21,* 29 (1981).
4. J.M. Guss and H.C. Freeman, *J. Mol. Biol. 169,* 521 (1983).
5. E.T. Adman and L.H. Jensen, *Isr. J. Chem. 21,* 8 (1981).
6. G.E. Norris, B.F. Anderson, and E.N. Baker, *J. Mol. Biol. 165,* 501 (1981).
7. D.M. Dooley, J. Rawlings, J.H. Dawson, P.J. Stephens, L.-E. Andréasson, B.G. Malmström, and H.B. Gray, *J. Amer. Chem. Soc. 101,* 5038 (1979).
8. D.R. McMillin and M.C. Morris, *Proc. Natl. Acad. Sci. U.S.A. 78,* 6567 (1981).
9. M. Goldberg, S. Vuk-Pavlovic, and I. Pecht, *Biochemistry 19,* 5181 (1980).
10. R. Branden and B. Reinhammar, *Biochim. Biophys. Acta 405,* 236 (1975).
11. B.G. Malmström, B. Reinhammar, and T. Vänngärd, *Biochim. Biophys. Acta 156,* 67 (1968).
12. J.H. Dawson, D.M. Dooley, R. Clark, P.J. Stephens, and H.B. Gray, *J. Amer. Chem. Soc. 101,* 5046 (1979).
13. L. Morpurgo, G. Rotilio, A. Finazzi-Agrò, and B. Mondovì, *Biochim. Biophys. Acta 336,* 324 (1974).
14. D.M. Dooley, R.A. Scott, J. Ellinghaus, E.I. Solomon, and H.B. Gray, *Proc. Natl. Acad. Sci. U.S.A. 75,* 3019 (1978).
15. R.S. Himmelwright, N.C. Eickman, C.D. LuBien, K. Lerch, and E. I. Solomon, *J. Amer. Chem. Soc. 102,* 7339 (1980).
16. D.J. Spira and E.I. Solomon, *Biochem. Biophys. Res. Commun. 112,* 729 (1983).

17. D.J. Spira, M.S. Co, E.I. Solomon, and K.O. Hodgson, *Biochem. Biophys. Res. Commun. 112,* 746 (1983).
18. M.T. Graziani, L. Morpurgo, G. Rotilio, and B. Mondovì, *FEBS Lett. 70,* 87 (1976).
19. L. Morpurgo, M.T. Graziani, A. Finazzi-Agrò, G. Rotilio, and B. Mondovì, *Biochem. J. 187,* 361 (1980).
20. J.A. Larrabee and T.G. Spiro, *Biochem. Biophys. Res. Commun. 88,* 753 (1979).
21. B. Reinhammar, *Biochim. Biophys. Acta 205,* 35 (1970).
22. M.C. Morris, B.L. Hauenstein, Jr., and D.R. McMillin, *Biochim. Biophys. Acta 743,* 389 (1983).
23. B.G. Malmström, B. Reinhammar, and T. Vänngärd, *Biochim. Biophys. Acta 205,* 48 (1970).
24. M.M. Morie-Bebel, W.E. Antholine, and D.R. McMillin, to be submitted.
25. L. Morpurgo, A. Desideri, and G. Rotilio in *The Coordination Chemistry of Metalloenzymes,* Ed., I. Bertini, R.S. Drago, and Luchinat, D. Reidel Publishing Co., p. 207 (1983).
26. S. Katoh and A. Takamiya, *J. Biochem. (Tokyo) 55,* 378 (1964).

Biological & Inorganic Copper Chemistry,
ISBN 0-940030-11-X, Eds., K. D. Karlin & J. Zubieta, Adenine Press, ©Adenine Press, 1985

Thermodynamics of Ligand Substitution Reactions of Tetragonal Cu(II) Sites in Proteins

David M. Dooley, Michele A. McGuirl, and Phoebe A. Mix
Department of Chemistry
Amherst College
Amherst, Massachusetts 01002

Abstract

Thermodynamic parameters (K, $\Delta H°$, $\Delta S°$) have been measured for azide and thiocyanate reactions with $Cu(dien)^{2+}$, bovine plasma amine oxidase, and bovine liver Cu, Zn superoxide dismutase. $\Delta H°$ and $\Delta S°$ were determined by monitoring the temperature dependence of the $N^-/SCN^- \Rightarrow Cu(II)$ LMCT bands. $Cu(dien)^{2+}$ ligand-substitution thermodynamics have been investigated in order to identify possible protein effects on the ligand substitution chemistry of tetragonal Cu(II). Entropy contributions dominate the enzyme-anion equilibria, whereas the enthalpy effects are larger in reactions of $Cu(dien)^{2+}$. The effects of ionic strength, pH, and buffer composition have also been examined.

Introduction

Most copper proteins, except those containing a single blue copper center, display rich ligand-substitution chemistry. In fact spectroscopic and chemical studies of exogenous ligand coordination have proved extremely useful approaches for elucidating the structural and functional properties of copper sites in proteins. Essential information has been obtained from ligand-binding experiments on the binuclear sites in hemocyanin and tyrosinase (1,2), the Type 2 and 3 sites in multicopper oxidases (1-3), the mononuclear sites in galactose oxidase (4), various amine oxidases (5-7), and superoxide dismutase (8,9). All of these copper sites can be characterized as tetragonal, that is, Cu(II) is five- or six-coordinate with four ligands roughly defining an equatorial coordination plane with one or two axial ligands. The available evidence correlates with nitrogen/oxygen donor ligands, known to be imidazole and water in some cases (1-11). Bovine erythrocyte superoxide dismutase is the only protein containing a tetragonal Cu(II) site to be structurally characterized by X-ray crystallography (8,9,12). Three imidazoles and one imidazolate ligand define the equatorial "plane," which is significantly distorted away from planarity (8,9,12). A water molecule is coordinated axially to give a five-coordinate structure, perhaps best described as a distorted square-pyramid. Ligand substitution reactions of the superoxide dismutase and other enzymes containing tetragonal Cu(II) centers are especially interesting, since substrate coordination to Cu(II) may be mechanistically important. Moreover, exogenous ligands can be selected to model substrate or product binding in some cases. Equilibrium constants for enzyme-ligand binding have been measured frequently, but there is still a need for systematic measurements in order to facilitate comparisons among proteins and to model complexes. $\Delta H°$ and $\Delta S°$ have not previously been determined for Cu(II) ligand-substitution reactions in proteins despite their fundamental importance to understanding the factors that control the chemistry. Here we report the thermodynamics of azide and thiocyanate binding to bovine liver superoxide dismutase and bovine plasma amine oxidase. Thermodynamic data have also been obtained for anion substitution reactions of the diethylenetriamine (dien) Cu(II) complex, which is a reasonable model for tetragonal Cu(II) sites in proteins (13,14).

Materials and Methods

Bovine plasma amine oxidase was purified by a published method (15). Bovine liver Cu,Zn SOD was purchased from DDI (Mountain View, CA) and used as received. All other chemicals were the highest grade commercially available. Ligand solutions were freshly prepared prior to each experiment. Titrations were carried out as previously described (16,17) in 5.0 mM PIPES buffer (pH 7.0) containing 0.1M NaCl at 15-16°C. Temperatures were measured by inserting a calibrated thermocouple into the thermostatted cell assembly next to the cuvette. Samples were allowed to equilibrate at least one-half hour following each change in temperature. All absorption spectra were obtained on a Cary 219 spectrophotometer, interfaced to an Apple II computer. Equilibrium constants were determined by a standard method (18); $\Delta H°$ and $\Delta S°$ were obtained as described by Gorman and Darnall (19) or by using the extinction coefficients obtained from titration experiments to calculate K at each temperature. Corrections for temperature dependent baseline changes were made when necessary.

Results and Discussion

Ligand field theory and an extensive body of physical data have established that the highest-occupied (half-filled) orbital in tetragonal Cu(II) complexes is $d_{x^2-y^2}$, which is located within the equatorial plane, giving a ^2B ground state. Thus equatorial σ,π-donor ligands will give rise to intense electric-dipole allowed LMCT transitions. Since the transitions are electric-dipole allowed, their extinction coefficients will not be significantly temperature-dependent in our range. Hence the observed variations in band intensities can be attributed to the temperature dependence of the relevant equilibrium constant. As Gorman and Darnall recently pointed out, absorption spectroscopy then becomes a simple but powerful technique for obtaining thermodynamic data (19). Our data are set out in Table I. A common set of conditions must be established for all the proteins and model complexes in order to make meaningful comparisons. For a number of reasons we settled on the conditions given in Table I. This is by no means the only valid choice. It should be noted, however, that phosphate buffers are particularly poor for ligand-substitution experiments. We and others (13) have observed that simple Cu(II) complexes, like

Cu(dien)$^{2+}$, display complicated chemistry in phosphate solutions; phosphate is also known to alter the reactivity of superoxide dismutase (20) and we have found very different (and more complex) amine oxidase ligand-substitution chemistry in phosphate buffer (21). Not unexpectedly the thermodynamic parameters are also a function of ionic strength and pH. For example, in 5 mM PIPES (pH 7.0) K(N$_3^-$) for Cu(dien)$^{2+}$ is 150 M^{-1}, but falls to 75 M^{-1} in 5 mM PIPES plus 0.1 m NaCl (pH 7.0). The temperature dependence of the N$_3^-$/SCN$^-$ $\Rightarrow$ Cu(II) LMCT transitions in Cu(dien)$^{2+}$$-X^-$ complexes is shown in Figures 1 and 2, which yields ΔH° and ΔS° for the reaction below.

$$Cu(dien)^{2+}-OH_2 + X^- \Rightarrow Cu(dien)^{2+}-X^- + H_2O$$
$$X^- = N_3^-, SCN^-$$

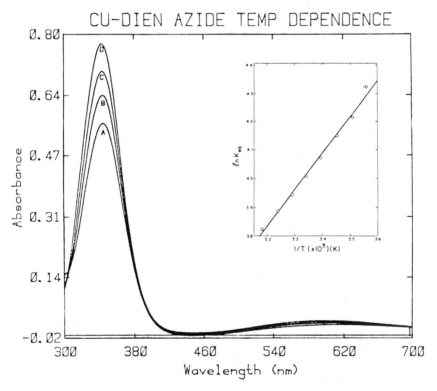

Figure 1. Temperature dependence of the Cu(dien)$^{2+}$-N$_3^-$ complex LMCT transition. [Cu^{2+}] = 1.0 × 10^{-3} M; [N$_3^-$] = 7.94 × 10^{-3} M. Temperatures ranged from 41.40° C (A) to 7.85° C (D). Inset: van't Hoff plot.

In contrast to its behavior in phosphate buffered solutions, amine oxidase displays only a single equilibrium constant in reactions with azide or thiocyanate under conditions used here. Figure 3 displays the temperature dependence of the amine oxidase-N$_3^-$ LMCT band. Convincing evidence has been presented that H$_2$O is the leaving group in amine oxidase reactions with exogenous Cu(II) ligands (10). Therefore

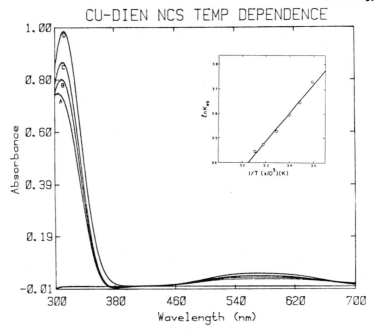

Figure 2. Temperature dependence of the Cu(dien)$^{2+}$−SCN$^-$ complex. LMCT transition. [Cu^{2+}] = 3.0 × 10^{-3} M; [SCN$^-$] = 13.8 × 10^{-3} M. Temperatures ranged from 40.00°C (A) to 9.25° C (D). Inset: van't Hoff plot.

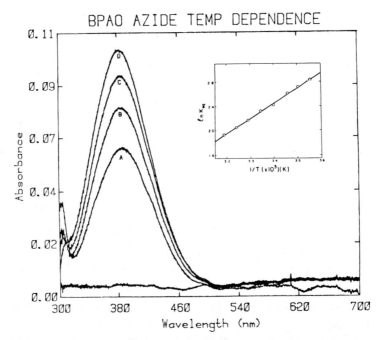

Figure 3. Temperature dependence of the amine oxidase-N$_3^-$ complex LMCT transition. [Enzyme] = 1.8 × 10^{-4} M; [N$_3^-$] = 59.3 × 10^{-3} M. Temperatures ranged from 40.65° C (A) to 8.25° C (D). Inset: van't Hoff plot.

ΔH° and ΔS° for the amine oxidase reactions with azide and thiocyanate are remarkable and clearly point to large protein effects on the Cu(II) ligand-substitution chemistry. Anion-binding induced protein conformational changes were not detected by UV difference spectroscopy in our previous work conducted in phosphate buffers, but may be a possible explanation for the very negative ΔS° values here.

The equilibrium constant for the superoxide dismutase-azide reaction compares well to the value established by Mota de Freitas and Valentine for non-coordinating buffers (20); Figure 4 displays the temperature dependence. Surprisingly, titrations with thiocyanate cannot be analyzed in terms of a single equilibrium constant. Superoxide dismutase reactions with thiocyanate are not completely understood (8,9). Our data may imply that SCN^- can coordinate to Cu(II) in more than one way or there is cooperativity between the active sites. The position and intensity of the superoxide dismutase$-SCN^-$ band is consistent with equatorial coordination as in $Cu(dien)^{2+}$-SCN^-. We suggest, very tentatively, that perhaps different leaving groups may be involved in the ligand-substitution reactions with thiocyanate and azide. Thermodynamic parameters (Table I) were obtained at both relatively high and low ionic strength and indicate that the superoxide dismutase-thiocyanate equilibrium

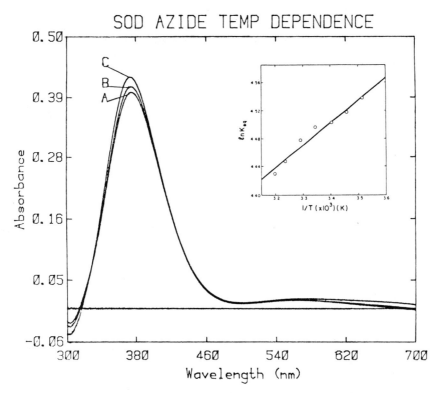

Figure 4. Temperature dependence of the superoxide dismutase-N_3^- complex LMCT transition. [Enzyme] = 2.9×10^{-4} M; $[N_3^-] = 10.0 \times 10^{-3}$ M. Temperatures ranged from 39.75° C (A) to 11.40° C (C). Inset: van't Hoff plot.

Table I

Thermodynamic Parameters for Cu(II) Ligand Substitution Reactions

Reaction	$K_{eq}(M^{-1})$*	$\Delta H°$(kJ/mole)	$\Delta S°$(J/mole-K)	$\Delta G°$(kJ/mole)**
BPAO + N_3^-	12.3 ± 0.7	-20.7 ± 0.6	-50 ± 2	-5.8 ± 0.1
BPAO + NCS⁻	4.7 ± 0.3	-38 ± 3	-119 ± 10	-2.6 ± 0.2
SOD + N_3^-	88 ± 2	-2.7 ± 0.4	28 ± 2	-11.2 ± 0.1
SOD + NCS⁻	22 ± 3	11.7 ± 1.2	64 ± 4	-7.4 ± 2.4
Cu(dien)$^{2+}$ + N_3^-	74.6 ± 1.6	-10.6 ± 0.7	-2 ± 2	-10.0 ± 0.5
Cu(dien)$^{2+}$ + NCS⁻	35.7 ± 1.2	-9.7 ± 1.0	-3 ± 3	-8.8 ± 0.1

Conditions: Buffer — 5 mM PIPES 0.1 M NaCl pH 7.0
　　　*T = 288 K, determined directly via titrations.
　　　**T = 298 K, calculated.

is ionic strength dependent. Unlike the Cu(dien)$^{2+}$ ligand-substitution reactions, $\Delta S°$ is the major contributor to the favorable equilibrium constants for both superoxide dismutase reactions. A sizable, positive value for $\Delta S°$ may be understood in terms of increasing disorder in the water structure in the copper's vicinity that accompanies partial charge neutralization. Even more intriguing is the positive $\Delta H°$ value obtained for thiocyanate coordination. Clearly Cu(dien)$^{2+}$ ligand-substitution is not a good model for the superoxide dismutase reaction with thiocyanate, which perhaps suggests that a leaving group other than H_2O is involved.

In our opinion the results obtained to date indicate that thermodynamic measurements will be useful in understanding and correlating an important part of the active-site chemistry in copper proteins. More extensive experiments along these lines are in progress.

Acknowledgements

This research was supported by the American Heart Association (Grant 82-972) with funds contributed in part by the Massachusetts Affiliate and by the NIH (Grant GM-27659). We thank Cheryl Coté for many helpful discussions.

References and Footnotes

1. E.I. Solomon in *Copper Proteins,* Ed., T.G. Spiro, Wiley, New York, p. 41 (1981).
2. E.I. Solomon, K.W. Penfield, and D.E. Wilcox, *Structure and Bonding 53,* 1 (1983).
3. a. B. Reinhammer in *Copper Proteins and Copper Enzymes V. III,* Ed., R. Lontie, CRC Press, Boca Raton, p. 1 (1984); b. L. Ryden, ibid., p. 37; c. B. Mondovì and L. Avigliano, ibid, p. 101.
4. M.J. Ettinger and D.J. Kosman in *Copper Proteins,* Ed., T.G. Spiro, Wiley, New York, p. 219 (1981).
5. G.A. Hamilton in *Copper Proteins,* Ed., T.G. Spiro, Wiley, New York, p. 193 (1981).
6. P.F. Knowles and K.D.S. Yadav in *Copper Proteins and Copper Enzymes V. II,* Ed., R. Lontie, CRC Press, Boca Raton, p. 103 (1984).
7. B. Mondovì, S. Sabatini, and O. Befani, *J. Mol. Cat. 23,* 325 (1984).

8. E.M. Fielden and G. Rotilio in *Copper Proteins and Copper Enzymes V. II,* Ed., R. Lontie, CRC Press, Boca Raton, p. 27 (1984).

9. J.S. Valentine and M.W. Pantoliano in *Copper Proteins,* Ed., T.G. Spiro, Wiley, New York, p. 291 (1981).

10. R. Barker, N. Boden, G. Cayley, S.C. Charlton, R. Henson, M.C. Holmes, I.D. Kelly, and P.F. Knowles, *Biochem. J. 177,* 289 (1979).

11. R.A. Scott and D.M. Dooley, manuscript in preparation.

12. J.A. Tainer, E.D. Getzoff, K.M. Beem, J.S. Richardson, and D.C. Richardson, *J. Mol. Biol. 160,* 181 (1982).

13. L. Morpuro, C. Giovagnoli, and G. Rotilio, *Biochim. Biophys. Acta 322,* 204 (1973).

14. R.S. Himmelwright, N.C. Eickman, C.D. LuBien and E.I. Solomon, *J. Amer. Chem. Soc. 102,* 5378 (1980).

15. P. Turini, S. Sabatini, O. Befani, F. Chimenti, C. Casanova, P.L. Riccio, and B. Mondovì, *Anal. Biochem. 125,* 294 (1982).

16. D.M. Dooley and K.C. Golnik, *J. Biol. Chem. 258,* 4245 (1983).

17. D.M. Dooley, C.E. Coté and K.C. Golnik, *J. Mol. Cat. 23,* 243 (1984).

18. W. Byers, G. Curzon, K. Garbet, B.E. Speyer, S.N. Young, and R.J.P. Williams, *Biochim Biophys. Acta 310,* 38 (1973).

19. E.G. Gorman and D.W. Darnall, *Biochemistry 20,* 38 (1981).

20. D. Mota de Freitas and J.S. Valentine, *Biochemistry 23,* 2079 (1984).

21. D.M. Dooley and C.E. Coté, submitted for publication.

Biological & Inorganic Copper Chemistry,
ISBN 0-940030-11-X, Eds., K. D. Karlin & J. Zubieta, Adenine Press, ©Adenine Press, 1985

Modulations of Heme Environments by Protein Modifications in Copper Reconstituted Hemoglobins

Periakaruppan T. Manoharan*, Kenneth Alston[†] and Joseph M. Rifkind
Laboratory of Cellular and Molecular Biology
Gerontology Research Center, NIH/NIA, Baltimore, MD 21224
and
[†]Department of Natural Sciences
Benedict College, Columbia, SC 29204

Abstract

Visible and ESR spectral analysis has been performed on copper substituted myoglobin (CuMb), human hemoglobin (CuHbA), carboxypeptidase-A treated hemoglobin-A (CPA-CuHbA) and sickle cell hemoglobin (CuHbS). CuHbA which does not bind oxygen and is in the unliganded conformation (T) has two heme environments as indicated by both visible and ESR spectra. CuHbS which has a modification near the amino acid end of the β-chain has nearly identical ESR and visible spectra. However, modifications of the carboxy end of the β-chain by treatment of CuHbA with carboxypeptidase-A (CPA) to produce CPA-CuHbA results in the presence of a single heme environment as identified by both ESR and visible spectra. This heme environment is apparently identical to that of CuMb and to one of the two environments found in CuHbA and CuHbS.

These results demonstrate that reaction with CPA at sites far removed from the heme does dramatically perturb the heme environment. This can be related to the alteration of the protein conformation from the unliganded T to the liganded R form. Substitution of iron by copper apparently amplifies the heme modification produced by CPA. Interestingly an excellent correlation exists between the ligand affinity and heme environment detected in the copper substituted heme proteins. Thus the modifications of the heme conformations by CPA to produce the high affinity hemoglobin conformation has nearly identical heme environment as high affinity CuMb.

The presence of two heme environments for electrophoretically pure T-state CuHbA and CuHbS where one of these are identical to that of CuMb can best be explained if the heme environment in T-state is controlled by subunit interactions which are relaxed in the R-state. Our results demonstrate the value of copper as a probe to detect changes in the heme environment which have not been observed for iron hemoglobin.

Introduction

One of the most interesting problems in hemeproteins is the relationship between protein conformation and function (1). The functional role of the heme iron is

*On leave from the Department of Chemistry, Indian Institute of Technology Madras 600 036 India

recognized as the principal site of interaction with the substituent ligands and inhibitors. This important role of the porphyrin metal in the function has been emphasized in the crystallographic studies of metalloporphyrins and hemoglobins (1-3). It is in this context that the substitution of the natural iron porphyrin moiety of hemoglobin with other transition metal porphyrins has proved to be an important tool in the investigation of the intrinsic role of the central metal ion (4-5). Earlier work on reconstituted hemoglobins has been largely due to Hoffman et al. (4-6) and Yonetani and his coworkers (7-13) which mainly dealt with cobalt as its central ion.

Some of the recent work (14-18) on nickel(II) and copper(II) reconstituted hemoglobins reveal certain interesting features and differences from those of cobalt and iron. Reconstituted hemoglobins with nickel (NiHbA) and copper (CuHbA) at the porphyrin site do not bind oxygen in contrast to the reversible oxygen binding properties of iron and cobalt hemoglobins. Previous immunochemical studies have shown (18) that the substitution of nickel for iron in hemoglobin-A yields a molecule that is antigenically distinct from R-state oxy, carboxy and methemoglobin-A. This protein is known to be in the T-state based on evidence from circular dichroism (CD) spectral changes, sulfhydryl reactivity, haptoglobin binding and x-ray crystallography (14). In these respects, the substitution of copper in hemoglobin-A seems to give properties similar to that of nickel in hemoglobin-A (17). Our findings on reconstituted copper hemoglobin based on optical and electron paramagnetic resonance (EPR) spectral data adds a new dimension to the existing data.

The optical spectral data of NiHbA, NiMb and carboxypeptidase-A (CPA) treated NiHbA (referred to as CPA-NiHbA) are quite similar to the corresponding reconstituted copper proteins. While these results suggest two types of active sites, the EPR spectra demonstrate the existence of two different types of active sites in CuHbA and a single active site after CPA treatment of CuHbA which is similar to CuMb. The existence of two types of active sites in oxyCoHbA has been identified by Yonetani and coworkers (10,13) from EPR spectral information, however, our studies on T-state CuHbA and its modifications provide new information on the T-conformation. These facts indicate that substitution with copper provides an opportunity to study the subunit interactions of T-state hemoglobin.

Moreover, the CPA treatment at sites far removed from the heme does dramatically perturb the heme environment and this can be related to the alteration of the protein conformation from the unliganded T to the liganded R-form. Substitution of iron by copper apparently amplifies this heme modification produced by CPA. Several interesting aspects of the EPR spectra of these reconstituted hemoglobins give testimony to the value of copper as a probe to detect changes in the heme environment which could not be so easily observed in iron hemoglobin.

Experimental

CuHbA, CuHbS (Sickle Cell) and NiHbA were prepared according to the methods reported earlier (14). In preparing $^{63}CuHbA$, ^{63}CuO (99.89% pure) purchased from Union Carbide Corp., Oak Ridge National Laboratories was used after converting it into the acetate form. In preparing the CPA modified CuHbA and NiHbA, electrophoretically pure CPA-HbA was prepared first by the method of Antonini (19). This was then converted into the corresponding CPA-^{63}CuHbA and CPA-NiHbA by the usual procedures (14). CuMb and NiMb were made by the method of Alston and Storm (20).

EPR spectra were measured in the temperature region 10-300K using a JEOL-JES-ME-1 X-band EPR instrument and an Airproducts cryogenic unit equipped with an Airproducts temperature controller. Q-band frequency measurements were made at lower temperatures using a Varian E-112 EPR instrument with a similar low temperature unit. All measurements were made at 100 KHz field modulation with DPPH as a g-marker. Magnetic field sweep was calibrated using Mn^{2+} in SrO. Optical spectra were recorded on a Varian-Cary 219 spectrophotometer.

The reactivity of the sulfhydryl groups in the various heme proteins were measured by reacting 4,4'-dipyridine disulphide (4-PDS) in 0.15 M NaCl solution to a known quantity of the hemeprotein. The increase in the intensity of 324 nm band, as a function of time was measured and plotted against change of absorbance relative to the absorbance of the heme protein in the absence of 4-PDS (21).

Results

The EPR spectra of CuHbA with the natural isotopic abundances of ^{63}Cu and ^{65}Cu gave a complex superhyperfine spectra due to ^{14}N on each of the separated parallel components from electron-copper nuclear hyperfine interaction. In order to simplify the spectra, the EPR spectra were measured with $^{63}CuHbA$. This spectrum is compared with CPA treated $^{63}CuHbA$ and CuMb in Figure 1 as measured at the X-band frequency. Four points emerge from these spectra: (i) $^{63}CuHbA$ and $^{63}CuHbS$ (not given in Figure 1) give identical X-band spectra; (ii) if the superhyperfine lines due to ^{14}N arise only from the porphyrin nitrogens one should observe only 9 lines on each one of the parallel components due to ^{63}Cu; on the contrary the X-band CuHbA and CuHbS reveal the presence of more than 9 lines on the parallel components indicating either an involvement of an additional nitrogen in the super-hyperfine pattern or the presence of more than one type of copper site; however, the parallel components in CuMb and CPA-^{63}CuHbA show only nine superhyperfine components in each one of the separated parallel resonances due to ^{63}Cu; (iii) it is clear that $A_{\parallel}$ (^{63}Cu) from CuMb and CPA-^{63}CuHbA are smaller than that of CuHbA and CuHbS; (iv) also some differences are apparent in the perpendicular part of the spectra due to $^{63}CuHbA$ and $^{63}CuHbs$ on the one hand and CPA-^{63}CuHbA and CuMb on the other. It is necessary to point out there that there is no temperature dependence in the EPR spectra except for higher resolution and intensity at lower temperature.

Hence, the EPR spectra of all these hemeproteins were measured at the higher

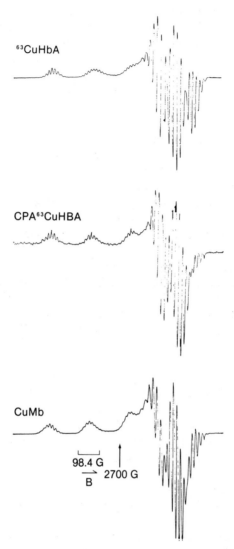

Figure 1. X-band EPR spectra of ^{63}CuHbA, CPA-^{63}CuHbA and CuMb at 12 K. The spectrum of ^{63}CuHbS is identical to that of CuHbA.

frequency. The Q-band frequency spectra are shown in Figure 2. The EPR spectra of ^{63}CuHbA clearly indicates the presence of two different copper environments. The parallel lines due to ^{63}Cu completely separates out at this frequency and two sets of four lines are partially superimposed. The two sets of lines have almost equal integrated intensities. Again, the perpendicular part of ^{63}CuHbA is made up of two components, one with a distinctly narrowed syperhyperfine spectra and another with broadened fine structure. On the contrary, the spectra of CPA-^{63}CuHbA and CuMb have similar spectra with the perpendicular part totally broadened out (less

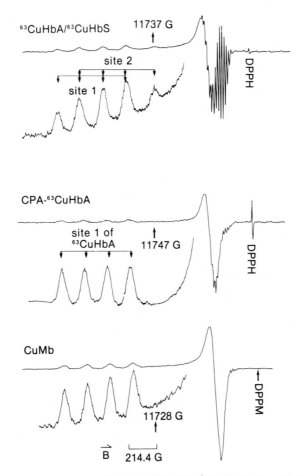

Figure 2. Q-band EPR spectra of ^{63}CuHbA, ^{63}CuHbS, CPA-^{63}CuHbA and CuMb at 120 K.

so in CPA treated ^{63}CuHbA) and have characteristics similar to one of the sites of ^{63}CuHbA in every respect. The ESR parameters obtained from the X- and Q-band measurements for all the reconstituted copper hemeproteins are given in Table I.

The site 1 of CuHbA and CuHbS has identical g- and A(^{63}Cu) tensor values which again are the same as those found for the CPA treated CuHbA and CuMb. Even the hyperfine coupling constants due to ^{14}N nuclei are similar. However, all the ESR parameters due to site 2 are quite different from those of site 1 of ^{63}CuHbA, CPA-^{63}CuHbA and CuMb.

As the existence of two different copper sites or environments in CuHbA is clear from EPR results, the optical spectral results seem to provide similar evidence. A single Soret band in CuMb occurs at 424 nm and in CPA treated CuHbA at 419 nm while the Soret band is split in CuHbA with band maxima at 398 nm and 420 nm.

Manoharan, Alston and Rifkind

Table I

ESR Parameters of Reconstituted Hemoglobins and Myoglobin*

Reconstituted Hemoglobin	$g_\parallel$	$g_\perp$	$A_\parallel(^{63}Cu)$	$A_\perp(^{63}Cu)$	$A_\parallel(^{14}N)$	$A_\perp(^{14}N)$
CuHbA Site 1	2.215	2.048	179.1	16.8	14.20	16.59
Site 2	2.175	2.040	193.6	13.4	14.08	14.44
CuHbS Site 1	2.215	2.048	177.6	16.7	14.3	16.6
Site 2	2.175	2.042	190.3	13.4	14.1	14.5
CPA-CuHbA	2.213	2.045	179.6	16.8	14.2	16.6
CuMb	2.214	2.045	178.5	17.0	14.1	16.6

*Error estimates for $g = \pm .001$; for $A = \pm 2.0$
All A values in 10^{-4} cm^{-1}

The corresponding nickel hemoglobins and myoglobin have similar properties. NiMb and CuMb, CPA-NiHb and CPA-CuHb have single Soret bands located in the longer wavelength region of the hemoglobin bands while NiHbA and CuHbA have an additional band at lower wavelength as seen from Figures 3-5. Soret band maxima for different heme proteins are listed in Table II.

Yet another interesting feature comes from the fact that the tetrameric β-subunit of NiHbA referred to as $Ni(II)\beta^{SH}$ has an optical spectrum very similar to the split Soret observed for NiHbA and CuHbA while that of separated α-chains $Ni(II)\alpha^{SH}$ is markedly different from that of NiHbA. Figure 6 shows the spectral differences between $Ni(II)\beta^{SH}$ and $Ni(II)\alpha^{SH}$. It is of importance to note that the intensity ratio of 399 nm/418 nm bands is 1.3 in NiHbA and $Ni(II)\beta^{SH}$ as compared to 3.3 in $Ni(II) \alpha^{SH}$.

The 4-PDS rate constant serves as a measure of "-SH reactivity" which is related to a conformational change in this region of the protein. In order to ascertain the

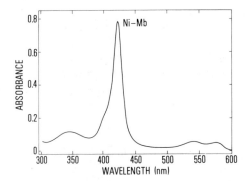
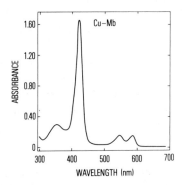

Figure 3. Visible spectrum of NiMb and CuMb in phosphate buffer at room temperature.

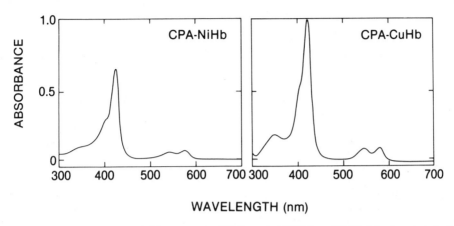

Figure 4. Room temperature visible spectrum of CPA treated NiHbA and CuHbA in phosphate buffer.

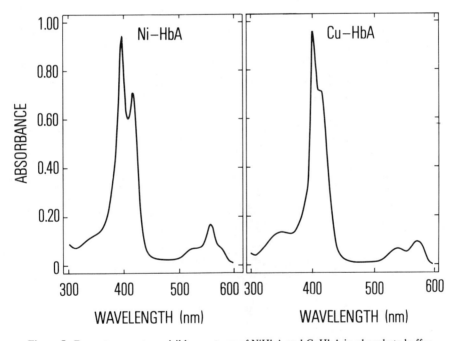

Figure 5. Room temperature visible spectrum of NiHbA and CuHbA in phosphate buffer.

conformational state of CuHbA and NiHbA and their CPA treated forms, the 4-PDS reactivity profile was measured and compared with the R-state FeHbCO and its CPA treated form. It is clear from Figure 7 that NiHbA and CuHbA have much slower reactivity than either FeHbCO or CPA treated hemoproteins.

Table II
Soret Band Maxima (in nm) in Hemoglobins and Myoglobins

			Ref.
NiHbA	398	420	a
CuHbA	404	417	a
CuHbS	404	419	a
CPA·NiHbA		422	a
CPA·CuHbA		418	a
NiMb		420	a
CuMb		424	a
Spermwhale Mb		434	b
Human Hb		430	b
Human HbO$_2$		415	b
Human HbCO		419	b
CPA·Human HbCO		418	b

a—This work;

b—E. Antonini and M. Brunori, *Hemoglobins and Myoglobins in Their Reactions with Ligands,* North-Holland Publishing Co., Amsterdam, London (1971) p. 19.

Discussion

The EPR spectra of [63]CuHbA measured at two frequencies combined with the optical split Soret band in both NiHbA and CuHbA does indicate the presence of

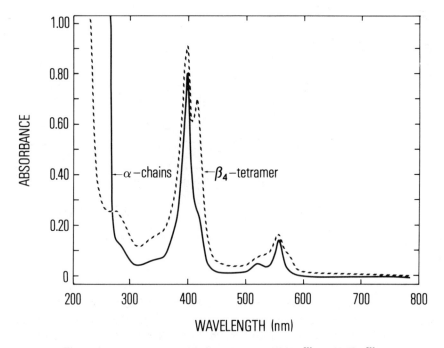

Figure 6. Visible spectral difference between Ni(II)α^{SH} and Ni(II)β^{SH}.

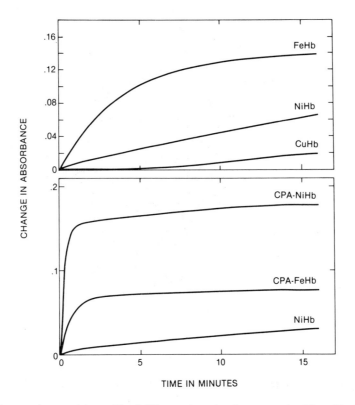

Figure 7. Comparative reactivity profile of -SH group in various heme proteins. The sulfhydryl reagent is 4-PDS. FeHb mentioned above is the R-state FeHb-CO.

two differing metal environments in these reconstituted hemoglobins. Furthermore, that CPA treated NiHbA and CuHbA have a single Soret band in the longer wavelength region of the hemoglobin bands and are similar to NiMb and CuMb (Figures 3-5) is again in accord with the presence of a single site in CPA treated CuHbA which is (a) identical to site 1 of CuHbA and (b) CuMb itself (Figures 1 and 2). A sketch of the β-subunit of hemoglobin and its modification by CPA treatment and in sickle cell is shown in Figure 8. CPA treatment which removes histidine β-146 (HC3) and tyrosine β-145 (HC2) produces noncooperative oxygen binding to Fe-hemoglobin. Perutz et al. (22,23) and Moffat (24) have shown that at least for horse hemoglobin both deoxy and oxy CPA treated hemoglobins crystallize in the oxy form. These changes are attributed to alterations primarily at the $\alpha_1\beta_2$ subunit contacts which stabilize the oxy form. Our results demonstrate that in Cu(II) and Ni(II) hemoglobin, this modification at a site far removed from the heme perturbs the heme environment.

A delineation of the nature of ligation at the two different porphyrin metal environments should be the first task. Table III gives a comparison of known ESR spectral parameters of copper porphyrin moieties with and without axial ligation. The ESR parameters of the site 1 is very comparable to those of strong axially

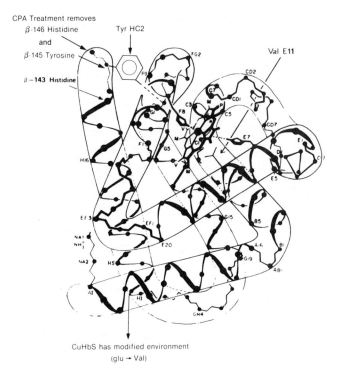

Figure 8. A sketch of the β-subunit of hemoglobin and modifications produced by CPA treatment and found in sickle cell hemoglobin.

Table III
Comparison of ESR Spectral Parameters in Some Cu(II)-Porphyrin Environments

	$g_{\parallel}$	$A_{\parallel}(^{63}Cu)$ (cm^{-1})
CuTPP[a] in chloroform (no axial ligand)	2.187	0.0209
CuTPP in H$_2$TPP[b] (no axial ligand)	2.190	0.0210
CuTTP-l-methyl imiadazole (stron axial ligand)[c]	2.225	0.0186
CuHb Site 1	2.215	0.0179 (consistent with the presence of axial ligand)
Site 2	2.175	0.0194 (consistent with the absence of axial ligand)

[a]TPP is Tetraphenyl Porphyrin
[b]Reference 25
[c]Reference 20

ligated copper tetraphenylporphyrin-l-methyl imidazole (20). This point has been made use of in predicting strong 5-coordination in CuMb (20). Again, since the ESR parameters of CuMb are very close to those of site 1 of CuHbA it is inferred that the site 1 copper environment has a strong axial ligand which is presumably the proximal histidine. When the axial ligation is absent as in the case of $CHCl_3$ solution of the same CuTPP (25) or in the case of CuTPP doped with H_2TPP (25) the $g_{\parallel}$ value decreases with a concommitant increase in the magnitude of $A_{\parallel}$ (^{63}Cu). This is also seen in the case of site 2 of CuHbA indicating either the absence of axial ligation or perhaps the presence of very weak axial ligation. The EPR results are thus consistent with the presence of two types of sites in CuHbA with the first one similar to CuMb with a strong axial ligand and the second one with no or very weak axial ligation.

The comparison of the visible and EPR spectra for CuHbA and CuMb permits the assignment of the longer wavelength Soret band to the 5-coordinated complex (site 1) and the shorter wavelength Soret band to much weaker axial ligation (site 2). In the latter site the central atom is perhaps weakly coordinated to both the proximal and distal histidine. As seen in Table 2, the short wavelength band is unique only for NiHbA, CuHbA and CuHbS. The presence of a myoglobin-type site 1 for some of the porphyrin in CuHb and presumably NiHbA is borne out by the results of carboxypeptidase A treated CuHbA where all the metal environments become equivalent and are similar to those in CuMb as seen both by EPR and visible spectroscopy.

Thus the ESR and optical results on reconstituted hemoglobins revealing the presence of two heme environments may be interpreted in one of the following three possibilities within the confines of quaternary structure: (i) NiHbA and CuHbA do not represent a pure T-conformation but could be a mixture of T and R structure; (ii) one of the sites in these reconstituted hemoglobins could be due to α-subunit and the other due to β-subunit; (iii) two different heme environments could be present within the structural component of a T-conformation.

The first possibility is ruled out by comparing sulfhydryl reactivity of NiHbA, CuHbA, FeHbCO, CPA-NiHbA, CPA-FeHbCO (Figure 7). The extremely slow reactivity of NiHbA and CuHbA as compared to FeHbCO (R structure) and a much faster reactivity of CPA modified NiHbA which is even faster than the R-structured CPA-FeHbCO not only clearly rules out the presence of a mixture of T and R conformations in NiHbA and CuHbA but also provides evidence for the T-state conformation of NiHbA and CuHbA.

The second possibility is again ruled out by measuring the optical spectra (Figure 6) of isolated α and β chains of NiHbA, referred to as Ni(II)α^{SH} and Ni(II)β^{SH} respectively, where the latter is a β_4 tetramer. Ni(II)β^{SH} exhibits a spectrum identical to NiHbA. Hence, the split Soret is not due to differences between nickel(II) protoporphyrin IX incorporated into α and β-chains. Moreover, Ni(II)α^{SH} has a markedly different spectrum than that of NiHbA with a Soret band maximum at 399 nm and a small shoulder at 418 nm. The 399 nm/418 nm intensity ratio is 1.3 in NiHbA compared to 3.3 in Ni(II)α^{SH}. This probably reveals that the two different metal environments are present even in the isolated chains which, however, becomes highly amplified by the dominant effects of the quaternary structure when α-chains become part of the $\alpha_2\beta_2$ tetramer or when β-chains associate into a β_4 tetramer.

Hence, the presence of two different metal ion environments in NiHbA, CuHbA and CuHbS within the T-conformation must be the only logical possibility. These two environments must result from subunit interactions in the quaternary structure and hence due to the consequent conformational restraints, which perturb the metal ion environments favored by the isolated subunits. The large conformational restraints associated with these subunit interactions explains the relative insensitivity of the optical spectrum of NiHbA to temperature variation (26). The presence of two metal environments within the T-state of the reconstituted hemoglobins receives support from the Mossbauer experiments on deoxyHb (T-form) by Levy *et al.* (27), wherein they have observed the presence of two types of metal environments due to conformational fluctuation. The deoxyhemoglobin which undergoes limited conformational fluctuations produces a complex with distal histidine in frozen solutions above 200 K. Hence the formation of two complexes in NiHbA, CuHbA and CuHbS must be considered more possible because of the presence of the metal in the porphyrin ring.

The presence of two types of metal environments has again been found in oxyCoHb by the use of EPR (8). However, the EPR spectrum of the α-chain of oxyCoHb showed a distinctly narrowed hyperfine structure in comparison with the oxy β chain indicating that the environment around the paramagnetic center is different between these chains, whereas in the deoxy form, the EPR spectrum of α and β-chains were indistinguishable. The observation of the indistinguishability of α and β chains of the deoxy CoHb is in line with our conclusion that the two sites observed for the T-form in NiHbA, CuHbA and CuHbS are not due to differences in α and β-chains. It is possible that the differences in the two metal centers in CoHb are more difficult to observe as in the case of deoxy FeHb (27).

Finally the CPA treatment of CuHbA gives rise to only one site, namely site 1 of CuHbA which seems to be identical to CuMb. Again, the optical spectrum of CPA treated CuHbA and NiHbA are in accord with the presence of a single site not only on the basis of a single Soret band in the longer wavelength region but also on their similarity to CuMb as seen in Figures 2-5. Furthermore, the sulfhydryl reactivity profile indicates that the CPA modified NiHbA has an R-structure. It is not surprising since even deoxy HbA on treatment with CPA acquires the R-conformation. Hence the CPA treatment alters the quaternary structure of CuHbA and NiHbA (because of changes in the $\alpha_1\beta_2$ subunit contacts) converting the site 2 type environment into the site 1 type.

It is possible to rationalize the change in the CuHbA EPR and visible spectra produced by CPA treatment in terms of the changes which occur in the positions of the proximal and distal histidines relative to the heme plane during the T $\Rightarrow$ R conformational change and the effect on their coordination with the Cu(II). Thus the movement of the proximal histidine closer to the heme plane and the distal histidine away from the ligand binding site in the ligand pocket would stabilize the 5-coordinated complex with one strong axial ligand analagous to that found in myoglobin as opposed to weak axial interaction with two ligands. In Fe-hemoglobin these changes in the movement of these histidines are coupled with movement of the iron toward the heme plane and no changes in ligand coordination are therefore produced.

Finally the Ni(II)α^{SH} visible spectrum with a short wavelength Soret band indicates site 2 type bonding with two weak axial ligands unlike the single subunit myoglobin which indicates site 1 type bonding with one strong axial ligand. This difference can be attributed to differences in ligand pocket dynamics between hemoglobin and myoglobin as has been suggested by Levy *et al.* (26) on the basis of Mossbauer and EPR results on the low temperature formation of a distal histidine complex in the iron hemeprotein.

The relationship between increased ligand pocket dynamics and the conversion from site 1 strong axial ligand in reconstituted myoglobin to two weak axial ligands in Ni(II)α^{SH} chains further suggests a coupling between movement on the distal and proximal sides of the heme whereby movement of the distal histidine towards the heme results in a weakening of the proximal histidine bond.

Conclusion

The reconstituted hemoglobins CuHbA, CuHbS and NiHbA are present in T-form. Also, two different metal environments are present within the confines of the quaternary T-structure; one with a strong axial ligand as in CuMb and another possibly very weakly coordinated to distal and proximal histidines. Moreover, the reaction with CPA at sites far removed from the heme does dramatically perturb the heme environment which is related to the alteration of its protein conformation from the unliganded T to the liganded R form. Modified heme conformations by CPA to produce the high affinity hemoglobin conformation has nearly identical heme environment as high affinity CuMb. Our results also demonstrate the value of copper as a probe to detect changes in the heme environment which have not been observed for iron hemoglobin.

Acknowledgement

We would like to express our sincere thanks to Professor James Hyde and Dr. W. Antholine for allowing one of us (PTM) to carry out Q-band ESR measurements at the National Biomedical ESR Center at Milwaukee, Wisconsin.

References and Footnotes

1. E. Antonini and M. Brunori in *Hemoglobins and Myoglobins in Their Reactions with Ligands,* North Holland Publishing Company, Amsterdam pp. 348-378 (1971).
2. M.F. Perutz, *Nature 228,* 726 (1970).

3. J.L. Hoard in *Hemes and Heme Proteins,* Eds. B. Chance, R.W. Estabrook and T. Yonetani, Academic Press, New York, pp. 9-24 (1966).
4. B.M. Hoffman and D.H. Petering, *Proc. Natl. Acad. Sci. USA 67,* 637 (1970).
5. T. Yonetani, H. Yamamoto and T. Iizuka, *J. Biol. Chem. 249,* 2168 (1974).
6. G.C. Hsu, C.A. Spilburg, C. Bull and B.M. Hoffman, *Proc. Natl. Acad. Sci. USA 69,* 2122 (1972); B.M. Hoffman in *Prophyrins* 7 (Part B), Ed. D. Dolphin, Academic Press, New York, pp. 403-444 (1979).
7. T.S. Srivastava and T. Yonetani, *Proc. Fed. Am. Soc. Exp. Biol. 33,* 1449 (1974).
8. T. Yonetani, H. Yamamoto and G.V. Woodrow III, *J. Biol. Chem. 249,* 682 (1974).
9. H. Yamamoto, F.J. Kayne and T. Yonetani, *J. Biol. Chem. 249,* 691 (1974).
10. M. Ikeda-Saito, H. Yamamoto, K. Imai, F.J. Kayne and T. Yonetani, *J. Biol. Chem. 252,* 620 (1977).
11. K. Imai, T. Yonetani and M. Ikeda-Saito, *J. Mol. Biol. 109,* 83 (1977).
12. K. Imai, M. Ikeda-Saito, H. Yamamoto and T. Yonetani, *J. Mol. Biol. 138,* 635 (1980).
13. T. Inubushi and T. Yonetani, *Biochemistry 22,* 1894 (1983).
14. K. Alston, A.N. Schechter, J.P. Arcoleo, J. Greer, G.R. Parr and F. K. Friedman, *Hemoglobin 8,* 47 (1984).
15. K. Alston, F.K. Friedman and A.N. Schechter, *Hemoglobin 6,* 15 (1982).
16. K. Alston, C.M. Park, D.W. Rodgers S.J. Edelstein and R.L. Nagel, *Blood,* in press.
17. P.T. Manoharan, K. Alston and J.M. Rifkind, *Bull. Mag. Res. 5,* 255 (1983).
18. K. Alston, A. Dean and A.N. Schechter, *Mol. Immunol. 17,* 1475 (1980).
19. E. Antonini, J. Wyman, R. Zito, A. Rossi-Fannelli and A. Caputo, *J. Biol. Chem. 236,* PC60 (1961).
20. K. Alston and C.B. Storm, *Biochemistry 79,* 4292 (1979).
21. R.S. Ampulski, V.E. Ayers and S.A. Morell, *Anal. Biochem. 32,* 163 (1969).
22. M.F. Perutz, *Proc. Roy. Soc. Ser. B173,* 113 (1969).
23. M.F. Perutz and L.F. TenEcyk, *Cold Spring Symposia on Quantitative Biology,* Vol. XXXVI, 295 (1971).
24. J.K. Moffat, *J. Mol. Biol. 58,* 79 (1971).
25. P.T. Manoharan and M.T. Rogers in *ESR of Metal Complexes,* Ed. T.F. Yen, Plenum Press, New York, pp. 143-173 (1969).
26. P. Chuknyiski and J.M. Rifkind (to be published).
27. A. Levy, K. Alston and J.M. Rifkind, *J. Biomol. Struct. Dynamics 1,* 1299 (1984).

Biological & Inorganic Copper Chemistry,
ISBN 0-940030-11-X, Eds., K. D. Karlin & J. Zubieta, Adenine Press, ©Adenine Press, 1985

DNA-scission and Antiproliferative Activities of L-ascorbate in the Presence of Copper Ion and a Copper-tripeptide Complex

Shyh-Horng Chiou*, Naoyuki Ohtsu† and Klaus G. Bensch‡
*Linus Pauling Institute of Science and Medicine
Palo Alto, CA. 94306, USA
†Kai Memorial Hospital, Hakuji-Kai Kinen Byoin
Tokyo, Japan
‡Department of Pathology, Stanford University School of Medicine
Stanford, CA. 94305, USA

Abstract

Kimoto et al. reported the antitumor activity of copper-diglycyl-L-histidine (Cu-GGH) in combination with L-ascorbate against Ehrlich ascites tumor cells *in vivo* (E. Kimoto, H. Tanaka, J. Gyotoku, F. Morishige and L. Pauling, Cancer Res., 43, 824 (1983)). Our *in vitro* studies with Cu-GGH (5-50μM) and ascorbate (100μM) demonstrated growth inhibition of mouse sarcoma, neuroblastoma and human endometrial carcinoma cells with cytocidal effect. Neither ascorbate nor copper tripeptide alone had a large cytostatic effect on these tumor cells. Incubation of solutions of viral DNA, calf liver RNA and various proteins with Cu/or Cu-GGH and ascorbate resulted in damage of these biological macromolecules. The addition of catalase, but not superoxide dismutase, partially prevented the observed DNA-scission by ascorbate and copper complex, suggesting that oxygen-derived free radicals may be involved in the process. Preliminary microscopic study indicated changes in the surface morphology of the cell membrane and alterations of the mitochondria without apparent damage to the nuclei. It is proposed that the observed cytostatic and cytocidal effect on the tumor cells is probably caused by free radicals formed by the interaction of L-ascorbate with the catalytic copper in the tripeptide complex.

Introduction

The importance of L-ascorbic acid as a biochemical reductant and its complex chemistry in most eucaryotic organisms cannot be overemphasized. Despite the voluminous reports on various aspects of ascorbic acid in regard to its medical (1) and technological (2) applications, the physiological roles of ascorbic acid at the cellular and molecular levels have not been described in a satisfactory manner. The antiviral effect of ascorbate is well documented (1,3,4) despite the lack of a convincing biochemical interpretation. The selective cytotoxic action of ascorbate in the presence of copper ion against malignant melanoma cells has been reported (5). Recently Kimoto et al. (6) also reported an enhancement of antitumor activity of ascorbate on Ehrlich ascites tumor cells by the combination with a coppper-peptide complex. In the previous study (7), it was shown that *in vitro* incubation of the viral DNA and proteins with the mixture of ascorbate and the copper-diglycylhistidine complex resulted in extensive degradation of these biological macromolecules within minutes. The impressive *in vitro* DNA-scission activity of this copper complex in the presence of ascorbate has prompted this study into the effect of this complex and ascorbic acid on various tumor cells.

Material and Methods

Chemicals—$CuCl_2$ (99.999%) was purchased from Aldrich Chemical Co. L-Ascorbic acid, 2,2'-biquinoline, EDTA, glutathione, dithiothreitol (DTT), beta-NADH, xanthine, xanthine oxidase, catalase, sodium azide, superoxide dismutase, lambda bacteriophage DNA and ethidium bromide were from Sigma Chemical Co. All buffers and culture media were of the highest grade commercially available. Copper-binding peptide, diglycyl-L-histidine was synthesized as described previously (7).

DNA Gel Electrophoresis—Electrophoresis in 0.7% agarose was carried out in a horizontal slab gel apparatus according to a previous procedure (7). The electrophoresis was run in a continuous, low ionic strength buffer system of 5 mM Tris-HCl, 5 mM boric acid, 5 mM sodium acetate and 0.2 mM EDTA, pH 8.0. Gels were stained with ethidium bromide in the running buffer for 30 min. The stained gels were photographed with a Polaroid camera using a U.V. transilluminator.

Cytotoxicity Assays—SN1a, a tumor cell line derived from human endometrial carcinoma was kindly supplied by Dr. Nelson Teng of the Stanford University School of Medicine. Mouse sarcoma (S-180) and neuroblastoma (N2a) cell lines were obtained from the American Type Culture Collection, Rockville, MD. The cell lines were maintained in the growth media specified by the suppliers. To each medium were added antibiotics at a concentration of 100 units penicillin and 100 μg streptomycin per ml. The cells were plated at about 2×10^5 cells per well into 6-well plates (3.5×1.0 cm) with 2.0 ml/well of the required medium plus 10% fetal bovine serum. The cells were allowed to attach to the plates for 24 hr before the start of the experiments. All culture plates were incubated at 37°C for 24 hr and the [^{3}H]-thymidine was added 2 hr before the end of incubation period. Cell monolayers were rinsed with Dulbecco's phosphate buffered saline and harvested with trypsin-EDTA. Viable cells were counted in triplicate using a hemocytometer. The cell suspensions of the trypsinized cultures were lysed in 2 ml of 0.12% SDS-2 mM EDTA pH 7.4, at 37 C for 30 min. An aliquot of the solubilized cells were removed for protein determination and the equivalent amount was precipitated with 5% cold trichloroacetic acid. The precipitates obtained after centrifugation at 1500xg for 30 min were dissolved in 0.5 ml of 2 M NH_4OH and counted in a vial containing 5 ml of Aquasol-2 scintillation cocktail (New England Nuclear) using a Beckman LS-8000 counter.

Results and Discussion

The presence of an enediol group in L-ascorbic acid accounts for its acidic property and ease of oxidation. It is readily oxidized by oxygen or other oxidants and is a relatively weak reducing agent with a redox potential of about $+0.058$ V at pH 7 and $25°C$ (8). It has been demonstrated that ascorbic acid and some catecholamines possessing an enediol group can inhibit tumor growth and react with nucleic acids, and that the inhibition is greatly enhanced by cupric ions (9,10). We have been interested in the beneficial effect of ascorbate and its possible clinical applications in the prevention of viral diseases and inhibition of tumor growth (11). Kimoto et al. first demonstrated the effect of a copper complex, Cu(II)-diglycylhistidine, in combination with ascorbate on Ehrlich ascites tumor cells in animals (6). In this report, we show the DNA-scission activity of ascorbate-copper complex *in vitro* and its antiproliferative property on several tumor cell lines.

Using gel electrophoresis it was shown that ascorbate was more effective in cleaving DNA, proteins and calf liver RNA (data not shown) than other reducing agents such as glutathione, dithiothreitol and beta-NADH (Fig. 1) even though the latter

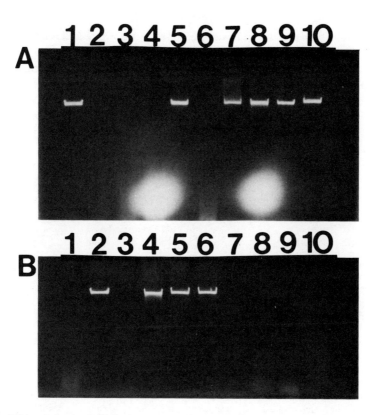

Figure 1. DNA scission by Cu^{2+}/AsA.

compounds possess higher reducing powers than ascorbate. The uniqueness of ascorbate as a reductant in the scission reaction may depend on its ability to generate hydrogen peroxide in the presence of oxygen and metal ions whereas other reducing agents having a thiol group are known to produce the superoxide radical (12), which rapidly undergoes dismutation in aqueous solution (13). Substitution of hydrogen peroxide for ascorbate in the DNA cleavage reaction mixture also produced the diffuse, smeared electrophoresis patterns similar to that observed for the scission reaction of Cu/ascorbate (Fig. 1A). This indicates that hydrogen peroxide is important in the DNA-scission reaction of ascorbate and copper ion. The inhibition of the scission reaction by catalase instead of superoxide dismutase further corroborates the role of hydrogen peroxide in the scission reaction (Fig.1B). In the absence of metal ions or metal complexes, hydrogen peroxide by itself did not show any discernible cleavage of DNA molecules (7). The role of the superoxide radical in the scission reaction appears to be limited since *in vitro* generation of O_2^- by xanthine oxidase and xanthine does not effect DNA cleavage (Fig. 1B). A Fenton-type reaction (14) involving hydroxyl radicals formed by the mixing of hydrogen peroxide and copper ion probably plays a role in the scission activity. It is also of interest to note that free copper ion and its chelated peptide complex are able to generate oxygen-derived free radicals from their interaction with reducing agents (Fig. 1).

The different sensitivities of three tumor cell lines to ascorbate and copper tripeptide are shown in Table I. A significant and observable growth inhibition of tumor cells was obtained at 100 μM ascorbate and 50 μM copper ion or copper-peptide complex. This is also borne out by the decrease of [3H]-thymidine incorporation into the tumor cells. The reason for employing the copper-chelating peptide in combination with ascorbate in the anticancer therapy of Kimoto et al. (6) is to minimize the toxicity of copper ion on normal cells while achieving a more selective cytotoxic

Table I
The Effects of Ascorbate and Copper-peptide Complex on Tumor Cells

Conditions[a]	% Cytotoxicity[b]		
	S-180	N2a	SN1a
Control without additions	0	0	0
Ascorbate (100μM)	21	23	14
Copper ion (5μM)	0	0	0
Copper ion (100μM)	14	16	8
Diglycylhistidine (1 mM) (GGH)	0	0	0
Cu-GGH complex (50μM)	12	8	10
Ascorbate plus Cu (50μM)	28	68	41
Ascorbate plus Cu-GGH (50μM)	44	80	39

a. The concentrations indicated were the final concentrations after mixing.
b. % Cytotoxicity was estimated from the numbers of viable cells at the end of 24 hr incubation. Data shown were percentages of dead cells after treatments. The estimation of growth inhibition from radioactivity uptake was about 8-15% lower than the values shown here.

effect against malignant cells. However in this study most tumor cell lines seemed to be able to tolerate the copper ions alone at very high levels without showing significant cytotoxicity (Table 1). Cytotoxicity and cell-killing effect were shown only in the cases of those cells treated with the copper ion or copper-peptide complex in conjunction with ascorbate. The detailed mechanism of the antiproliferative activity of copper or copper-peptide complex in combination with ascorbic acid is still unknown. The effect probably belongs to the class of free radical-generating agents which would account for the observed efficient DNA scission and antitumor properties. Preliminary microscopic observations indicate that cell membrane damage accompanies cell growth inhibition, but morphologically nuclei remain intact. Changes in the morphology of mitochondria was also evident.

Acknowledgements

We thank Dr. Nelson Teng of the Stanford University School of Medicine for providing human endometrial carcinoma cells in this study. Thanks also go to Mr. Stephen Lawson for the assistance in the preparation of cell cultures. This work was supported in part by the private donors of the Linus Pauling Institute.

References and Footnotes

1. E. Cameron, L. Pauling and B. Leibovitz, *Cancer Res. 39,* 663 (1979).
2. P.A. Seib and B.M. Tolbert in *Ascorbic Acid: Chemistry, Metabolism, and Uses* (Eds., P.A. Seib and B.M. Tolbert), American Chemical Society, Washington, D.C. (1982).
3. C.W. Jungeblut, *J. Exp. Med. 62,* 517 (1935).
4. C.W. Jungeblut, *J. Exp. Med. 70,* 315 (1939).
5. S. Bram, P. Froussard, M. Guichard, C. Jasmin, Y. Augery, F. Sinoussi-Barre and W. Wray, *Nature 284,* 629 (1980).
6. E. Kimoto, H. Tanaka, J. Gyotoku, F. Morishige and L. Pauling, *Cancer Res. 43,* 824 (1983).
7. S.-H. Chiou, *J. Biochem. 94,* 1259 (1983).
8. S. Lewin in *Vitamin C: Its Molecular Biology and Medical Potential,* Academic Press, New York, p.43 (1976).
9. K. Yamafuji, H. Murakami and M. Shinozuka, *Z. Krebsforsch. 73,* 195 (1970).
10. K. Yamafuji, Y. Nakamura, H. Omura, T. Soeda and K. Gyotoku, *Z. Krebsforsch. 76,* 1 (1971).
11. E. Cameron and L. Pauling, *Proc. Natl. Aca. Sci. U.S.A. 75,* 4538 (1978).
12. H.P. Misra, *J. Biol. Chem. 249,* 2151 (1974).
13. D.T. Sawyer and J.S. Valentine, *Acc. Chem. Res. 14,* 393 (1981).
14. C. Walling, *Acc. Chem. Res. 8,* 125 (1975).

Biological & Inorganic Copper Chemistry,
ISBN 0-940030-11-X, Eds., K. D. Karlin & J. Zubieta, Adenine Press, ©Adenine Press, 1985

Formation of Adducts Between Cupric Complexes of Known Antitumor Agents and Ehrlich Ascites Tumor Cells

W. E. Antholine
Department of Radiology, The Medical College of Wisconsin,
Milwaukee, Wisconsin, 53226

and

Susanne Lyman and David H. Petering
Department of Chemistry, University of Wisconsin-Milwaukee,
Milwaukee, Wisconsin, 53201

and

Loren Pickart
Virginia Mason Research Center
Seattle, Washington, 98101

Abstract

The ESR spectra of several cupric complexes of known antitumor agents have been detected after uptake of the complexes by Ehrlich ascites tumor cells. It is shown that at least some of the adducts formed in cells are comprised of tridentate cupric complex and a sulfhydryl donor atom from a macromolecule. The use of room temperature ESR at three different frequencies (Q, X, and S-band) is illuminating in these studies, because two of the complexes are shown to interact with cells to become effectively immobilized during the process involved in net reduction. S-band ESR studies were also used to detect adduct formation between cupric bleomycin and pyridine and to suggest that cupric bleomycin forms adducts in the presence of cells similar to the pyridine adduct.

Introduction

During the past thirty years the search for antitumor agents has been eminated by studies of organic compounds. Yet two of the clinically useful antitumor drugs, numbering about thirty, contain or probably require metal ions for activity— dichlorodiammine Pt(II) and bleomycin (1,2). Several copper complexes are known to be cytotoxic to cells in culture and in some cases to have activity against animal tumors (3-6 and Fig. 1). Previous studies of the reactions of Cu(II)KTS and Cu(II)L$^+$ with cells suggested that a redox cycle is set up in which Cu(II) is reduced to Cu(I) by cellular thiols such as glutathione, GSH (7). The cuprous species is reoxidized to

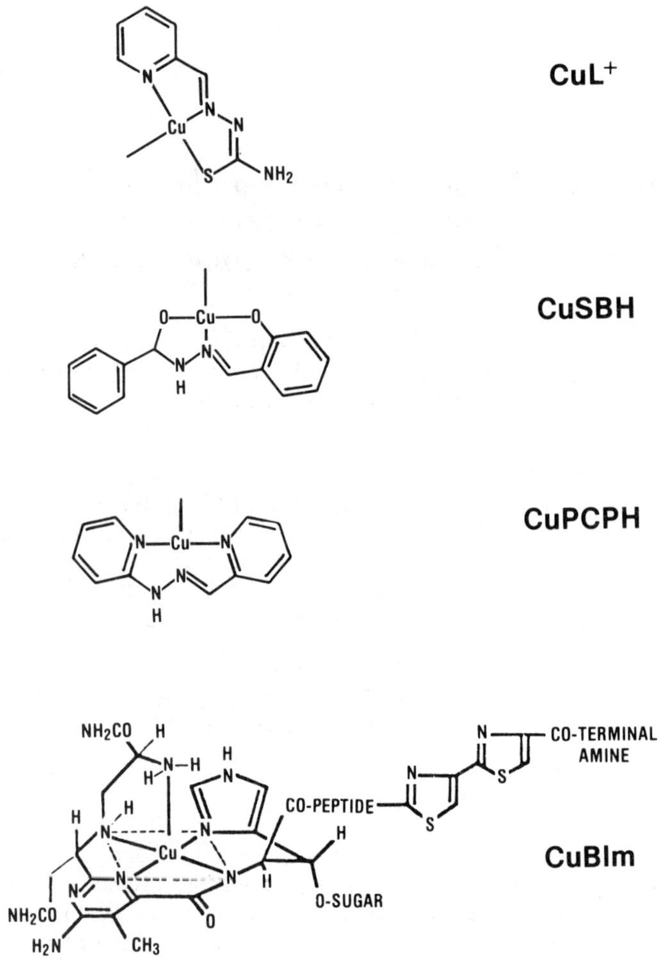

Figure 1. Probable structure of cupric complexes with known cytotoxicity against Ehrlich cells: 2-formylpyridine monothiosemicarbazonato copper (II), CuL$^+$; salicylaldehydebenzoylhydrazonato copper II, CuSBH; pyridine-2-carboxaldehyde-2'-pyridylhydrazonato copper (II), CuPCPH; cupric bleomycin, CuBlm.

the cupric form by oxygen. During the process, radicals including O$_2^-$ and ·OH have been detected utilizing spin trapping techniques (7). ESR data for one of the complexes, Cu(II)L$^+$, 2-formylpyridine thiosemicarbazonato Cu(II), indicates that the tridentate complex completes the square planar configuration by forming an adduct with a thiol ligand as part of the redox cycle of reactions (7-9). Although the adduct was not identified, it was presumed to involve glutathione as the third donor because GSH is present in large concentrations and because the ESR spectrum of the adduct can be modeled by CuL plus GSH (7,9).

This work focuses on the structure of the fraction of several cupric complexes which can be detected by ESR after uptake of the complexes by Ehrlich ascites tumor cells. Emphasis is placed on the use of room temperature ESR so that spectral measurements are made under conditions similar to those used to test the biological effects of the complexes. It is shown that at least some of the adducts formed in cells are comprised of tridentate cupric complex and a donor atom from a macromolecule.

Materials and Methods

Reagents and Materials. The preparation of 2-formylpyridine thiosemicarbazone ligand, and salicylaldehydebenzolhydrazone and their copper complexes have been described previously (10,5). Bleomycin was supplied by Bristol Laboratories under the trade name Bleonoxane and pyridine-2-carboxaldehyde-2'-pyridylhydrazone was purchased from Aldrich Chemical Co. The preparation of cupric bleomycin and (pyridine-2-carboxaldehyde-2'-pyridylhydrazonato)-copper(II) dichloride have also been previously described (5,6). All other chemicals were reagent grade.

The Ehrlich ascites tumor is a transplantable tumor derived from a mouse mammary carcinoma. These cells are grown in mice, which survive about 17 days after intraperitoneal injection of 5×10^6 cells. For studies of the room temperature ESR spectra of copper complexes in the presence of Ehrlich cells, copper complexes were rapidly mixed with washed cells using a vortex mixer in a medium of 0.01M PO_4 pH 7.2 + 0.15M NaCl. ESR tubes were then filled with the cell suspension.

Physical Measurements. The ESR studies were conducted at the National Biomedical ESR Center. The S-band spectrometer includes a microwave bridge operating at about 2.3GHz. The S-band cavity is a loop-gap resonator (11). Cell suspensions were placed in a 3 mm O.D. quartz tube for S-band analysis. These cells settled to the bottom of the tube resulting in packed cells. Cell suspensions for X-band analysis were inserted into a flat cell which was placed horizontally in the ESR cavity to prevent settling of cells over time.

Results

ESR Spectra of Copper Complexes at 77°K. ESR spectra (Fig. 2) of several copper complexes were taken at 77°K to define the ESR parameters and concentration before addition of drugs to cells (Table I). In three of these complexes copper is bound to a tridentate ligand and a fourth donor atom, presumably an oxygen atom from the medium provided by either DMSO or H_2O. Thus, the square plane for CuL is comprised of two nitrogen atoms, a sulfur donor atom, and one oxygen atom (N-N-S-O), O-N-O-O for CuSBH, and N-N-N-O for CuPCPH. The coordination environment for CuBlm is thought to be a pyramidal square plane of nitrogens (12-14).

A good indication of the presence of nitrogen donor atoms comes from the values of $g_{||}$ and $A_{||}$ (Table I), which can be compared to known values with the aid of Peisach-Blumberg plots (15), and from the hyperfine structure in the $g_{\perp}$ region (Fig. 2). The perpendicular region is complicated by superposition of perpendicular,

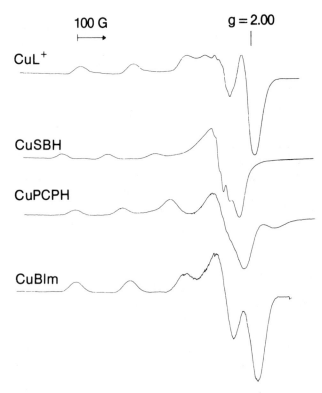

Figure 2. X-band ESR spectra at −196°C for CuL⁺, CuSBH, and CuPCPH, in DMSO and CuBlm in 0.1M NaCl at pH 7. Spectrometer conditions: incident microwave power 5mW, microwave frequency 9.061 GHz, modulation amplitude 5 Gauss, modulation frequency 100 KHz.

Table I
ESR parameters for copper complexes of known antitumor agents

sample[a]	temp.	g_{iso}	A_{iso}	A_N	$g_{\parallel}$	$g_{\perp}$	$A_{\parallel}$	A_N	Ref.
⁶³CuL⁺	−196°C				2.20	∼ 2.05	172G	12.5G	(8)
CuL⁺	R.T.	2.10	∼ 71G	—	—	—	—	—	(7)
CuL⁺ (in cells)	R.T.	—	—	—	2.12	∼ 2.02	152G	∼ 12G	this work
CuL⁺−GSH	R.T.	2.07	∼ 79G	14G	—	—	—	—	(7)
⁶⁵CuL−GSH	−196°C	—	—	—	2.14	2.035	180G	12.6G	(9)
CuSBH	−196°C	—	—	—	2.28	2.07	157G	—	this work
CuSBH	R.T.	2.11	∼ 68G	∼ 15G	—	—	—	—	this work
CuSBH (in cells)	R.T.	—	—	—	2.21	2.05	172G	—	this work
CuSBH	R.T.	2.14	∼ 66G	—	—	—	—	—	this work
CuSBH (S-band in cells)	R.T.	—	—	—	2.21	—	175G	—	this work
CuPCPH	R.T.	2.12	∼ 68G	—	—	—	—	—	this work

[a]X-band data for all samples except when S-band indicated.

parallel, "overshoot" lines, and hyperfine structure from both cupric isotopes and nitrogen splittings. Thus, determination of the number of donor atoms from the number of resolved lines in the perpendicular region presents difficulties. Recent studies using spin echo ESR, and ENDOR have implicated the nitrogen donor atoms for CuBlm (14,16).

Room temperature ESR spectra of copper complexes. Studies have shown that the rigid limit ESR parameters calculated from room temperature data for some cupric complexes may differ from the those obtained from frozen spectra (17,18). The ESR parameters from the room temperature spectra for CuL$^+$, CuSBH, and CuPCPH (Fig. 3) are similar to those for the frozen samples (Table I), whereas the parameters for CuBlm, at room temperature, appear to differ from the frozen solution parameters (18).

The hyperfine structure is best resolved at room temperature at X-band in the high field $M_I = +3/2$ lines (Fig. 3). Even though the spectra contain splittings from two isotopes of copper $^{63}Cu \sim 70\%$ and $^{65}Cu \sim 30\%$, five lines from CuL$^+$ are consistent with two approximately equivalent nitrogen donor atoms. In the case of CuSBH,

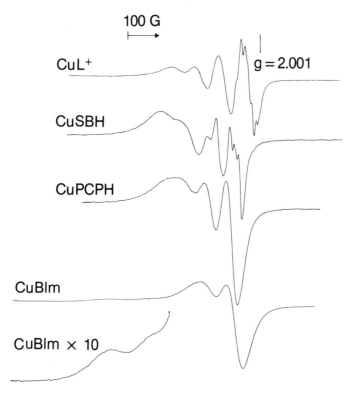

Figure 3. X-band spectra at room temperature for CuL$^+$, CuSBH, CuPCPH in DMSO and CuBlm in 0.1M NaCl at pH7. Spectrometer conditions: incident microwave power 200 mW, microwave frequency 9.504 GHz, modulation amplitude 5G, modulation frequency 100 KHz, ESR flat cell used for samples.

the three line splitting is consistent with the presence of a single donor atom. These spectra will be compared with the spectra of these copper complexes upon addition to Ehrlich ascites tumor cells as discussed below (Fig. 6). A change in rigid limit parameters may indicate a change in a donor atom(s). Further, a change from an isotropically averaged spectrum indicative of a mobile or rapidly tumbling complex to a rigid limit spectrum or slow motion spectrum suggests (1) an adduct has formed in which the molecular weight has increased above about 1600 gms/mole, (2) the cupric ion has been transferred to a binding site on a molecule with a large molecular weight, or (3) the viscosity has increased such that the complex can no longer rapidly tumble with respect to the ESR time frame.

Reaction of CuBlm with pyridine. Cupric complexes made from tridentate ligands readily acquire a Lewis base to form adducts. However, CuBlm is already pyramidal square planar making adduct formation more difficult. A large excess of pyridine was added to CuBlm to demonstrate that pyridine adducts could be formed (Figs. 4 and 5). The frozen solution, X-band ESR spectrum of CuBlm in the presence of pyridine appears to sharpen up in the perpendicular region with little apparent change in the positions of the lines (Fig. 4). Changes in the room temperature spectra in the presence of pyridine are more substantial (Fig. 5). In the absence of pyridine the room temperature ESR spectrum for CuBlm is nicely resolved using

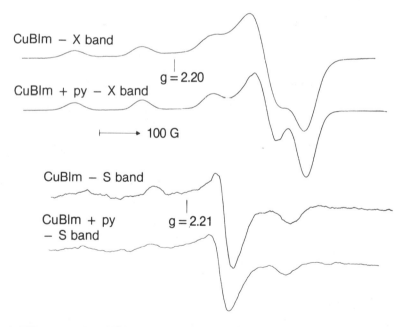

Figure 4. ESR spectra at $-196°C$ for CuBlm in the presence and absence of pyridine. Top spectra: X-band (9.1 GHz), 20mM CuBlm in 0.15 M NaCl at pH 7 and 10mM CuBlm after addition of pyridine (6.0 M). Spectrometer conditions: incident microwave power 5mW; modulation amplitude 5G, modulation frequency 100 KHz. Bottom spectra: S-band (3.36 GHz); 2mM CuBlm in 0.10 M NaCl at pH 7 and 1mM CuBlm after addition of pyridine (1 M).

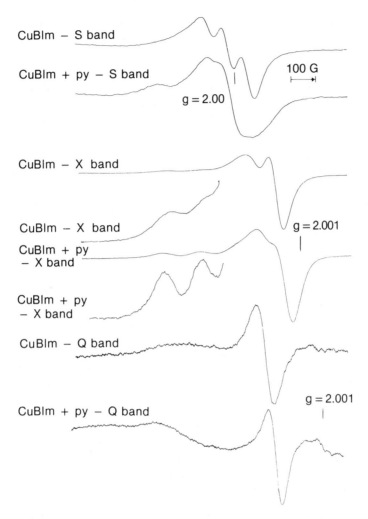

Figure 5. ESR spectra at room temperature for CuBlm (20mM) in 0.15 M saline at pH 7 in the absence of pyridine and for CuBlm (10mM) in the presence of pyridine (6 M) at three microwave frequencies. Spectrometer conditions: S-band (3.461 GHz), incident microwave power OdB, modulation amplitude 12.5 G, modulation frequency 100 KHz, X-band (9.504 GHz), incident microwave power 200mW, modulation amplitude 5G, modulation frequency 100 KHz; Q-band (34.722 GHz) incident microwave power 4dB, modulation amplitude 5G, modulation frequency 100 KHz.

the low frequency S-band spectrometer (18). Three lines in the fast tumbling domain are well resolved at S-band, whereas only the high field line is in the fast tumbling domain at X-band. Two lines in the $g_{||}$ region are in the slow tumbling domain. In the presence of pyridine the ESR spectrum is no longer well resolved and a line in the $g_{||}$ region appears to indicate that the motion of the complex is slower. The $g_{||}$ lines at X-band are more prominent and the position of the only resolved line at Q-band has changed. Recent studies suggest either that CuBlm is not spherical but rather cigar shaped or it has segmented flexibility and rotates about a hinge (18). Since the presence of pyridine affects this motion, it is proposed that an excess of Lewis bases in cells might affect the ESR spectrum in a manner similar to the effect of excess pyridine.

ESR spectra of copper complexes associated with Ehrlich cells. Upon addition of the cupric complexes to Ehrlich ascites tumor cells several changes are immediately evident (Fig. 6): (1) the intensity of the signal decreases; (2) the motion of the

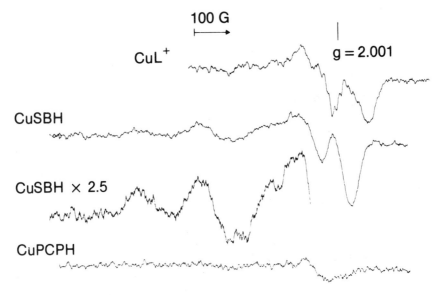

Figure 6. X-Band ESR spectra at room temperature of CuL' (initial conc. 6mM), CuSBH (initial conc. 7mM), and CuPCPH (initial conc. 8mM) in 10^8 Ehrlich cells suspended in 0.15 M NaCl.

complex is slow resulting in an immobilized spectrum; and (3) the ESR parameters have changed (Table I). The shift in $g_{||}$ from 2.18 to 2.12 and the improved resolution of the nitrogen hyperfine structure are consistent with the formation of a CuL-SR adduct. The spectrum of CuL^+ in cells after freezing (Fig. 7) is identical with previous results for a CuL-SR adduct in which RSH is either glutathione or a cysteine amino acid residue from cat hemoglobin (7-9). If the adduct was formed from CuL^+ and GSH, the room temperature spectrum would be the isotropically averaged spectrum due to rapid motion of a low molecular weight complex (7). Thus, as previously observed, CuL^+ most likely forms an adduct with a cysteine amino acid residue from a protein and the motion of the complex is slowed. Similarly, when CuSBH interacts with cells its motion is slowed and the apparent g-value in the parallel region changes from 2.28 to 2.21 consistent with a possible shift in donor atoms from O-N-O-O to O-N-O-S. The intensity of the CuPCPH signal decreased rapidly. The $g_{||}$ region of its ESR spectrum was not detected, so that little ESR data was obtained. The change from the mobile to the immobile form upon

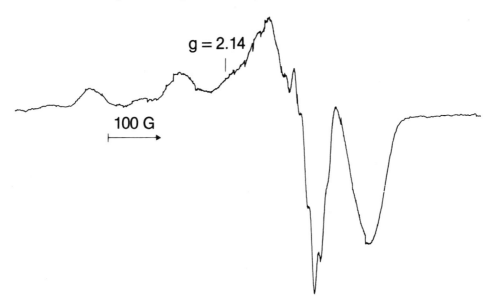

Figure 7. X-band ESR spectrum at $-196°C$ of CuL^+ (initial conc. 7mM) in 10^8 Ehrlich cells (7-9).

addition of CuSBH to cells was repeated using low frequency spectroscopy. Similar results were obtained using a low frequency S-band spectrometer (Fig. 8 and Table I).

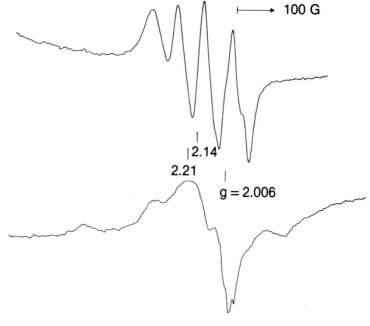

Figure 8. S-band ESR spectra at room temperature of CuSBH (initial conc. 4mM) in the absence and presence of 10^8 Ehrlich cells. Spectrometer conditions: incident microwave power OdB, microwave frequency 3.4485 GHz, modulation amplitude 12G, modulation frequency 100 KHz.

The rate of decrease of ESR observable CuL^+ in cells was similar when CuL^+ was dissolved in DMSO and added to cells or whether solid CuL^+ was added to cells (Fig. 9 and 10). When solid CuL^+ was added to cells, the ESR spectrum can be attributed to aggregated particles for which exchange or superexchange through the aggregates results in narrow lines for $g_{||}$ and $g_{\perp}$ and the loss of the cupric hyperfine lines. Comparison of the rate of reduction of these complexes in cells indicates that the adduct form can be detected in cells for up to two hours (Fig. 10).

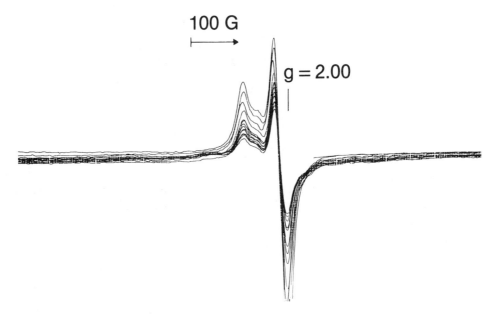

Figure 9. S-band ESR spectra of CuL^+ (initial conc. 2.9mM) after addition of solid CuL^+ to 10^8 Ehrlich cells. Spectrometer conditions: microwave frequency 3.4682 GHz, incident microwave power OdB, modulation amplitude 12G, modulation frequency 100 KHz.

Discussion

Three types of reactions are known to occur when copper complexes are added to cells. The cupric complex is either reduced, the copper (II or I) complex is dissociated in a ligand exchange reaction, or the complex forms an adduct (17). As described in the introduction, the redox chemistry of copper naturally intersects with oxygen redox reaction under aerobic conditions in cells. Thus, when copper is reduced, it is likely that reoxidation through reaction with O_2 will occur and reactive reduced oxygen species will be formed.

In this study all of the tridentate copper complexes are apparently reduced in cells as indicated by their loss of ESR spectral intensity. CuPCPH reacts very rapidly according to Fig. 10. Given the larger affinity of sulfhydryl groups for Cu(I), it is

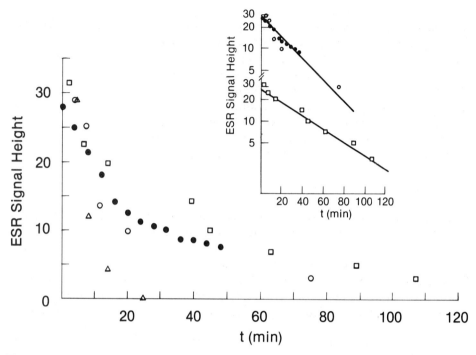

Figure 10. Plot of decrease in ESR signal height of cupric complexes as measured from peak maximum to peak minimum in the $g_\perp$ region versus time upon addition to 10^8 Ehrlich cells. CuL$^+$, $\bigcirc$, solid CuL$^+$, $\bullet$, CuSBH, $\square$, and CuPCPH, $\triangle$. Insert shows semilog plot of signal height versus time. Spectrometer conditions: see legends for Figures 8 and 9.

likely that the reaction occurs as follows:

$$Cu(II)PCPH^{2+} + RSH \Rightarrow Cu(I)PCPH^{1+} + RS^{\cdot} + H+ \tag{1}$$

$$Cu(I)PCPH^{1+} + RSH \Rightarrow Cu(I)SR + PCPH + H^+ \tag{2}$$

The complex is reduced (RXN 1) and the Cu(I) transferred to thiol in a reaction which is fast in comparison with the reoxidation of Cu(I)PCPH. Copper is then distributed throughout the cell in analogy to reactions of 3-ethoxy-2-oxobutyraldehyde bis(thiosemicarbazonato) Cu(II), CuKTS, with Ehrlich cells (19). In particular, the first site to be clearly populated by Cu from CuKTS is Ehrlich cell metallothionein(Mt) in a metal exchange reaction (20).

$$Cu(I) + ZnMt \Rightarrow Cu(I)Mt + Zn \tag{3}$$

This reaction may significantly disrupt cellular zinc metabolism and thereby inhibit cell proliferation.

CuL and CuSBH are apparently reduced much more slowly by Ehrlich cells (Fig. 10). This is in qualitative agreement with previous studies of CuL, which monitored the disappearance of a charge transfer band of the complex. However, according to the ESR data, the pseudofirst order decline in ESR intensity of CuL is about $6 \times 10^{-4}sec^{-1}$ or an order of magnitude faster than the constant calculated from absorbance changes of the complex. CuSBH also reacts with cells with a slow, small rate constant of $4 \times 10^{-4}sec^{-1}$. According to past work, the net reduction of CuL and presumably CuSBH is accompanied by many redox cycles of copper and the generation of a large flux of reduced species of O_2 (7). Thus, in these cases reaction (4) competes effectively with ligand substitution (RXN 2) so that cycling can occur.

$$Cu(I)L + O_2 \Rightarrow Cu(II)L^+ + O_2^- \qquad (4)$$

Since species such as H_2O_2 and $\cdot OH$ are highly toxic to cells, these complexes may exert some of their biological effects on cells in this manner.

The use of room temperature ESR is illuminating in these studies, for both CuL and CuSBH are shown to interact with cells to become effectively immobilized during the processes involved in net reduction. It is probable that the complexes bind to proteins forming adducts with SH groups on these macromolecules (RXN 5).

$$Cu(II)L + P-SH \quad \rightleftarrows \quad Cu(II)L \cdot S-P + H^+ \qquad (5)$$
$$\text{(protein)}$$

Such adducts have been observed in the reaction of CuL with hemoglobin (Hb). In the case of Hb, the adduct perturbs its oxygen binding processes, and so in general such adducts might alter protein function (8). It may also be that such adduct formation precedes the redox reaction (RXN 1), so that these complexes carry out the oxidation of protein sulfhydryl groups as they are reduced. Alternatively, the protein-complex adduct may be relatively stable as with CuL·Hb. Then, only the free form of CuL in RXN 5 is reduced by reactive thiols such as glutathione.

The use of room temperature, multifrequency ESR is also helpful for determining whether the structure of a copper complex reacting with cells at $25\text{-}37^\circ C$ is the same as that commonly studied at $77^\circ K$. In the case of CuBlm, there are apparent differences described elsewhere (18). Using S-band frequencies one can also detect probable adduct formation between CuBlm and a Lewis base, pyridine. Because so little Blm or CuBlm is taken up into cells, it has been difficult to study the cellular reaction of CuBlm (21). Preliminary studies near the limit of sensitivity for room temperature studies do suggest that CuBlm forms adducts in the presence of cells similar to the pyridine adduct.

Acknowledgements

Supported by NIH Grants CA-22184, CA-28858 and RR-01008 and by funds from the University of Wisconsin-Milwaukee for William E. Antholine.

References and Footnotes

1. B. Rosenberg in *Metal Ions in Biological Systems*, Eds. H. Sigel, *Vol. II*, Marcel Dekker, New York, Chap. 3 (1980).
2. S.K. Carter in *Bleomycin: Current Status and New Developments*, Eds., S.K. Carter and S.T. Crooke, Academic Press, New York, p. 9 (1978).
3. W.E. Antholine, J.M. Knight and D.H. Petering, *J. Med. Chem. 19(2)*, 339 (1976).
4. G.J. Van Giessen, H.G. Petering, *J. Med. Chem. 11*, 695 (1968).
5. L. Pickart, W.H. Goodwin, W. Burgua, T.B. Murphy and D.K. Johnson, *Biochem. Pharm. 32(24)*, 3868 (1983).
6. E.A. Rao, L.A. Saryan, W.E. Antholine and D.H. Petering, *J. Med. Chem. 23*, 1310 (1980).
7. L.A. Saryan, K. Mailer, C. Krishnamurti, W. Antholine and D.H. Petering, *Biochem. Pharm. 30(12)*, 1595 (1981).
8. W. Antholine and F. Taketa, *J. Inorg. Biochem. 16*, 145 (1982).
9. W.E. Antholine and F. Taketa, *J. Inorg. Biochem. 20*, 69 (1984).
10. W.E. Antholine, J. M. Knight and D.H. Petering, *Inorg. Chem. 16*, 569 (1977).
11. W. Froncisz and J.S. Hyde, *J. Mag. Res. 47*, 515 (1982).
12. Y. Iitaka, H. Nakamura, T. Nakatani, Y. Muraoka, A. Fujii, T. Takita and H. Umezawa, *J. Antibiot. (Tokyo) 31*, 1070 (1978).
13. J.C. Dabrowiak, *J. Inorg. Biochem. 13*, 317 (1980).
14. W.E. Antholine, J.S. Hyde, R.C. Sealy and D.H. Petering, *J. Biol. Chem. 259(7)*, 4437 (1984).
15. J. Peisach and W.E. Blumberg, *Arch. Biochem. Biophys. 165*, 691 (1974).
16. R.M. Burger, H.D. Adler, S.B. Horwitz, W.B. Mims and J. Peisach, *Biochem. 20*, 1701 (1981).
17. R. Basosi, W.E. Antholine, W. Froncisz and J.S. Hyde, *J. Chem. Phys., 81(11)*, 4849 (1984).
18. W.E. Antholine, G. Riedy, J.S. Hyde, R. Basosi and D.H. Petering, *J. Biomolecular Structure and Dynamics, 2(2)*, 469 (1984).
19. D.T. Minkel and D.H. Petering, *Cancer Res. 38*, 117 (1978).
20. A. Kraker, S. Krezoski, J. Schneider, J. Schmidt and D. Petering in *Platinum Coordination Complexes in Cancer Chemotherapy*, Eds. M.P. Hacker, E.B. Douple and I.H. Krakoff, Martinus Nijhoff Publishing, Boston, p. 354 (1984).
21. W.E. Antholine, D. Solaiman, L. Saryan and D.H. Petering, *J. Inorg. Biochem. 17*, 75 (1982).

Biological & Inorganic Copper Chemistry,
ISBN 0-940030-11-X, Eds., K. D. Karlin & J. Zubieta, Adenine Press, ©Adenine Press, 1985

Possible Medicinal Uses of Copper Complexes

Rosalie K. Crouch
Department of Ophthalmology
Medical University of South Carolina
Charleston, South Carolina 29425 U.S.A.

Thomas W. Kensler
School of Hygiene and Public Health
Johns Hopkins University
Baltimore, Maryland 21205 U.S.A.

Larry W. Oberley
Radiation Research Laboratory
University of Iowa
Iowa City, Iowa 52242 U.S.A.

John R. J. Sorenson
College of Pharmacy
University of Arkansas for Medical Sciences
Little Rock, Arkansas 72205 U.S.A.

Abstract

Copper-dependent enzymes required for tissue maintenance, repair, and prevention of toxic metabolic end-product accumulation are found in all cells. The increase in plasma copper concentration associated with many diseases can be viewed as a component of the physiologic response intended to provide cells of affected tissue with copper for de novo synthesis of these enzymes and a return to normal. This view is consistent with observations that copper complexes have antiinflammatory, antiulcer, anticonvulsant, antidiabetic, anticancer, anticarcinogenic, antimutagenic, and radioprotectant activities in animal models of these disease states. Copper complexes are known to have antiinflammatory in Man as a result of their effectiveness in the treatment of arthritic diseases. The above pharmacologic activities are reviewed in support of the possibility that copper complexes offer a physiological approach to therapy of chronic diseases.

Introduction

Like essential amino acids, essential fatty acids, and essential cofactors (vitamins), essential metalloelements such as copper are required for normal metabolic processes but can not be synthesized *in vivo* and dietary intake and absorption are required to obtain them. The adult body contains between 1.4 and 2.1 mg of copper

per kilogram of body weight (1). Infants contain 3 times this amount (1) which is consistent with the fact that their metabolic needs are much greater than adults. All tissues of the body need copper for normal metabolism but some tissues have greater metabolic needs than others and tissue copper content reflects this fact. Amounts of copper found in various body tissues and fluids are shown in Table I.

Table I
Mean Concentration* of Cu in Tissues and Fluids (see references in 2)

Adrenal	210	Milk	
Aorta	97	colostrum	0.35-0.50 ug/ml
Bile	547	mature	0.20-0.50 ug/ml
Blood (total)	1.01 ug/ml	Muscle	85
erythrocytes	0.98 ug/ml	Nails	23 ug/g
plasma	1.12 ug/ml	Omentum	190
serum	1.19 ug/ml	Ovary	130
Bone	25 ug/g	Pancreas	150
Brain	370	Pancreatic Fluid	105
Breast	6 ug/g	Placenta	4 ug/g
Cerebrospinal Fluid	0.22 ug/g	Prostate	110
Diaphragm	150	Saliva	0.08 ug/ml
Esophagus	140	Skin	120
Gall Bladder	750	Spleen	93
Hair	19 ug/g	Stomach	230
Heart	350	Sweat	0.55 ug/ml
Intestine		Testes	95
Duodenum	300	Thymus	4 ug/g
jejunum	250	Thyroid	100
ileum	280	Tongue	4.6 ug/g
cecum	220	Tooth	
sigmoid colon	230	dentine	2 ug/g
rectum	180	enamel	10 ug/g
Kidney	270	Trachea	65
Larynx	59	Urinary Bladder	120
Liver	680	Urine	0.04 ug/ml
Lung	130	Uterus	110
Lymph Node	60		

*ug/g of tissue ash or as shown

The amount of copper in each tissue correlates with the number and kind of metabolic processes requiring copper in that tissue. In this regard, it is of interest to point out that the brain and heart contain more copper than all other tissues except the liver which is the major copper storage organ. Because the gall bladder and bile serve as the major excretory vehicle for copper, bile and gall bladder also contain a large amount. Bile may also contain a mobile form of copper suitable for reabsorption. Organs with the next most abundant copper content in decreasing order are stomach, intestine, and adrenal glands. Remaining tissues have lesser amounts of copper because of their relatively lower metabolic activity but it is just as important for normal metabolism in these tissues as it is in all others.

Although bile may serve as the major excretory vehicle for excess copper, significant but lesser amounts are lost *via* hair, stratum corneum, finger- and toe-nails, sweat, and urine as end-products of metabolism. These losses point out the need for a compensating daily intake and absorption to replenish this essential metalloelement.

Ionic copper has a particularily high affinity for other molecules (Ligands) capable of bonding with it. A consequence of this is that nearly all copper in biological systems exists as complexes or chelates composed of copper bonded to organic components of these systems. Calculated amounts of ionic copper suggested to be present in biological systems are too small to be measured using the most sensitive instrumentation available. As a result, tissue copper contents reflect tissue contents of copper complexes and these complexes account for the absorption, distribution, and biologically active forms of copper *in vivo*.

Fates of ingested copper complexes likely follow the pathway presented in Figure 1. Considering one of a large number of possible copper complexes that might be found in foods and/or beverages, CuL_2, following ingestion and digestion, leads to the conclusion that other copper complexes are formed as a result of exchange with other ligands (L) such as amino acids, fatty acids, amines, etc., formed in the digest

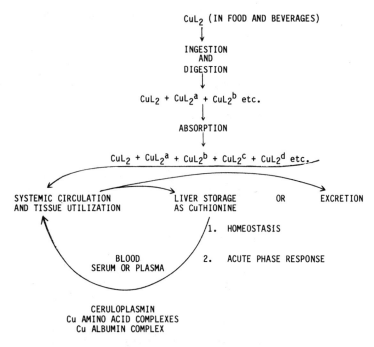

Figure 1. Fate of copper complexes following ingestion, digestion, absorption and tissue distribution.

but some of the originally ingested complex may remain intact. Additional complexes may also be formed by ligand exchange following absorption but some of the original complex may still remain unchanged. These copper complexes then undergo systemic circulation to all tissues and are: 1) utilized by tissues following ligand exchange with apoenzymes and apoproteins to form metalloenzymes and metallo-proteins, 2) stored in the liver following exchange with thionine to form copper-thionine, or 3) excreted in the event tissue needs have been met and stores replenished.

As it is shown in Figure 1, stored copper complexes are released by the liver into blood to meet normal metabolic needs. This homestatic release of copper complexes from the liver meets normal copper-dependent physiologic requirements of body tissues. Copper is primarily released from the liver as ceruloplasmin, an enzyme containing 6 to 8 atoms of copper. Two remaining forms of less firmly bound copper are amino acid complexes and an albumin complex. Larger quantities of copper complexes are known to be released as a component of the acute-phase response to infections, arthritides, seizures, and neoplasias (1-5). It is likely that this response also occurs in other disease states. This response accounts for a 2 to 3 fold increase in blood copper complex concentrations as shown in Figure 2 and reflects a greater physiologic need in these states. These complexes have a role in distribution of copper to cells to facilitate *de novo* synthesis of copper-dependent enzymes needed for normal biochemical processes, listed in Table II.

Table II. RECOGNIZED COPPER-DEPENDENT ENZYMES AND THEIR CHEMICAL FUNCTION (1,2,6-8)

Enzyme	Function
Cytochrome c Oxidase	Reduction of Oxygen:

$$O_2 \xrightarrow{H+,e-} HO_2 \xrightarrow{H+,e-} H_2O_2 \xrightarrow{H+,e-} H_2O + HO\cdot \xrightarrow{H+,e-} H_2O$$

Enzyme	Function
Superoxide Dismutase	Dismutation of superoxide:

$$2O_2^- + 2H^+ \longrightarrow O_2 + H_2O_2$$

Enzyme	Function
Tyrosinase	Hydroxylation of tyrosine:

DOPA

Enzyme	Function
Dopamine-β-Hydroxylase	Hydroxylation of dopamine:

NOREPINEPHRINE

Enzyme	Function
Lysyl Oxidase	Oxidation of terminal amino group of lysyl amino acids in specific peptides to an aldehyde group:

$$-CH_2-CH_2-NH_2 \longrightarrow -CH_2-\underset{O}{\overset{}{C}}H$$

Enzyme	Function
Amine Oxidases	Oxidation of primary amines to aldehydes:

$$R-CH_2-NH_2 \longrightarrow R-\underset{O}{\overset{}{C}}H$$

Cytochrome c Oxidase is required by all cells to produce energy required to drive energy-requiring biochemical reactions. Superoxide Dismutase is required to disproportionate superoxide and prevent cellular destruction associated with its accumulation, which is thought to play a role in causing pathology associated with affected tissues in chronic diseases. This has been documented for arthritides, seizures, and cancers (9-13). Tyrosinase is the enzyme required for synthesis of dihydroxyphenylalanine (DOPA) and its subsequent transformations to melanin, required for pigmentation. Dopamine-β-Hydroxylase is required for conversion of dopamine to norepinephrine, which is then converted to epinephrine. Lysyl Oxidase is required for cross-linking of collagen and elastin in maintenance and repair of all connective tissues. Amine Oxidases are required for removal of primary amines which are no longer needed for hormonal activity, norepinephrine or dopamine, or other amines which are toxic metabolic end-products. In addition, copper-dependent processes appear to be required for modulation of prostaglandin syntheses, lysosomal membrane stabilization, and modulation of histaminic activity (2).

Since copper is needed for activity of these enzymes, which are required for normal metabolism and prevention of disease, great care should be taken to assure that dietary intake provides required amounts of copper. Unfortunately, many or nearly all modern diets studied (see references in 14) do not supply required amounts of this and other essential metalloelements. It is then reasonable to suggest that marginal or deficient intakes may lead to impaired enzyme function and manifestations of acute disease in the short term as well as manifestations of chronic disease in the long term. The above considerations led us to suggest that copper complexes might be effective in treating inflammation, ulcers, seizures, neoplasia, and diabetes, as well as preventing ionizing radiation-induced pathology.

In the not too distant past it was thought that the elevation in blood copper levels, illustrated in Figure 2, associated with arthritic disease was pathologic. This notion

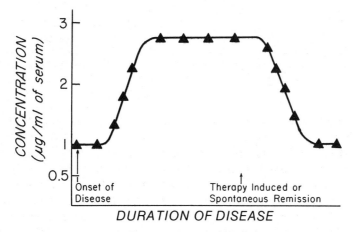

Figure 2. Alteration of serum copper content in the general acute phase response to various diseases.

still persists in the interpretation of the significance of elevated blood copper compounds found in patients with inflammatory, epileptic, or neoplastic diseases. However, observations that copper complexes have antiinflammatory activity, anticonvulsant activity, and anticancer activity suggest that these elevations in blood copper compounds are physiologic and play a role in bringing about remissions of these disease states.

Antiinflammatory and Antiarthritic Activity of Copper Complexes

To date, over 70 copper complexes have been studied as antiinflammatory agents. Results of these studies have been reviewed recently (2,16) and confirm as well as extend original observations that copper complexes of inactive ligands and active antiinflammatory drugs are more active than the parent ligand or inorganic copper. The following is a brief presentation of some of the data from the original report suggesting that copper complexes are the active metabolites of antiarthritic drugs (17).

As shown in Table III, $Cu(II)_2(acetate)_4$ was found to be active in the initial test (carrageenan paw edema) for antiinflammatory activity but inactive in the two follow-up antiinflammatory screens (cotton wad granuloma and adjuvant arthritis).

Table III
Antiinflammatory activities of some copper complexes

Compound	Carrageenan Paw Edema	Cotton Wad Granuloma	Adjuvant Arthritis	Copper (%)
$Cu(II)_2(acetate)_4$	A at 8	I at 100	I at 30	31.8
anthranilic acid	I at 200	NT	I at 30	
3,5-dips acid	I at 200	NT	I at 30	
$Cu(II)(anthranilate)_2$	A at 8	A at 25	A at 1.2	18.9
$Cu(II)(3,5-dips)_2$	A at 8	A at 5	A at 1.2	12.5
Aspirin	A at 64	A at 200 i.g.	A at 6	
$Cu(II)_2(aspirinate)_4$	A at 8	A at 10	A at 1.2	15.0
D-Penicillamine	I at 200	I at 100	I at 30	
$Cu(I)D-pen(H_2O)1.5$	A at 8	A at 10	NT	26.7
$Cu(II)(D-pen\ disulfide)(H_2O)_2$	A at 8	A at 25	A at 30	15.4

A = lowest active dose tested; I = inactive; NT = not tested. All compounds were given by subcutaneous injection unless indicated as intragastric (i.g.) and expressed as milligrams per kilogram of body weight (mg/kg).

Copper chloride had no activity in any of these models of inflammation. Ligands such as anthranilic acid and 3,5-diisopropylsalicylic acid (3,5-dips) which were anticipated to be inactive were found to be inactive. However, their copper complexes were found to be potent antiinflammatory agents in all three models of inflammation. These observations supported the notion that complexed copper was a more active antiinflammatory form of copper and led to the suggestion that copper complexes of active antiinflammatory agents might be more active than the parent antiinflammatory drugs. Representative data obtained by comparing Aspirin and D-penicillamine with their copper complexes are also presented in Table III. These data showed that these complexes are more effective than their parent drugs and supported the hypothesis that active metabolites of antiarthritic drugs are their copper complexes. Since amounts of copper in these complexes do not appear to correlate with activity of these complexes, it is suggested that pharmacologic activity is due to the physicochemical properties of these copper complexes.

Two general chemical mechanisms are immediately apparent possibilities. Small molecular weight copper complexes may serve as transport forms of copper that allow activation of copper-dependent enzymes or they may have chemical reactivities that facilitate correction of the chemical problem that led to the disease state. Activitation of lysyl oxidase, which is ultimately required to catalyze cross-linking of connective tissue components in the tissue repair phase of antiinflammatory action, is an important mechanistic consideration in accounting for antiinflammatory activity of copper complexes (18). Activation of the copper-dependent superoxide dismutase (Cu-ZnSOD), which is required to prevent accumulation of superoxide in the cellular fluid matrix is another important mechanistic consideration since accumulation of superoxide as a result of reduced Cu-ZnSOD activity has been suggested as the cause of arthritic and other inflammatory diseases (9-11). Small molecular weight copper complexes have been shown to disproportionate superoxide (19-20). This chemical reactivity of copper complexes has attracted a great deal of attention in accounting for antiinflammatory activity of copper complexes (2). Other less well understood possible mechanisms involve modulation of inflammation mediators such as histamine (17,26), lysosomal membrane stabilization, and prostaglandin systheses (2).

These results explain the earlier observations by Fenz, Forestier, and Hangarter that copper complexes are effective in treating arthritic and other degenerative diseases in Man (21). Results obtained by Hangarter with his copper-salicylate preparation (Permalon) are presented in Table IV. These results are particularly

Table IV

Copper-Salicylate therapy of acute rheumatic fever, rheumatoid arthritis, cervical spine-shoulder and lumbar-spine syndromes, and sciatica (21)

Disease	Total number of patients	Clinical Results			
		Symptom Free	Improved	Slightly Improved	Unchanged
Acute rheumatic fever	78	78(100%)			
Rheumatoid arthritis	620	403(65%)	143(23%)		74(12%)
Cervical spine-shoulder and lumbar spine syndromes	162	95(57%)	52(32%)		18(11%)
Sciatica					
without lumbar involvement	120	76(63%)	38(32%)	6(5%)	
with lumbar involvement	160	95(59%)	39(24%)	10(6%)	16(11%)
Total	1140	744(65%)	272(24%)	16(1%)	108(10%)

noteworthy since most of these patients had previously been unsuccessfully treated with drugs commonly used to treat these diseases.

Antiulcer Activity of Copper Complexes

Copper complexes were also found to be unique antiinflammatory agents when it was demonstrated that they were potent antiulcer agents, as shown in Table V. Copper(II)$_2$(acetate)$_4$ had only very weak antiulcer activity and the antiarthritic drugs, from which the copper complexes were synthesized, are known to be potent ulcer causing agents. Nevertheless, their copper complexes have been found to be effective antiulcer agents in six different models of ulcer (2). Most remarkable is the observations by West and his colleagues that copper complexes of antiarthritic drugs are able to treat or prevent ulcers due to their parent drugs (22-24).

Table V
Antiulcer activity of some copper complexes

Compound	Antiulcer Activity[a]
Cu(II)$_2$(acetate)$_4$(H$_2$O)$_2$	225
Cu(II)(anthranilate)$_2$	4.5
Cu(II)(3,5-dips)$_2$	2.3
CU(II)$_2$(aspirinate)$_4$	11.3
Cu(II)$_n$(niflumate)$_{2n}$	4.5
Cu(II)(D-pen disulfide)·3H$_2$O	4.5
Cu(II)$_n$(fenamole)$_n$(acetate)$_{2n}$	4.5
Cu(II)$_n$(fenamole)$_{2n}$(HCL)$_{2n}$	4.5
Cu(II)(salicylate)$_2$·4H$_2$O	4.5
Cu(II)$_2$[1−(p-chlorobenzoyl)-5-methoxy-2-methylindole-3-acetate]$_4$(CH$_3$COCH$_3$)$_2$	4.5
Cu(II)$_n$(4-n-butyl-1,2-diphenyl-3,5-pyrazolidinedione)$_{2n}$	4.5

[a]All doses were given intragastrically and are expressed as the lowest active dose in milligrams per kilogram of body weight (mg/kg).

Potent antiulcer activity coupled with antiinflammatory activity has distinguished copper complexes as a unique class of antiarthritic drugs since all other antiarthritic drugs cause ulcers (17,21). While all known copper-dependent biochemical processes have been cited as possibly accounting for some aspect of these activities, the superoxide disproportionating reactivity of copper complexes (19,20) is especially interesting since Cu-ZnSOD has been found to be less than normal in the joints of adult arthritics (9) and in polymorphonuclear leukocytes from children with juvenile rheumatoid arthritis (10,11).

DeAlvare, Goda, and Kimura (19) in addition to suggesting a mechanism for superoxide disproportionation which has received some useful comment (25) and support (26) in the literature, pointed out that a basis for the greater activity of small molecular weight copper complexes when compared to Cu-ZnSOD may be due to their ability to cross cell membranes. This is consistent with their greater lipid solubility.

Anticonvulsant Activity of Copper Complexes

Being aware that copper deficiency in animals and Man is associated with seizures, we submitted copper complexes to the National Institute of Neurological and Communicative Disorders and Stroke-Antiepileptic Drug Development Program (NINCDS-ADD) for evaluation as anticonvulsants in their models of seizure. Preliminary data obtained with copper complexes of salicylates and aminoacids in the maximal electroshock (MES) and Metrozol (M) models of seizures are presented in Table VI. These data demonstrate that copper complexes of salicylates and aminoacids are effective anticonvulsants. Since neither salicylates nor aminoacids are known to have anticonvulsant activity and neither copper chloride nor copper acetate, given subcutaneously, had anticonvulsant activity, it was suggested that the observed activity was due to complexed forms of copper. This led to the hypothesis that the active forms of the anticonvulsant drugs are also their copper complexes. Supporting evidence was provided when it was shown that the copper complex of amobarbital was more effective than sodium amobarbital as an anticonvulsant in protecting against the MES model of seizure (28). In addition, Cu(II)(amobarbital)$_2$ was found to be less toxic than sodium amobarbital. We continue to find that copper complexes

Table VI
Anticonvulsant activities of some copper complexes (27,28)

Complexes	%Cu	MES	Metrozol
Salicylates			
Cu(II)(salicylate)$_2$	19	I[a]	A[b] at 30 min; A at 300 at 4 hr
Cu(II)(4-tertiarybutyl-salicylate)$_2$·½H$_2$O	14	I	A at 300 at 30 min; A at 300 at 4 hr
Cu(II)(3,5-dips)$_2$	13	A at 300 at 4 hr; A at 100 at 6 hr; A at 300 at 8 hr	A at 30 at 30 min; A at 100 at 4 hr; A at 100 at 6 hrs. A at 100 at 8 hr
Amino acids			
Cu(II)(L-threoninate) (L-serinate)	22	I(i.p.)	A at 30 at 30 min and 4 hr
Cu(II)(L-threoninate) (L-alaninate)	24	I(i.p.)	A at 30 at 30 min and 4 hr
Cu(II)(L-valinate)$_2$H$_2$O	20	A at 600 at 30 min (i.p.)	A at 30 at 30 min and 4 hr
Cu(II)(L-threoninate)$_2$H$_2$O	20	I(i.p.)	A at 30 at 30 min and 4 hr
Cu(II)(L-alaninate)$_2$	27	I(i.p.)	A at 30 at 30 min and 4 hr
Cu(II)(L-phenylalaninate)$_2$	16	I(i.p.)	A at 30 at 30 min
Cu(II)(L-cystinate)$_2$H$_2$O	20	I(i.p.)	A at 100 at 30 min
Cu(II)(L-tryptophan)$_2$	14	I(i.p.)	A at 100 at 30 min and 4 hr (i.p.)

[a]Inactive (I) at doses studied;

[b]Activity (A) at doses and times indicated. All doses (mg/kg) were given subcutaneously or, when indicated, intraperitoneally (i.p.)

of various antiepileptic drugs which dismutate superoxide (unpublished observation) have anticonvulsant activity (29). More detailed comparisons, in progress, are required to fully investigate the possibility that these copper complexes can be distinguished from their parent drugs.

Biological mechanisms of action of anticonvulsant drugs are not well understood. There are, however, a number of reports suggesting that seizures occur with depletion of norepinephrine synthesis in the brain (1,30,31). These suggestions are consistent with the observation that copper complexes have anticonvulsant activity and the copper-dependency of dopamine-β-hydroxylase, the enzyme required for norepinephrine synthesis.

The notion that a small molecular weight copper complex might facilitate transport of copper to the brain and enable activation or increase activity of Cu-ZnSOD in preventing seizures also has merit. Epileptic seizures resulting from brain trauma, infection, and tumors (32,33) are clearly associated with inflammatory processes wherein superoxide release or accumulation may have an etiologic role. Such a role for superoxide in induction of seizures has been documented in an animal model of seizure and related to trauma-induced seizures in Man (13). If superoxide accumulation is a cause of seizures then superoxide disproportionating reactivity of copper complexes or their possible role in activation or synthesis of this enzyme in brain tissue merit consideration as plausible mechanisms. Perhaps an understanding of coordination chemistry involved in anticonvulsant activity of copper complexes will shed light on biological mechanisms of action of these drugs.

Antineoplastic Activity of Copper Complexes

Following the report that neoplastic cells were deficient in superoxide dismutase activity and Cu-ZnSOD decreased growth of a solid sarcoma 180 tumor (12) as well as increased survival of the implanted mice (34), a variety of superoxide disproportionating copper salicylates were examined for anticancer activity. The copper complex of aspirin, $Cu(II)_2(acetylsalicylate)_4$, was tested and found to produce a rapid and marked reduction of an ascites neuroblastoma tumor in mice (29) and a marked reduction in growth of a solid Ehrlich tumor accompanied by an increase in survival of implanted mice. Dimethylsulfoxide and pyridine solvates of this complex were even more effective than the parent complex in the solid Ehrlich tumor model (34). Since these complexes were thought to be more lipid soluble and lipid solubility appeared to increase activity, the ether soluble complex, $Cu(II)(3,5\text{-dips})_2$, was selected for evaluation as an anticancer agent. This complex was found to be the most effective of all salicylate complexes tested to date (35-37).

Subsequent mechanistic studies support the suggestion that superoxide disproportionation by $Cu(II)(3,5\text{-dips})_2$ or facilitated *de novo* synthesis of Cu-ZnSOD and production of hydrogen peroxide may account for its antineoplastic activity (37). Data presented in Figure 3 show that survival of male Swiss mice bearing an intraperitoneally implanted Ehrlich cell tumor following a single intraperitoneal

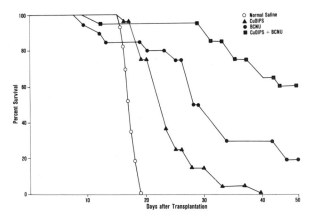

Figure 3. Survival of mice intraperitoneally implanted with Ehrlich tumor cells and treated with Cu(II)(3,5-dips)$_2$, BCNU, or Cu(II)(3,5-dips)$_2$ plus BCNU (Reproduced with permission of Humana Press).

injection of Cu(II)(3,5-dips)$_2$ (14.5 mg/kg, 0.4 mg/mouse) plus 1,3-bis(2-chloroethyl-2-nitrosourea) (BCNU) (30 mg/kg) combination exceeded survivals found for a single injection of BCNU (30 mg/kg), Cu(II)(3,5-dips)$_2$ (14.5 mg/kg), or saline. Administration of N-acetylcysteine (109 mg/kg) or reduced glutathione (209 mg/kg) to Cu(II)(3,5-dips)$_2$-treated mice increased the neoplasia-induced death rate slightly. Treatment with N-acetylcysteine or reduced glutathione alone had no antineoplastic activity and could not be distinguished from saline-treated controls. BCNU was expected to potentiate the effects of Cu(II)(3,5-dips)$_2$ since it inhibits glutathione reductase and may allow an increase in cellular hydrogen peroxide concentration. Administration of N-acetylcysteine or reduced glutathione were expected to reduce the antineoplastic activity of Cu(II)(3,5-dips)$_2$ because they facilitate the removal of hydrogen peroxide by serving as oxidizable cofactors of glutathione peroxidase.

Research directed toward the re-establishment of normal superoxide dismutase levels in neoplastic cells merits serious consideration as an approach to cancer therapy. This suggestion is consistent with the recent report that ascorbic acid plus Cu(II)glycylglycylhistidine has a marked inhibitory effect on growth of an Ehrlich cell ascites tumor and markedly increased survival of the implanted mice (38). Cu(II) glycylhistidyllysine (39), Cu(II) pyridine-2-carboxaldehye-2-pyridylhydrazonate, Cu(II) salicylaldehyde-benzoylhydrazonate (40), Cu(II) bleomycin (41), copper amino acid complexes (42), and a large variety of other chemical classes of copper complexes (43,44) have also been reported to be effective in the same or similar animal tumor models as well as tumor cell cultures. In the past it was thought that these complexes were effective because they affected DNA synthesis. Currently, scavenging of superoxide seems to be another likely rationale for anticancer activity of copper complexes.

Anticarcinogenic Activity of Copper Complexes

Induction of cancer by chemicals involves multiple stages as the target cell progresses from its normal phenotype to a malignant neoplasma. In the simplest and best studied model system, mouse skin, two stages—initiation and promotion—can be operationally defined. The first stage, initiation, is a phenomenon of gene alteration such as may be effected by carcinogen interaction with DNA and subsequent fixation of a permanent lesion in the genetic apparatus. The second stage, promotion, is a phenomenon of gene activation in which the latent altered genotype of the initiated cell becomes expressed. Unlike initiation, which in summation is an irreversible event, many of the components of promotion are reversible. As such, the promotion stage of carcinogenesis may be particularly amenable to interruption or reversal by chemoprotective agents.

The involvement of oxygen radicals in the multistep process of carcinogenesis is becoming evident (45). Not only are these species important in the metabolic activation of some carcinogens, but they may be an obligatory component of tumor promotion. The induction of ornithine decarboxylase(ODC) activity is a prominent, early, and transient event following exposure of mouse skin to tumor promoters and can be inhibited by a spectrum of antipromoting agents (46,47). As shown in Figure 4, $Cu(II)(3,5\text{-dips})_2$ inhibited 12-tetradecanoylphorbol-13-acetate (TPA)-mediated induction of ODC in a log-dose response manner over the range of 0.1 to 10 μmol ($ID_{50} = 1$ μmol). Applications of equimolar amounts of 3,5-dips, $Zn(II)(3,5\text{-dips})_2$, or $Cu(II)(EDTA)^{2-}$, which are compounds devoid of SOD activity (48), as well as the hydrophilic complex $Cu(II)_2(\text{acetate})_4$, were without effect, underscoring the specificity of the action of $Cu(II)(3,5\text{-dips})_2$ which is lipophilic and disproportionates superoxide. Maximal inhibition of ODC induction was observed when $Cu(II)(3,5\text{-dips})_2$ was applied several minutes after the tumor promoter, and greater than 50% inhibition was maintained if $Cu(II)(3,5\text{-dips})_2$ was given within 2 hr before or after TPA.

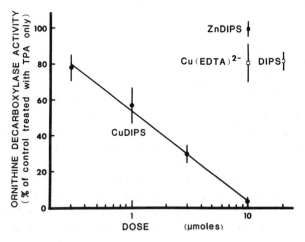

Figure 4. Inhibition of TPA-induced ODC activity by topically applied Cu(II) $(3,5\text{-dips})_2$, ●; $Cu(II)(EDTA)^{2-}$, ■; $Zn(II)(3,5\text{-dips})_2$, □; 3,5-dips, ○.

It has also been demonstrated that $Cu(II)(3,5\text{-dips})_2$ is a potent inhibitor of tumor promotion in mouse epidermis (49). As shown in Table VII, topical administration

Table VII

Inhibition of multistage carcinogenesis by Cu(II)(3,5-dips)$_2$

Group	Treatment[a]				mice alive at 20 wk	mice with papillomas at 20 wk	papillomas per mouse at 20 wk
	Modifier	Initiator	Modifier	Promoter			
1	Ether	DMBA	Ether	Acetone	20	0	0
2	Ether	DMBA	Ether	TPA	20	18	13.6
3	Cu(II)(3,5-dips)$_2$	DMBA	Ether	TPA	20	19	10.9
4	Ether	DMBA	Cu(II)(3,5-dips)$_2$	TPA	20	7[b]	1.6[b]
5	Ether	DMBA	Zn(II)(3,5-dips)$_2$	TPA	20	18	11.5
6	Ether	DMBA	Ether	DMBA	19	18	5.4
7	Cu(II)(3,5-dips)$_2$	DMBA	Cu(II)(3,5-dips)$_2$	DMBA	20	9[b]	0.9[b]

[a]Female CD-1 mice (7-9 weeks) were shaved with surgical clippers 2 days before treatment and only those mice not exhibiting hair growth were used. Twenty mice were used for each treatment group. All mice were initiated with a single topical application of 0.2 μmol 7,12-dimethylbenz(a)anthracene (DMBA) in 0.2 mol acetone. Beginning 10 days after initiation, mice were promoted twice a week with 4 nmol 12-tetradecanoylphorbol-13-acetate (TPA) (groups 2-5) or 0.2 μmol DMBA (groups 6-7) for 18 weeks. Mice were also treated with either diethylether or 2 μmol Cu(II)(3,5-dips)$_2$ 15 min prior to each DMBA application (groups 3 and 7) or 30 min prior to each TPA application (group 4). Mice in group 5 were treated with 2 μmol Zn(II)(3,5-dips)$_2$ 30 min prior to each TPA application. The number and incidence of papillomas were recorded weekly.
[b]Differ from control, p < 0.05.

of 2 μmol Cu(II)(3,5-dips)$_2$ 30 min prior to each of 40 semiweekly treatments with 4 nmol TPA to mice initiated with a single dose of 7,12-dimethylbenz[a]anthracene (DMBA) resulted in a 60% reduction in tumor incidence and an 85% reduction in number of papillomas per mouse, compared to those initiated mice receiving vehicle and promoter. No significant inhibition of tumor formation was observed with either Zn(II)(3,5-dips)$_2$ (Table VII, group 5), Cu(II)$_2$(acetate)$_4$ or 3,5-dips (49). Thus, SOD-mimetic activity and lipophilicity are essential properties for the antipromoter action of copper complexes. In confirmation, Solanki *et al.* (50) recently reported that Cu(II)(3,5-dips)$_2$ inhibited initiation by DMBA in their mouse skin multistage tumorigenesis study. Our results show that in the CD-1 mouse Cu(II)(3,5-dips)$_2$ is a more effective inhibitor of promotion than initiation (Table VII, groups 4 vs 3). In addition, when the complete carcinogen, DMBA, is administered twice weekly, prior treatment with Cu(II)(3,5-dips)$_2$ substantially reduces both incidence and number of tumors. Whether or not this inhibitory action reflects antagonism of only the "promoter" component of DMBA carcinogenesis is unclear. Overall, the finding that a low molecular weight, lipophilic, copper complex with SOD-mimetic activity can inhibit phorbol diester-induced biochemical and biological responses strengthens arguments for an essential role of oxygen radicals in the promotion stage of carcinogenesis and of SODs or SOD-like compounds in the homeostatic prevention of carcinogenesis.

Antimutagenic Activity of Copper Complexes

In addition to confirming the observation that Cu(II)(3,5-dips)$_2$ has anticarcinogenic activity, Solanki *et al.* (50) demonstrated that this complex, also has antimutagenic activity. The DMBA-induced mouse keratinocyte-mediated Chinese hamster V-79 cell mutagenesis was inhibited and replating efficiency increased in a dose-related manner. Concentrations ranging from 0.01 to 5 μg of Cu(II)(3,5-dips)$_2$ per ml of culture medium produced up to 60% inhibition of mutagenesis and increased challenged replated-cell viability from 64 to 100%. The ability of Cu(II)(3,5-dips)$_2$ to reduce DMBA-induced mutations provides additional evidence in support of an obligate role of oxygen radical mediation of mutagenesis.

Antidiabetic Activity of Copper Complexes

It has been demonstrated that copper complexes have antidiabetic activity in the streptozotocin-induced diabetic rat (51). These data, presented in Figure 5, show that glucose utilization is impaired in streptozotocin-treated mice as well as streptozotocin and salicylic acid or 3,5-dips-treated mice when compared to the control (vehicle alone) group at time zero. With injection of glucose a more marked impairment of glucose utilization is evidenced by the subsequent rise in plasma glucose over the 60 minute glucose tolerance test period.

A less pronounced impairment of glucose utilization was found in the streptozotocin and Cu(II)(salicylate)$_2$ or Cu(II)(3,5-dips)$_2$-treated groups as evidenced by the lower plasma glucose values at time zero. Glucose tolerance was significantly (p<0.001)

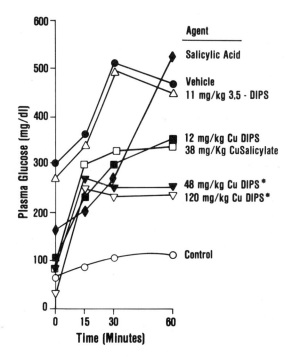

Figure 5. Antidiabetic activity of copper complexes in the streptozotocin treated rat. Male Wistar rats (n≥4) were pretreated with agents by IP injection 15 minutes before streptozotocin (IV injection, 50 mg/kg). Plasma glucose concentrations were measured on day 3 after IP bolus of glucose (1 g/kg). *Significantly different from streptozotocin-injected control rat; p<0.001. (Reproduced with permission of Humana Press).

improved in the two Cu(II)(3,5-dips)₂-treated groups when compared with the streptozotocin-treated group. Plasma glucose levels 15 and 30 minutes after Cu(II)(salicylate)₂ and Cu(II)(3,5-dips)₂ injection were normal, eliminating the possibility of protection *via* hyperglycemia at the time of streptozotocin injection. Liver function tests were normal at the time of glucose tolerance testing. A slight elevation of blood urea nitrogen was seen in rats receiving Cu(II)(3,5-dips)₂ (22-38 mg/100 ml vs 13-20 mg/100 ml in controls). Glycosuria of rats treated with streptozotocin alone or streptozotocin plus 3,5-dips was 3-4+ and 2-3+ for streptozotocin plus salicylic acid. Glycosuria for Cu(II)(3,5-dips)₂ pretreated rats was 0-1+ at all doses studied and 0-2+ in the Cu(II)(salicylate)₂-treated group. Thus hepatic dysfunction or renal glycosuria did not account for the improved glucose tolerance.

It is noteworthy that compounds possessing Cu-ZnSOD-like chemical reactivity can attenuate streptozotocin diabetes. This activity is attributed to the combination of superoxide disproportionating reactivity and lipophilicity of the complexes, which may allow cellular penetration and re-establishment of disproportionating reactivity or a facilitation of *de novo* synthesis of pancreatic β cell Cu-ZnSOD. This suggestion has merit since it has been demonstrated that streptozotocin decreases Cu-ZnSOD activity in pancreatic β cells (52) and intravenous administration of Cu-ZnSOD attenuates streptozotocin-induced diabetes (53,54). Testing Cu-ZnSOD-like copper complexes for their ability to prevent or attenuate experimental diabetes may be worthwhile since it is possible that the etiology of Type I diabetes involves oxygen radical mediated β cell damage following the loss or reduction of Cu-ZnSOD activity.

Radiation Protection Activity of Copper Complexes

Recognizing that ionizing irradiation of aerated aqueous solutions produces superoxide, Petkau and his colleagues (55-57) demonstrated that Cu-ZnSOD given to mice intravenously afforded protection against doses of x-irradiation ranging from 300 to 1000 rads. They observed 17% survival (83% mortality) with Cu-ZnSOD treatment both pre-and post-irradiation using the 1000 rad radiation dose which produced 100% mortality in the control group. Since Cu(II)(3,5-dips)$_2$ was thought to penetrate cell membranes and disproportionates superoxide, it was evaluated as a radioprotectant.

Two groups of 24 mice were treated with one subcutaneous injection of 5 mg of Cu(II)(3,5-dips)$_2$ per mouse. One group was treated 3 hours before irradiation and the other was treated 24 hours before irradiation. A control group of 22 mice was given a subcutaneous injection of vehicle. All of the mice were bilaterally irradiated with a total dose of 1000 rads of gamma irradiation delivered at a rate of 40 rads per minute.

Data presented in Figure 6 show that there was 100% mortality for the control group by day 18. However, there was only 67% mortality (33% survival) and 42% mortality (58% survival) in the respective 3 hour and 24 hour pretreated groups. Deaths occurred in the treated groups up to day 18 or 19 with no subsequent deaths for the remaining term of the experiment, 30 days. Even though these data are preliminary, the possibility that small molecular weight copper complexes might be useful as radioprotectants necessitates careful evaluation of this observation.

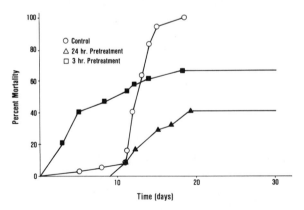

Figure 6. Radioprotectant activity of Cu(II)(3,5-dips)$_2$.

Radioprotectant activity of $Cu(II)(3,5\text{-dips})_2$ provides additional dimension to an approach to antineoplasia. First, ionizing radiation is a recognized inducer of neoplasia. Second, an effective radioprotectant would be useful in protecting non-neoplastic tissue of patients undergoing radiation therapy of neoplastic tissue. Development of an effective radioprotectant with anticancer, anticarcinogenic, and antimutagenic activities is an extremely exciting possibility. This possibility is supported with the recognition that ionizing radiation produces inflammation, gastric ulcers, and seizures as the amount of radiation is increased and copper complexes have antiinflammatory, antiulcer, and anticonvulsant activities.

Acknowledgements

We are indebted to the American Cancer Society, Grants SIG-3; the Arthur Armbrust Cancer Research Foundation; the American Diabetes Association; the International Copper Research Association; The Kroc Foundation; the National Cancer Institute, grant T32-CA-09125 and CA-36380; and the National Institute of Environmental Health Sciences, Grants ESOO454; for financial support. We are also most grateful to the NINCDS for their evaluation of our copper complexes as anticonvulsants and to Cmdr. Brian Gray of the Armed Forces Radiobiology Research Institute for his efforts in obtaining radioprotectant data with $Cu(II)(3,5\text{-dips})_2$.

References and Footnotes

1. E.J. Underwood, *Trace Elements in Human and Animal Nutrition,* Academic Press, New York, p. 57 (1977).
2. J.R.J. Sorenson in *Metal Ions in Biological Systems, Vol. 14,* Ed., H. Sigel, Marcel Dekker, New York, p. 77 (1982).
3. M.C. Powanda in *Inflammatory Diseases and Copper,* Ed., J.R.J. Sorenson, Humana Press, Clifton, New Jersey, p. 31 (1982).
4. A. Flynn in *Inflammatory Diseases and Copper,* Ed., J.R.J. Sorenson, Humana Press, Clifton, New Jersey, p. 17 (1982).
5. J.R.J. Sorenson, *Inorg. Perspect. Biol. Med. 2,* 1 (1978).
6. P. George in *Oxidases and Related Redox Systems, Volume 1,* Eds., T.E. King, H.S. Mason and M. Morrison, John Wiley, New York, p. 3 (1965).
7. B.L. O'Dell in *Trace Elements in Human Health and Disease, Vol. 1, Zinc and Copper,* Eds., A.S. Prasad and D. Oberleas, Academic Press, New York, p. 391 (1976).
8. G.A. Hamilton, in *Copper Proteins,* Ed., T.G. Spiro, John Wiley, New York, p. 193 (1981).
9. J.M. McCord, *Science 185,* 529, (1974).
10. M. Rister in *Trace Elements in the Pathogenesis and Treatment of Inflammation,* Eds., K.D. Rainsford, K. Brune and M.W. Whitehouse, Birkhauser Verlag, Basel, p. 137 (1980).
11. M. Rister, K. Bauermeister, U. Gravert and E. Gladtke, *Lancet* May 20, 1094 (1976).
12. L.W. Oberley and G.R. Buettner, *Cancer Res. 39,* 1141 (1979).
13. J.J. Rubin and L.J. Willmore, *Exptl. Neurol., 67,* 472 (1980).
14. J.R.J. Sorenson, L.W. Oberley, V. Kishore, S.W.C. Leuthauser, T.D. Oberley, and A. Pezeshk. *Inorg. Chim. Acta 91,* 285 (1984).
15. J.R.J. Sorenson, *Prog. Med. Chem. 15,* 211 (1978).
16. J.R.J. Sorenson in *Inflammatory Diseases and Copper,* Ed., J.R.J. Sorenson, Humana Press, Clifton, New Jersey p. 289 (1982).
17. J.R.J. Sorenson, *J. Med. Chem. 19,* 135 (1976).

18. E.D. Harris, R.A. Di Silvestro and J.E. Balthrop in *Inflammatory Diseases and Copper,* Ed., J.R.J. Sorenson, Humana Press, Clifton, New Jersey p. 183 (1982).

19. L.R. DeAlvare, K. Goda and T. Kimura, *Biochem, Biophys. Res. Commun. 39,* 687 (1976).

20. U. Weser, C. Richter, A. Wendel, and M. Younes, *Bioinorg. Chem. 8,* 201 (1978).

21. J.R.J. Sorenson and W. Hangarter, *Inflammation 2,* 217 (1977).

22. L.J. Hayden, G. Thomas and G.B. West, *J. Pharm. Pharmacol. 30,* 244 (1978).

23. R. Goburdhun, K. Gulrez, H. Haruna and G.B. West, *J. Pharmacol. Meth. 1,* 109 (1978).

24. G.B. West, *J. Pharmacol. Methods 8,* 33 (1982).

25. C.L. Young and S.J. Lippard, *J. Am. Chem. Soc. 102,* 4920 (1980).

26. M. Nappa, J.S. Valentine, A.R. Mikszal, H.J. Schugar and S.S. Iseid, *J. Am. Chem. Soc. 101,* 7744 (1979).

27. J.R.J. Sorenson, D.O. Rauls, K. Ramakrishna, R.E. Stull and A.N. Voldeng in *Trace Substances in Environmental Health XIII,* Ed., D.D. Hemphill, University of Missouri, Columbia, MO, p. 360 (1979).

28. J.R.J. Sorenson, R.E. Stull, R. Ramakrishna, B.L. Johnson, E. Riddell, D.F. Ring, T.M. Rolniak and D.L. Stewart in *Trace Substances in Environmental Health-XIV,* Ed., D.D. Hemphill, University of Missouri, Columbia, MO, p. 252 (1980).

29. J.R.J. Sorenson, L.W. Oberley, R.K. Crouch, T.W. Kensler, V. Kishore, S.W.C. Leuthauser, T.D. Oberley and A. Pezeshk, *Biol. Trace Elem. Res. 5,* 257 (1983).

30. W.M. Bourn, L. Chin and A.L. Picchioni, *J. Pharm. Pharmacol. 30,* 800 (1978).

31. P.C. Jobe, A.L. Picchioni and L. Chin, *J. Pharmacol. Expl. Ther. 184,* 1 (1973).

32. A.L. Rose and C.T. Lombroso, *Pediatrics 45,* 404 (1970).

33. J.M. Oxbury and C.W.M. Whitty, *Brain 94,* 733 (1971).

34. L.W. Oberley, S.W.C. Leuthauser, G.R. Buettner, J.R.J. Sorenson, T.D. Oberley and I.B. Bize in *Pathology of Oxygen,* Ed., A.P. Autor, Academic Press, New York, p. 207 (1982).

35. J.R.J. Sorenson, L.W. Oberley, T.D. Oberley, S.W.C. Leuthauser, K. Ramakrishna, L. Vernino and V. Kishore in *Trace Substances in Environmental Health-XVI,* Ed., D.D. Hemphill, University of Missouri Press, Columbia, MO, p. 362 (1982).

36. S.W.C. Leuthauser, L.W. Oberley, T.D. Oberley, J.R.J. Sorenson and K. Ramakrishna, *J. Nat. Cancer Inst. 66,* 1077 (1981).

37. L.W. Oberley, K.L. Rogers, L. Schutt, T.D. Oberley, S.W.C. Leuthauser and J.R.J. Sorenson, *J. Nat. Cancer Inst. 71,* 1089 (1983).

38. E. Kimoto, H. Tanaka, J. Gyotoku, F. Morishige and L. Pauling, *Cancer Res. 43,* 824 (1982).

39. L. Pickart, J.H. Freedman, W.J. Loker, J. Peisach, C.M. Perkins, R.E. Stenkamp and B. Weinstein, *Nature 288,* 715 (1980).

40. L. Pickart, *Biochem, Pharm. 32,* 3868 (1983).

41. E.A. Rao, L.A. Saryan, N.E. Antholine and D.H. Petering, *J. Med. Chem. 23,* 1310 (1980).

42. E.M. Treshchalina, A.L. Konovalova, M.A. Presnov, L.R. Chapurina, N.I. Belichuk and I.A. Diakon, *Doklady Akademic Nauk SSSR 248,* 1273 (1979).

43. P.J. Sadler, M. Nasr and V.L. Narayanan, The Design of Metal Complexes as Anticancer Drugs, Platinum Coordination Complexes in Cancer Chemotherapy, Ed., M.T. Hackler, I. Krakoff, E.B. Dauple, Martinus-Nijhoff, Boston November 1983.

44. J.R.J. Sorenson in *Copper in the Environment, Part II Health Effects,* Ed., J.O. Nriagu, John Wiley, New York, p. 83 (1979).

45. T.W. Kensler and M.A. Trush in *Superoxide Dismutase, Volume III,* Pathological States, CRC Press, Boca Raton, FL, in press.

46. T.G. O'Brien, R.C. Simsiman and R.K. Boutwell. *Cancer Res. 35,* 1662 (1975).

47. R.K. Boutwell in *Radioprotectors and Anticarcinogens,* Eds., O.F. Nygaard, and M.G. Simic. Academic Press, New York, p. 557 (1983).

48. T.W. Kensler and M.A. Trush, *Biochem Pharmacol. 32,* 3485 (1983).

49. T.W. Kensler, D.M. Bush and W.J. Kozumbo, *Science 221,* 75 (1983).

50. V. Solanki, L. Yotti, M.K. Logani, T.J. Slaga, *Carcinogenesis 5,* 129 (1984).

51. S.E. Gandy, M.G. Buse, J.R.J. Sorenson and R.K. Crouch, *Diabetologia 24,* 437 (1983).

52. R.K. Crouch, S.E. Gandy, G. Kimsey, R.A. Gailbraith, G.M.P. Gailbraith and M.G. Buse, *Diabetes 30,* 235 (1981).

53. M.J. Robbins, R.A. Sharp, A.E. Slonim and I.M. Burr, *Diabetologia 18,* 55 (1980).

54. S.E. Gandy, M.G. Buse and R.K. Crouch, *J. Clin. Invest. 70*, 650 (1982).
55. A. Petkau, W.S. Chelack, S.D. Pleskach, B.E. Meker and C.M. Brady, *Biochem. Biophys. Res. Comm. 65*, 886 (1975).
56. A. Petkau, K. Kelley, W.S. Chelack, S.D. Pleskach, C. Barefoot and B.E. Meeker, *Biophys. Res. Comm. 67*, 1167 (1974).
57. A. Petkau, W.S. Chelack and S.D. Pleskach, *Int. J. Radiat. Biol. 29*, 297 (1976).

Biological & Inorganic Copper Chemistry,
ISBN 0-940030-11-X, Eds., K. D. Karlin & J. Zubieta, Adenine Press, ©Adenine Press, 1985

Paraquat Toxicity is Mediated by Transition Metals

Ron Kohen and Mordechai Chevion
Department of Cellular Biochemistry
The Hebrew University of Jerusalem
Jerusalem 91 010, Israel
and
Gerontology Research Center
National Institute on Aging
Baltimore, Maryland 21224

Abstract

The involvement of transition metals ions in paraquat toxicity was studied in two models: bacteria and laboratory mice. Incubation of *E. coli* B with paraquat for 30 min resulted in 50% bacterial inactivation. The addition of micromolar concentration of copper sulfate dramatically enhanced the rate of bacterial inactivation (>99.9% after 17 min). In contrast, the addition of chelating agents, totally eliminated the killing of *E. coli*. No bacterial killing was observed under anaerobic exposure, both in the absence and presence of copper. However, in the presence of copper, the anaerobic addition of hydrogen peroxide resulted in complete restoration of the rate of inactivation as under aerobiosis. The protective effects of catalase and superoxide dismutase, were found to arise from their general properties as proteins rather than from their specific enzymatic functions. The role of paraquat is to either produce superoxide ions or to directly reduce bound copper ions. The reduced cuprous complexes react with hydrogen peroxide to locally form hydroxyl radicals which are, probably, responsible for the deleterious effects.

Chelation therapy of paraquat-poisoned mice with desferrioxamine or nitrilo-triacetate led to an extension of the life span of the animals by 45 and 60%, respectively, and resulted in 25 and 30% survivors, respectively. In contrast, loading of the animals with iron or copper prior to the poisoning with paraquat yielded a shortening of their life span by 56 and 41%, respectively. Similarly, therapy of the paraquat poisoned mice with desferrioxamine yielded 78-94% protection of the lung acetylcholine esterase, and significantly reduced their loss of total body weight.

This study is the first to indicate the involvement of copper and iron in paraquat toxicity in the metal-mediated Haber-Weiss mechanism. Consequently, chelation therapy is being suggested for treatment of paraquat-poisoned human subject.

Introduction

Paraquat (PQ^{+2}) (1,1'-dimethyl-4,4'-bipyridylium, dichloride) is a widely used herbicide (1) that was first synthesized at the end of the 19th century and was mainly used as an oxidation-reduction indicator (2) (also known as methyl viologen). Since 1966, with its increasing agricultural use throughout the world, there have been a large number of cases of systemic toxicity resulting from ingestion of paraquat (3). Today paraquat is known to be highly lethal to men and animals (4).

Studies of the chemistry of the paraquat radical ($PQ^{+\cdot}$) showed that it reacts fast with oxygen, yielding superoxide radical ($O_2^{\div}$) (10). Considerable biochemical understanding of the mechanism of paraquat toxicity in bacterial system has been gained (26,47,48). It was shown that bacterial killing requires molecular oxygen and carbon source, and that the induction of cellular superoxide dismutase led to a considerable protection.

In mammalian systems, paraquat poisoning is manifested mainly by a pulmonary injury (5). Although several mechanisms of its action were suggested (6-9) none satisfactorily explains the toxicity of paraquat and none indicates a promising means of treatment. After the initial absorption and distribution, paraquat is being actively concentrated in the lungs, and there it undergoes enzymatical reduction to $PQ^{+\cdot}$ (11). There it can similarly produce superoxide radical, suggesting that $O_2^{\div}$ could be an important mediator of paraquat toxicity. Alternatively, the superoxide radical itself may not be the toxic species, but rather may be transformed into another secondary reactive free radical such as the hydroxyl radical ($OH\cdot$) (12).

The toxicity of superoxide radical has been discussed in the last few years (13,14,46). The chemical as well as the biological reactivity of superoxide both *in vitro* and *in vivo* is low (13). There are recent reports incriminating the superoxide radical itself as responsible for deleterious effects in a number of processes of biological relevance (49). Nevertheless, it seems unlikely that superoxide *per se* would be the primary candidate for oxygen or oxygen-mediated toxicity (15).

It was shown that physiological systems contain significant concentrations of labile iron, copper and manganese (16) and that commercial paraquat contain considerable amounts of iron (17). As transition metals are known to enhance deleterious processes induced by superoxide and/or ascorbate in biological systems (18-23), we initiated this investigation of the role of transition metal ions in paraquat toxicity.

Materials and Methods

Escherichia coli B (SR-9) was used throughout. The cells were grown at 37° in a shaking incubator in medium containing KH_2PO_4 0.7%, K_2HPO_4 0.3%, Nacitrate 0.5%, $(NH_4)_2SO_4$ 0.1% at pH 7.0. Magnesium sulphate 1 mg/ml was added after sterilization in an autoclave, and glycerol 1% was used as carbon source. The bacteria were harvested at 90 Klett units and were washed three times in phosphate buffer (1 mM) containing glucose (0.5%).

The washed cells were suspended in phosphate buffer (1 mM, pH 7.14) containing glucose (0.5% w/v) and magnesium sulphate (1 mM) to a final density of 3×10^7

cells/ml. The following materials were added to the systems at different concentrations and combinations: methyl viologen (paraquat), etylenediaminetetraacetic acid disodium salt (EDTA), diethylenetriaamine-pentaacetic acid (detapac), superoxide dismutase or catalase, copper sulfate, desferrioxamine (Desferal, Ciba), hydrogen peroxide, tert-butyl alcohol, mannitol and histidine. Copper salicylate and copper tyrosine were prepared according to known procedures (50,51). Samples from the reaction mixture were taken at various times and were diluted in phosphate buffer (1 mM) containing detapac (0.01μM) and gelatin 0.5% in order to stop the reaction (23). The samples were diluted by a factor of 10^3-10^6 and were plated on agar dishes. Each sample was plated at least four times. All the solutions were prepared fresh before every experiment using triply distilled water.

To achieve anaerobic conditions, high purity nitrogen (>99.999%) was bubbled through the bacteria suspension for 20 min before the reaction and flushed over the suspension during the reaction.

The survival curves were evaluated from colony counts and represent at least 3 different experiments for each system.

Mice—male Balb/C weighing 30 ± 2 gr were given unlimited amounts of food and water. In the survival experiments groups of 10 mice in each group were tested. Each experiment was repeated 3 times and the results are the average of the replications. Paraquat was administered intra peritoneally (IP) (17 mg/kg). Desferrioxamine or nitrilo-triacetate injections began one hour *post* the intoxication with paraquat. The control group received injections of water. Loading of the animals with iron or copper was conducted by repeated injections (IP) of the mice (once daily for five days, prior to the day of intoxication with paraquat) with ferrous sulfate (75 mg/kg) or cupric sulfate (6.5 mg/kg).

Activity of lung acetylcholine esterase was determined in four groups, five animals in each, in every experiment. The animals received a single dose of paraquat (20 mg/kg). The group of mice that was treated with a combination of paraquat and desferrioxamine received a single dose of paraquat (20 mg/kg) followed by multiple treatment with desferal. Lungs from each group were excised daily, homogenized and the enzymatic activity of acetylcholine esterase was determined according to Brown and Mailing (52).

Results

The Effect of Copper on Bacterial Inactivation Induced by Paraquat

Exposure of *E. coli* B (3×10^7 cell/ml) for 30 min to paraquat in the concentration range 0.1-1.0 mM caused inactivation of less than 1 decimal logarithmic unit; 36-83% of the bacteria were killed depending on paraquat concentration (basic system) (Fig. 1). Similarly, incubation of these cells with *copper alone* for 30 min showed only marginal inactivation. For example, when copper concentration was

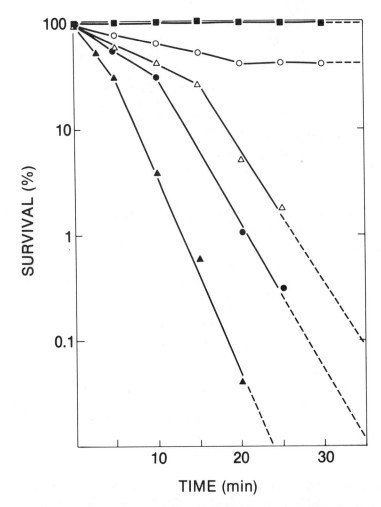

Figure 1. The Effect of Copper on Paraquat-Induced Bacterial Inactivation. All the incubation mixtures contained 3×10^7 E. coli B cells/ml, paraquat (0.25 mM), glucose (0.5% w/v) in phosphate buffer (1 mM, pH 7.4). Copper concentrations were 1 μM (▲), 0.5 μM (●), 0.1 μM (△), no added copper (○), and no added copper in the presence of desferrioxamine (0.1 mM) (■).

0.8 or below, 1 and 2 μM the observed inactivation was 0, 20 and 50% respectively (not shown).

By contrast, exposure of E. coli B cells to a *combination* of paraquat (0.25 mM) and copper(II) (1.0 μM) led to a rapid, exponential inactivation of the cells. For example, after 20 min incubation, the inactivation exceeded 3 decimal logarithmic units. This dramatic enhancement was dependent on copper concentration; increasing $[Cu^{+2}]$, using constant paraquat concentration, led to a higher rate of bacterial killing (Fig. 1).

When desferrioxamine was added to the incubation mixture that contained *E. coli* B cells and paraquat (no copper added) the residual inactivation was very small (2-3% after 30 min). Other chelating agents like EDTA or diethylenetriaminepenta-acetic acid (detapac) were also highly efficient in preventing the damage induced by paraquat. The rate (slope of the curve) of inactivation in the presence of paraquat (0.25 mM), and desferrioxamine was less than 1% of that exhibited for the reaction mixture containing *both* paraquat (0.25 mM) and copper (1 μM) (Fig. 1).

Anaerobic Inactivation

In an attempt to ascertain the role of oxygen in paraquat toxicity, some experiments were carried out in an anaerobic atmosphere. The same concentrations of paraquat and copper ions which had caused an inactivation of 3 logarithmic units of E. coli B in 17 min, under aerobic conditions (Fig. 1), caused bacterial inactivation of only 0.1 logarithmic units under anaerobic conditins (Fig. 2). Hydrogen peroxide (0.25 mM), itself, innocuous to the cells (not shown), was added to the reaction mixture that contained *both* paraquat and copper, and led to a marked increase in the rate of inactivation (Fig. 2). When paraquat and hydrogen peroxide were anaerobically

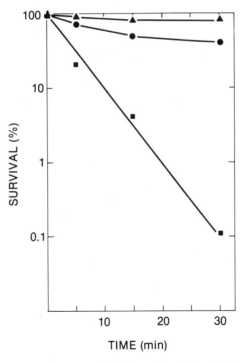

Figure 2. The Effect of the Combination of Hydrogen Peroxide and Copper on Paraquat-Induced Bacterial Inactivation Under Anaerobic Conditions. All the incubation systems contained 3×10^7 E. coli B cells/ml, paraquat (0.25 mM), glucose (0.5% w/v) in phosphate buffer (1 mM, pH 7.4), cupric sulfate (1 μM) (▲); H_2O_2 (0.1 mM) (●); cupric sulfate (1 μM) together with H_2O_2 (0.1 mM) (■).

introduced into the reaction mixture, the rate of inactivation was increased only slightly (Fig. 2). Hydrogen peroxide acted on the cells under aerobic atmosphere as well by raising the killing to 1.2 logarithmic units after 30 min (not shown). Also, the addition of desferrioxamine to the reaction mixture containing added hydrogen peroxide and paraquat (no copper added) almost completely prevented the bacterial inactivation.

The Effect of Superoxide Dismutase, Calalase and other Proteins

Superoxide dismutase (SOD) prevented the damage induced by paraquat and copper ions, *only* when all the reaction components were added simultaneously (Fig. 3a). In order to find out whether its ability to halt the inactivation of the cells had resulted from its enzymatic activity, SOD was heat-inactivated and subsequently added to the reaction mixture. The inactivated SOD was also efficient in reducing cell killing (Fig. 3a).

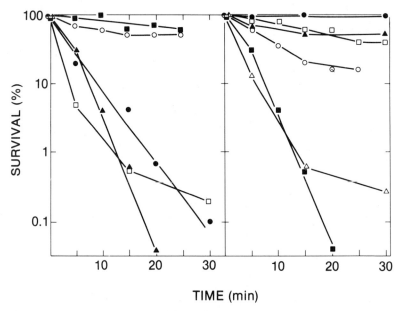

Figure 3. The Effect of Added Proteins on Paraquat-Induced Bacterial Inactivation. All the incubation systems contained 3×10^7 E. coli B cell/ml, paraquat (0.25 mM), glucose (0.5% w/v) in phosphate buffer (1 mM, pH 7.4). (a) cupric sulfate (1 μM) (▲); cupric sulfate (1 μM) added simultaneously with SOD (100 μg/ml) (■); cupric sulfate (1 μM) added simultaneously with heat-inactivitated SOD (○); preincubation of the bacteria with copper (1 μM, 12 min) followed by addition of SOD (100 μg/ml (□); copper salicylate (1 μM) (●). (b) cupric sulfate (1 μM) (■); simultaneous addition of the combination of cupric sulfate (1 μM) and catalase (100 μg/ml) (□); simultaneous addition of cupric sulfate (1 μM) and heat-inactivated catalase (100 μg/ml) (○); preincubation of the bacteria with cupric sulfate (1 μM, 12 min) followed by addition of catalase (100 μg/ml (△); no additions (▲).

By contrast, when the cells were pre-incubated with copper alone for 12 min and *then* paraquat and superoxide dismutase were added, SOD proved unable to stop the damage induced by paraquat and copper (Fig. 3a).

Copper salicylate (1 μM), which has been shown to possess SOD activity (24,25) failed to provide protection against paraquat toxicity. In fact, the slope of the curve of bacterial inactivation in the presence of copper salicylate was similar to that exhibited in the presence of copper sulfate (1 μM) and paraquat. Thus, copper salicylate was highly effective sensitizer to paraquat toxicity.

Catalase, like SOD, prevented the damage induced by paraquat and copper, *only* when all components were added together (Fig. 3b). Similarly, even heat-inactivated catalase reduced the rate of bacterial inactivation (Fig. 3b). By contrast, when the cells were first loaded with copper ions, and paraquat and catalase were added *only after* 12 min of pre-incubation, catalase failed to prevent bacterial killing (Fig. 3b).

In order to further verify that the protective effects of SOD and catalase are not due to their specific enzymatic activities, but rather could be attributed to their general properties as proteins, hexokinase and collagenase were tested, and were found equally effective protectants as SOD and catalase.

The Effect of Free Radicals Scavengers

Two OH-scavengers were used in trial to diminish the damage induced by the combined action of paraquat and copper. Mannitol (100 mM) or tert-butyl alcohol (100 mM) provided a small decrease in the rate of cellular inactivation (Fig. 4). Unlike these scavengers, low concentrations of histidine (1 mM), which is also an effective chelating agent, reduced the rate of inactivation more efficiently and proved to be a better protectant (Fig. 4). The bacterial killing was completely stopped after 15 min of incubation with histidine.

Survival of Paraquat Poisoned Mice

Mice that received a single dose of paraquat (17 mg/kg) began to die 24 hours after the injection, 50% of the mice were dead by 55 hours after the injection (Table I), and no survivors were left by the fourth day. In contrast, mice that received the repeated injections of desferrioxamine prior to, or following, the same dose of paraquat, began to die 40 hours after injection, 50% of these mice were dead only 80-82 hours after injection, and 20-30% of the mice survived subsequently for at least 3 additional months (Table I). Thus, desferrioxamine therapy significantly increased the life span of poisoned mice. Two groups were used as controls, one group was given repeated injections of desferrioxamine; and the second received injections of water only; both control groups survived the experiment.

Treatment of paraquat poisoned mice with desferrioxamine resulted in a smaller loss in body weight. Animals given only paraquat lost (19±3)% by day 2 and (25±4)% by day 3, whereas those intoxicated and treated with desferrioxamine showed a loss of (4±0.8)% by day 2 and (10±0.8)% by day 3.

To support our results with direct evidence that metals are involved in paraquat toxicity, another series of experiments was carried out. The survival time of these

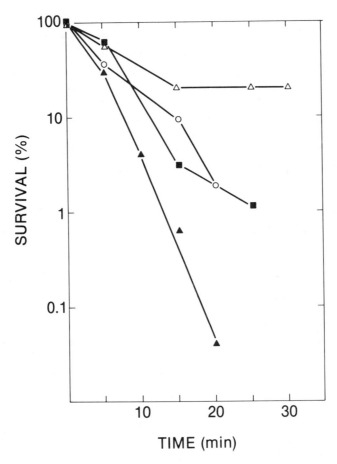

Figure 4. The Effects of Free Radicals Scavengers on the Paraquat-Induced Bacterial Inactivation. All the incubation systems contained 3×10^7 E. coli B cells/ml, paraquat (0.25 mM) copper sulfate (1 μM), glucose (0.5% w/v) in phosphate buffer (1 mM, pH 7.4) no additions (▲); with tert-butyl alcohol (100 mM) (■); with mannitol (100 mM) (○); with histidine (1 mM) (△).

mice was measured. In one group, ferrous sulfate was given IP each day for five days prior to the paraquat injection. A significant shortening of the life span of the animals was recorded (Table I); 25 and 30 hours after paraquat was injected into the iron loaded animals, 50% and 75% respectively of the mice had died, whereas the mice receiving paraquat alone showed no mortality within this time period. Similar findings were observed when the mice were pre-loaded with copper sulfate (6.5 mg/kg) (Table I).

The effect of chelating agents other than desferrioxamine was tested. Nitrilo-triacetate (NTA) was slightly more effective than desferrioxamine in protecting the paraquat intoxicated animals. A combination of desferrioxamine and NTA proved very efficient by yielding 70% survivors (Table I). In contrast, detapac, a potent general chelator did not provide any significant effect.

Table I

The Survival of Paraquat Poisoned Mice: The Effects of Chelators and Loading with Iron or Copper

Treatment	Life Span[1] (h)	R[2]	Survivors[3] (%)
1. Paraquat (17 mg/kg)	55	1.00	0
2. Paraquat $\Rightarrow$ desferrioxamine[4]	80	1.45	25
desferrioxamine $\Rightarrow$ Paraquat $\Rightarrow$ desferrioxamine[5]	82	1.49	25
3. Paraquat $\Rightarrow$ nitrilo-triacetate[5]	88	1.60	30
4. Paraquat $\Rightarrow$ (desferrioxamine + nitri-triacetate)[5]	>2200	>40.	70
5. Paraquat $\Rightarrow$ diethylenetriaminepentaacetic acid[5]	53	0.96	0
6. Ferrous Sulfate $\Rightarrow$ Paraquat	25	0.44	0
7. Copper Sulfate $\Rightarrow$ Paraquat	32	0.59	0
8. Paraquat $\Rightarrow$ Copper penicilamine[5]	49	0.90	0
Paraquat $\Rightarrow$ Copper salicylate[5]	48	0.87	0
Paraquat $\Rightarrow$ Copper Tyrosine[5]	41	0.75	0

[1]life span is determined as the time required for 50% of the poisoned animals to die.

[2]R=(life span of treated mice)/(life span of paraquat poisoned animals).

[3]survivors are mice who survived at least 90 day post poisoning and all external symptoms of the intoxication have disappeared.

[4]multiple injections of Desferal (3 times daily, for 2 days post poisoning with paraquat, 5 mg each).

[5]single injection daily (5 mg desferal, or 1.5 mg NTA, or 2.5 mg detapac, or 2.5 mg of ferrous sulfate, or 0.2 mg of copper sulfate, or 1 mg penicilamine) for five days prior to paraquat intoxication and once at the first day post intoxication.

Three copper chelates mimicking superoxide dismutase had only marginal sensitizing effects on the poisoned mice (Table I).

Another series of experiments dealt with the deleterious effects to the lungs consequent to paraquat intoxication. We chose to follow the activity of acetylcholine esterase in the lungs (52) (Table II). We found that the poisoned mice have lost 35, 45 and 60% of their enzymatic activity 1, 2 and 3 days post intoxication, and that the reduction in the enzymatic activity is not due to a simple competitive inhibition, because in in vitro experiments, paraquat failed to block the enzymatic activity.

In mice poisoned with paraquat and treated with desferrioxamine, the reduction in the enzyme activity of the lung was much smaller (6-12% only) than in the group that was given paraquat alone (Table II).

We studied the water content of the lungs after exposure to higher dose of paraquat (25 mg/kg) (25). The mice were killed at intervals, the lungs weighed, then freeze-dried for 72 hours, and weighed again. The water content was calculated as the difference between the two weights. Four groups (5 mice in each group) were used. The groups received injections of water (group 1), desferrioxamine (group 2), paraquat (group 3) and a combination of paraquat and desferrioxamine (group 4). The water content of the lungs of groups 1, 2 and 4 did not change 2 and 4 hours post

Table II
Activity of Lung Acetylcholine Esterase from Paraquat-Poisoned Mice

Group	Time 0	24h	48h	72h
1. Control	100	100	100	100
2. Desferrioxamine	100	107	107	112
3. Paraquat	100	65	55	40
4. Paraquat $\Rightarrow$ desferrioxamine	100	98	104	97
% protection by desferrioxamine		78	94	90

Five animals in each group, were used in each experiment. Injections were given intraperitoneally with one hour intervals. The first group (#1) was a control that was injected five times with sterile water. The second group was treated with desferrioxamine (3 injections of 5 mg followed by 2 injections of 2 mg of Desferal). The third group was treated with a single dose of paraquat (20 mg/kg), and the fourth group was treated with a combination of paraquat and desferrioxamine (a single dose of paraquat (20 mg/kg) followed by multiple treatment of desferrioxamine, 3 injections of Desferal 5 mg each, 2 injections of Desferal 2 mg each). Lungs from each group were excised daily, homogenized and the enzymatic activity determined according to Brown and Mailing (52).

injections $(75.0 \pm 0.2)\%$, $(p < 0.05)$ while the water content in the lungs of group 3 increased by $(1.0 \pm 0.2)\%$ and $(2.0 \pm 0.2)\%$ after 2 and 4 hours, respectively. Six hours after the poisoning the difference between group 3 and the other groups had reached its maximum (2.5%).

Discussion

E. coli System

Exposure of *E. coli* B to paraquat caused an inactivation of the bacteria cells of up to one logarithmic unit within an hour; a result consistent with that previously reported by Fridovich and Hassan (26,47,48). The demonstration of the involvement of transition metals in enhancing biological damage induced by paraquat was shown in two ways: the effect of chelators which minimized the bacterial inactivation caused by paraquat, and the effect of added copper ions enhanced dramatically (100 fold) the rate of the bacterial inactivation.

It is possible that the residual killing of *E. coli* in the basic system (no copper added) is due to contamination of transition metal ions. The fact that desferrioxamine, a specific chelator for iron (27), most efficiently blocked the reaction, may indicate that iron is the contaminant, when no metals are added.

It has been shown that paraquat radical reacts very fast with oxygen producing the superoxide radical (10) both in biological and chemical systems (10,30). Nevertheless, it is not yet clear whether the superoxide radical is the main cause of paraquat-induced damage in biology (46). Recently it was shown that superoxide radical by itself, being an unreactive species (13), is unable to induce enzymatic inactivation (18). Other radicals like the highly reactive hydroxyl radical (OH·), which may be obtained from superoxide radical (12), may be the responsible species for the deleterious effects of superoxide.

The Haber-Weiss reaction (31) is too slow under physiological conditions (32) in order to account for the deleterious processes in biology. However, trace metal ions may catalyse this reaction of superoxide by virtue of the Fenton reaction (33) (scheme).

BMM = BIOLOGICAL MACRO MOLECULES

Copper or iron ions can participate in a mechanism undergoing cyclic oxidation-reduction in chemical as well as in biological systems (34,53-55). Indeed, the superoxide radical can reduce metal complexes (18 and scheme), and also serve as a source for hydrogen peroxide. Thus, such a mechanism could explain the unusual enhancement of paraquat toxicity by copper. It is feasible to visualize an analogous mechanism in which paraquat radical is directly involved by replacing the role of superoxide radical ion.

The Detailed Mechanism in Bacterial System: paraquat had been shown to be reduced in various biological systems to the stable mono cation radical ($PQ^{+\cdot}$) (28,29,35,36). This stable radical reacts very fast with oxygen to generate O_2^- (10,26). It can also directly reduce biological complexes of transition metal ions (17,37). The superoxide radical thus formed can dismute, enzymatically or spontaneously, to produce hydrogen peroxide. Subsequently, the reduced metal complexes can react with hydrogen peroxide to produce OH· in a site spectific fashion (20) which may be responsible for the biological damage (scheme).

The component reactions of this suggested mechanism are substantiated by several sets of experiments. Thus, when paraquat was introduced in the absence of oxygen, no superoxide radical could be formed and no bacterial killing was recorded even in the presence of copper ions (Fig. 2). However, when H_2O_2 was added to this anaerobic system (containing paraquat and copper), the rate of bacterial killing was *similar* to that observed under aerobic conditions, in the absence of exogenous hydrogen peroxide. Oxygen formed in anaerobic systems by the catalatic decomposition of added hydrogen peroxide is estimated to be at least an order of magnitude lower than that in air-saturated solutions. This is so because the catalase is low in un-induced *E. coli* cells (38) and because the apparent K_m for hydrogen peroxide is very high. In addition, the continuous flushing of the reaction vessel with nitrogen would remove the liberated oxygen.

The observed protective effects of various proteins was possibly due to their chelation of metals (39-41) rather than to their specific enzymatic function. Copper-salicylate, which possesses SOD activity *in vitro* (24,25) failed to lower the bacterial killing, but rather enhanced the rate of inactivation.

Hydroxyl radicals are suggested as the primary cause for the biological damage observed. In principle, it is expected that OH· scavengers should protect. However, in the case of the recently proposed site specific metal mediated Haber-Weiss reaction (18,20,21) hydroxyl radical scavengers were shown to protect weakly, if at all (42,43). In such reactions OH· radicals are formed on biological macromolecules in close proximity to biological targets, and they react predominantly at the site of their formation, to which the scavenger may not enjoy free access. Tertiary butyl alcohol and mannitol reduced the rate of inactivation by a factor of 2. Histidine, on the other hand, a potent transition metal chelator (44), and a known scavenger of OH·, provided much higher protection at lower concentrations. Thus, it seems that the effect of histidine arises from the chelation of metal ions.

Mice System

We used four different parameters: the survival and loss of weight, the loss of activity of lung acetylcholine esterase and the water content of the lungs of paraquat intoxicated animals in order to demonstrate the involvement of transition metals in paraquat toxicity. Chelation therapy provided a significant protection while loading the animals with metals markedly exacerbated the poisoning. The rationale behind this approach arose from the bacterial system, in which the validity of the metal-mediated site-specific Haber-Weiss mechanism had been indicated. Nevertheless, it is very feasible that the effects of the chelators on one hand and those of the loading with metals on the other are due, in the whole animal, to a mechanism that is altogether different, such as modulation of the active transport of paraquat into the lungs of intoxicated animals.

In summary, based on these findings with iron and copper and with chelators we suggest that labile transition metals mediate paraquat toxicity, and thus, chelating agents should be tried out in treatment of paraquat poisoning in human subjects.

Acknowledgement

This research has been supported by a grant from the United States-Israel Binational Science Foundation (BSF).

References and Footnotes

1. A. Ledwith in *Biochemical Mechanisms of Paraquat Toxicity,* Ed., A.P. Autor, Academic Press, New York, pp. 21-37 (1977).
2. P. Smith and D. Heath, *Clin. Rev. Toxicol. 4,* 411-445 (1976).
3. J.F. Dasta, *Am. J. Hos. Pharm. 35,* 1368-1372 (1978).

4. A.P. Autor, *Life Sciences 14*, 1309-1319 (1974).
5. D. Heath and P. Smith in *Biochemical Mechanisms of Paraquat Toxicity*, Ed., A.P. Autor, Academic Press, New York, pp.39-57 (1977).
6. L. Kune, M. Kuncova, F. Soldan, R. Hodusa and L. Antalikova, *Bull. Eur. Physiopathol. Respir. 15*, 71-76 (1979).
7. J.M. Hutchison, *Diss. Abstr. Int. D-40*, 4619-4623 (1979).
8. D.B. Greenberg, S.A. Lyons and J.A. Last, *J. Lab. Clin. Med. 92*, 1035-1042 (1978).
9. P.J. Daugherty, *Arch. Intern. Med. 142*, 202-207 (1982).
10. S. Solar, W. Solar and N. Gestoff, *J. Chem. Soc. Faraday Trans. 78*, 2467-2477 (1982).
11. C.W.M. Sharp, A. Ottolenghi and H.S. Posner, *Toxicol. Appl. Pharmacol. 22*, 241 (1972).
12. C. Beauchamp and I. Fridovich, *J. Biol. Chem. 245*, 4641-4646 (1970).
13. J.A. Fee, *Trends Biochem. Sci.*, 84-86 (March 1982).
14. B. Halliwell, *Trends Biochem. Sci.*, 270-272 (August 1982).
15. A. Samuni and G. Cazpski, *Rad. Res. 76*, 624-632 (1978).
16. R.P.J. Williams, *FEBS Lett. 140*, 3-10 (1982).
17. D.C. Borg, K.M. Schaich and A. Forman in *Proc. Conf. on Oxygen Radicals in Chemistry and Biology*, Walter de Gruyter and Co., Berlin, in press.
18. A. Samuni, M. Chevion and G. Czapski, *J. Biol. Chem 256*, 12632-12635 (1981).
19. A. Samuni, M. Chevion, Y.S. Halpern, Y.A. Ilan and G. Czapski, *Rad. Res. 75*, 489-496 (1978).
20. E. Shinar, T. Navok and M. Chevion, *J. Biol. Chem. 258*, 14778-14783 (1983).
21. G. Czapski, J. Aronovitch, A. Samuni and M. Chevion in *Oxyradicals and Their Scavenger Systems — Molecular Aspects I*, Ed., Cohen and R.A. Greenwald, Elsevier, pp.111-115 (1983).
22. D.C. Borg, K.M. Schaich, J.J. Elmore and J.A. Bell, *Photochem. Photobiol. 28*, 887-907 (1978).
23. A. Samuni, J. Aronovitch, D. Godinger, M. Chevion and G. Czapski, *Eur. J. Biochem. 137*, 119-124 (1984).
24. R.J.Y. Youngman, A.D. Dodge, E. Lengfelder and E.F. Elstner, *Experienta 35*, 1295-1296 (1979).
25. E. Lengfelder, M. Saran and W. Bors, *Abstract Nr. L-3 International Conference on Singlet Oxygen and Related Species in Chemistry and Biology* (1977).
26. M. Hassan and I. Fridovich, *J. Biol. Chem. 253*, 8143-8148 (1978).
27. F. Knusel and J. Muesch, *Nature 206*, 674-676 (1965).
28. H.J. Forman, J. Nelson and A.B. Fisher, *J. Biol. Chem. 255*, 9879-9882 (1980).
29. J.S. Bus, S.Z. Cagen, M. Olguard and J.E. Gibson, *Toxicol. Appl. Pharmocol. 35*, 501-506 (1976).
30. H.K. Fisher, J.A. Clements and R.R. Wright, *Am. Rev. Resp. Dis. 107*, 246-252 (1973).
31. F. Haber and J. Weiss, *Proc. R. Soc. London Ser. A147*, 332-351 (1934).
32. B. Halliwell, *FEBS Lett. 92*, 321-326 (1978).
33. G. Czapski and Y. A.Ilan, *Photochem. Photobiol. 28*, 651-653 (1978).
34. H. Sigel in *Metal Ions in Biological Systems. Properties of Copper* Vol. 12, Marcel Dekker Inc. New York and Basel, p.4 (1981).
35. M.R. Montgomery, *Res. Commun. Chem. Pathol. Pharmacol. 16*, 155-158 (1979).
36. T.A. Farrington, N. Ebert, E.J. Land and K. Fletcher, *Biochim. Biophys. Acta 314*, 372-381 (1973).
37. E.J. Land and A.J. Swallow, *Ber. Bunsenges. Phy. Chem. 79*, 436 (1975).
38. H.E. Richter and P.C. Loewen, *Arch. Biochem. Biophys. 215*, 72-77 (1982).
39. M. Anbar and A. Levitzki, *Radiat. Res. 37*, 32-40 (1966).
40. E.K. Hodgson and I. Fridovich, *Biochemistry 14*, 5294-5299 (1975).
41. N.R. Bachur, S.L. Gordon and M.V. Gee, *Cancer Res. 38*, 1745-1750 (1978).
42. G. Czapski, *Israel J. Chem. 24*, 29-32 (1984).
43. D.C. Borg and K.M. Schaich, *Israel J. of Chemistry 24*, 87-90 (1984).
44. Eds., J. Peisach, P. Aisen and W.E. Blumberg, *The Biochemistry of Copper*, Academic Press, New York, pp.1-209 (1966).
45. D.R. William in *The Metals of Life. The Solution Chemistry of Metal Ions in Biological Systems*, Van Nostrand Reinhold Company, London pp.15 (1971).
46. R.M. Baum, *Chem. Engineer. News 62*, 20-26 (1984).
47. H.M. Hassan and I. Fridovich, *J. Biol. Chem. 254*, 10846-10852 (1979).
48. H.M. Hassan and I. Fridovich, *J. Biol. Chem. 252*, 7667-7676 (1977).
49. I. Fridovich, *Ann. Rev. Pharmacol. Toxicol. 23*, 239-257 (1983).

50. L.R. deAlvare, K. Goda and T. Kimura, *Biochem. Biophys. Res. Comm. 69,* 687-695 (1976).
51. K.E. Joesler, G. Jung, M. Weber and M. Weser, *FEBS Lett. 25,* 25-30 (1972).
52. E.A.B. Brown and H.M. Maling, *Biochem. Pharmacol. 29,* 465-473 (1980).
53. T. Navok and M. Chevion, *Biochem. Biophys. Res. Comm. 122,* 297-301 (1984).
54. K. Nakamura and E.R. Stadtman, *Proc. Natl. Acad. Sci. (USA) 81,* 2011-2015 (1984).
55. R.L. Levine, *J. Biol. Chem. 258,* 11823-11827 and 11828-11833 (1983).

Biological & Inorganic Copper Chemistry,
ISBN 0-940030-11-X, Eds., K. D. Karlin & J. Zubieta, Adenine Press, ©Adenine Press, 1985

Magnetic Properties of Copper(II) Chain Compounds

William E. Hatfield and Leonard W. ter Haar
Department of Chemistry, University of North Carolina
Chapel Hill, North Carolina 27514

Abstract

$LiCuCl_3 \cdot 2H_2O$ and Cu-KTS are alternating chains with alternation parameters near the uniform-chain limit ($\alpha = 0.89$ and 0.98, respectively), and both compounds show discontinuities in their magnetic susceptibilities. These phase transitions are unexpected in view of available theories. Cu-KTS·DMF and (isopropylammonium)$CuCl_3$ are alternating chains with intermediate values of the alternation parameter ($\alpha = 0.55$ and 0.35, respectively), and neither one of these displays a phase transition in the temperature region studied (>1.6 K). These results indicate that although the theory works reasonably well for moderately alternating systems, a more careful consideration of intra- and interchain exchange coupling, the alternation parameter, and the energy gap is required for precise descriptions of magnetic properties. $Cu(phthalato)(H_2O)$ presents an example of a new 1-D magnetic model system with a new twist to the alternating character. An analysis of the magnetic properties and superexchange pathways indicate that $Cu(pht)(H_2O)$ is an alternating next-nearest neighbor chain.

Introduction

Now that uniformly-spaced chains of copper(II) are reasonably well understood (1), attention has turned to chain compounds with more complicated structural features. These include alternatingly-spaced chains, alternatingly-bridged chains, alternating next-nearest neighbor chains, and chains which undergo transitions such as the magnetoelastic spin Peierls transition.

Such compounds are rare. The most thoroughly studied transition metal compound which exhibits alternating-chain magnetism is $Cu(NO_3)_2 \cdot 2.5H_2O$ (2). However, the room temperature crystal structure of $Cu(NO_3)_2 \cdot 2.5H_2O$ is ladder-like (3). Other transition metal compounds (4-16) which exhibit alternating-chain magnetism are listed in Table I. Recent work in our laboratory on chains of this sort are reviewed in the Article.

Theoretical Section

Uniformly-Spaced Linear Spin Chain

The Hamiltonian which describes the exchange interaction in a linear chain of

Table I

Exchange Coupled Transition Metal-ion Alternating Chain Compounds

Compound	α	J(cm^{-1})	g	Structure	Ref.
Cu$_2$(OAc)$_4$pyr[a]	3×10^{-4}	-160	2.18	Alternatingly bridged	4
Cu$_2$L(CH$_3$COO)$_2 \cdot$2CH$_3$OH[b]	0.19	-7.9	2.11	Alternatingly bridged	5
Cu(NO$_3$)$\cdot$2.5H$_2$O	0.27	-1.8	2.18	Ladder-like at RT	2,3
(IPA)CuCl$_3$[c]	0.35	-13.7	2.17	Alternatingly spaced	6,16
Fe(IV)(μ-O)(hpz)[d]	0.40	-133	2.30	Disordered bridges	7
Cu(N-MeImid)$_2$Br$_2$[e]	0.40	-7.2	2.14	Uniformly spaced at RT	8,9
Cu-KTS$\cdot$DMF	0.55	-2.6	2.07	No X-ray structure	16
Cu(4-Mepy)$_2$Cl$_2$[f]	0.67	-9.6	2.17	Uniformly spaced at RT	10,22
					11,12
Cu(3,6-DTO)Cl$_2$[g]	0.69	-2.7	2.08	Alternatingly bridged	13
LiCuCl$_3 \cdot$2H$_2$O	0.89	-3.7	2.14	Alternatingly spaced	14,16
Cu-OTS[h]	0.90	-12.9	2.11	No X-ray structure	22
Cu-HTS[i]	0.91	-10.1	2.06	No X-ray structure	22
Cu-KTS[j]	0.98	-4.5	2.08	Alternatingly spaced	15,16

[a] OAc = acetate, pyr = pyrazine;

[b] L^{2-} = dianion of N, N'-Bis[2-((o-hydroxybenzhydrylidene)amino)ethyl]-1,2-ethanediamine;

[c] IPA = isopropylammonium;

[d] hpz^{2-} = dianion of hemiporphyrazine;

[e] N-MeImid = N-(methyl)imidazole;

[f] 4-Mepy = 4-methylpyridine;

[g] 3,6-DTO = 3,6-dithiaoctane;

[h] OTS^{2-} = 2,3-octanedione bis(thiosemicarbazonate);

[i] HTS^{2-} = 2,3-hexanendione bis(thiosemicarbazonate);

[j] KTS^{2-} = 3-ethoxy-2-oxobutyraldehyde bis(thiosemicarbazonate).

uniformly-spaced, uniformly bridged magnetic ions is

$$\mathbf{H} = -2J \sum_{i \leq j}^{N} \alpha \hat{S}_i^z \hat{S}_j^z + \beta \hat{S}_i^x \hat{S}_j^x + \gamma \hat{S}_i^y \hat{S}_j^y \qquad (1.1)$$

where the parameter J is the exchange coupling constant describing the interaction between any two nearest neighbor spins. Although the exchange interaction is isotropic within the Heisenberg-Dirac-Van Vleck formalism (HDVV), anisotropy is often invoked to either simplify theoretical treatments or to explain experimental results. The anisotropy parameters α, β, and γ are used to denote the anisotropy. As a rule, the isotropic Heisenberg case ($\alpha = \beta = \gamma$) may be used to describe exchange coupling in copper (II) chains.

The most important work is that of Bonner and Fisher (17) who carried out calculations on finite chains and made extrapolations to the infinite limit for the generation of thermodynamic properties. The ground state consists of a band or continuum of degenerate singlet and triplet delocalized spin excitations (also known as spin waves) (18,19).

Hall (20) fit the numerical results of Bonner and Fisher (17) for the magnetic susceptibility of the $S = \frac{1}{2}$ uniform-chain to the expression

$$\chi_M = \frac{Ng^2\beta^2}{kT} \times \frac{0.25 + 0.14995x + 0.30094x^2}{1 + 1.9862x + 0.68854x^2 + 6.0626x^3} \qquad (1.2)$$

where $x = |J|/kT$. This expression has been used widely for the analysis of magnetic susceptibility data.

Alternatingly-Spaced Linear Spin Chain

The Hamiltonian for the alternating spin chain, in which the exchange coupling alternates in magnitude along the chain axis, is given by

$$\mathbf{H} = -2J \sum_{i=1}^{N/2-1} [\hat{S}_{2i} \cdot \hat{S}_{2i-1} + \alpha \hat{S}_{2i} \cdot \hat{S}_{2i+1}] \qquad (1.3)$$

where the parameter J is the exchange coupling between a spin and its left neighbor, and αJ is the exchange coupling between a spin and its right neighbor. The alternation parameter, α, is defined by the limits $0 < \alpha < 1$. The limit of $\alpha = 1$ corresponds to the uniformly-spaced chain, and the limit $\alpha = 0$ corresponds to the case of maximum alternations which is simply the isolated dimer. The effect of alternation on magnetic susceptibilities is shown in Figure 1.

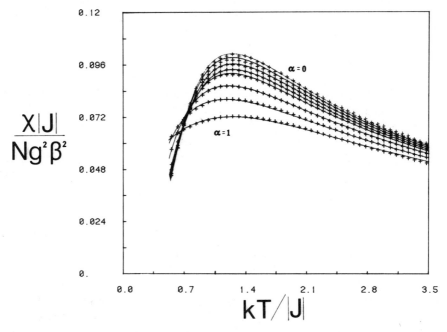

Figure 1. Reduced magnetic susceptibility plots for the $S = \frac{1}{2}$ alternating chain model.

Numerical calculations by Duffy and Barr (21) provided the first quantitative results for alternating chains. The calculations were performed on short S = ½ spin rings of up to 10 spins. Duffy and Barr concluded that the finite chain energy gap, which separates the singlet ground state from the band of triplet excited states, was unlikely to vanish in the limit of infinite chain length for $\alpha \leq 0.6$. They were unable to determine whether or not the energy gap vanishes for alternation parameter values of up to but not including the $\alpha = 1.0$ (uniform-chain) limit. Subsequently, Hatfield and co-workers (22) performed calculations on short rings of up to ten spins and developed the following expression for magnetic susceptibilities in terms of J, g, and α.

$$\chi_M(\alpha) = \frac{Ng^2\beta^2}{kT} \times \frac{A(\alpha) + B(\alpha)x \; C(\alpha)x^2}{1 + D(\alpha)x + E(\alpha)x^2 + F(\alpha)x_3} \tag{1.4}$$

where $x = |J|/kT = T_r^{-1}$, α = alternation parameter, and A-F are coefficients in a power series of α.

Bonner, et al. (23) calculated the ground state properties of short alternating rings (up to 12 spins) in an attempt to improve the uncertain conclusions about the existence of the energy gap in alternating-chains up to but not including $\alpha = 1.0$. These calculations represented an improvement over the results of Duffy and Barr (21) for $\alpha \leq 0.8$ and the extrapolations down to T = 0 K were also improved. However, the convergence of the finite-chain energy gap extrapolations are slow near the uniform limit, especially at the small kT/|J| values required by α values close to 1.0, and future calculations are required in order to improve the accuracy of the energy gap results for the higher alternation values (24).

Spin-Peierls Transition

From the above discussion it is clear that an important distinction between the alternating-chain model and the uniform-chain model is the occurrence of an energy gap in the ground state energy spectrum. Systems with $\alpha \leq 0.7$ have an energy gap and uniform chains ($\alpha = 1.0$) do not (24). As a result, the implications with respect to magnetic susceptibility are dramatic. Uniform chains have a nonzero, paramagnetic susceptibility at T = 0 K, but, alternating chains have a paramagnetic susceptibiltiy which goes to zero as the temperature approaches zero. It is interesting to ask what occurs at and near the uniform chain limit.

Magnetic systems often undergo transitions when the temperature is lowered and enter a long-range ordered magnetic phase, either LRO ferromagnetism or LRO antiferromagnetism. In the case of an ideal one-dimensional Heisenberg system, there can be no phase transition at any temperature greater than T = 0 K. However, any real chemical system will always consist of a 3-D lattice composed of chains. As a consequence, the magnetic chains are not isolated, and additional interactions must be considered in the quasi-one-dimensional systems. These interactions relax the stringent rule that disallows phase transitions in one-dimensional systems by "mixing" in some 3-D character from weak interchain interactions.

Now, consider a vibrational interaction between chains which may ultimately lead to an interaction of the phonon lattice with the spin lattice. Such spin-phonon coupling is characterized by a dimensionless spin-phonon coupling constant, λ. Because of the degeneracy of the ground state of the uniform-chain, a Jahn-Teller type lattice distortion can occur giving rise to a phase transition. The transition is known as the spin-Peierls transition and it occurs at temperature T_{SP} (25). At T_{SP}, the lattice distortion allows an energy gap to open since the driving force for the transition is a lowering of the net magnetic energy. The ground state of the system becomes similar to that of the alternating chain described above, with one exception. The magnitude of the energy gap is temperature dependent, and hence the alternation parameter is also temperature dependent. The spin-Peierls transition is a magneto-elastic phase transition and the spin-Peierls phase is only a LRO phase in the sense that 3-D phonons are involved. Ideally, the alternation parameter would decay from $\alpha = 1.0$ at T_{SP} to a value at T = 0 K which is determined by the magnitude of the transition temperature and the exchange interaction.

A large number of uniformly spaced, antiferromagnetically exchange-coupled, transition metal-ion spin chains have been structurally and magnetically characterized. Yet alternating chains are rarities among transition metal compounds. The work described in this Article deals with the identification and magnetic characterization of several such systems.

Lithium Copper (II) Trichloride Dihydrate, LiCuCl$_3$·2H$_2$O and Isopropylammonium Copper(II) Trichloride, (C$_3$H$_{10}$N)CuCl$_3$

The structures of the compounds LiCuCl$_3$·2H$_2$O (14) and (IPA)CuCl$_3$ (6) afford an opportunity of correlating the exchange coupling constants determined from an analysis of the magnetic data to the respective ligand bridges from which they arise.

Magnetic Properties

Magnetic susceptibility data for LiCuCl$_3$·2H$_2$O are given in Figure 2. The maximum in the magnetic susceptibility curve at 6.6 K provide strong evidence for antiferromagnetic exchange interactions. In view of the structures of the compound, these interactions occur along the chain of alternatingly-spaced, chloro-bridged, copper(II) ions. Above 4.4 K, the data were field independent in the range studied (0.1 to 10 kOe).

The exchange coupling constant and the alternation parameter for the alternating-chain compounds LiCuCl$_3$·2H$_2$O and (IPA)CuCl$_3$ were determined by fitting Equation 1.4 to the experimental data. The best fit obtained from a non-linear Simplex fitting procedure yielded J = -3.7 cm^{-1} and $\alpha = 0.89$ for LiCuCl$_3$·2H$_2$O; and J = -13.7 cm^{-1} and $\alpha = 0.35$ for (IPA)CuCl$_3$. The EPR g-values of 2.14 and 2.17, respectively, were held constant during all fitting procedure.

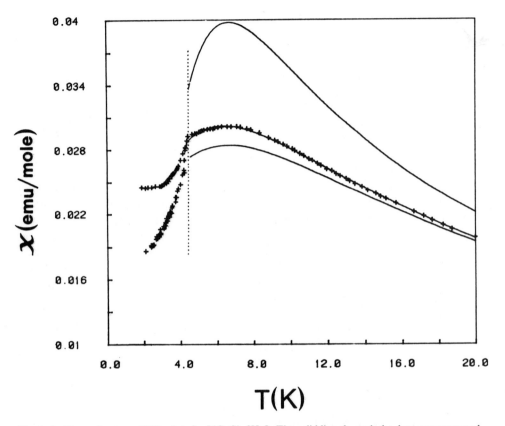

Figure 2. Magnetic susceptibility data for LiCuCl$_3$·2H$_2$O. The solid line through the data was generated by the expression given in the text for the alternating Heisenberg chain model with J $= -3.7$ cm^{-1} and a $= 0.89$. The upper and lower solid curves correspond to the best-fits to the data of the dimer ($a - 0.0$ and the uniformly-spaced chain ($a = 1.0$) models, respectively.

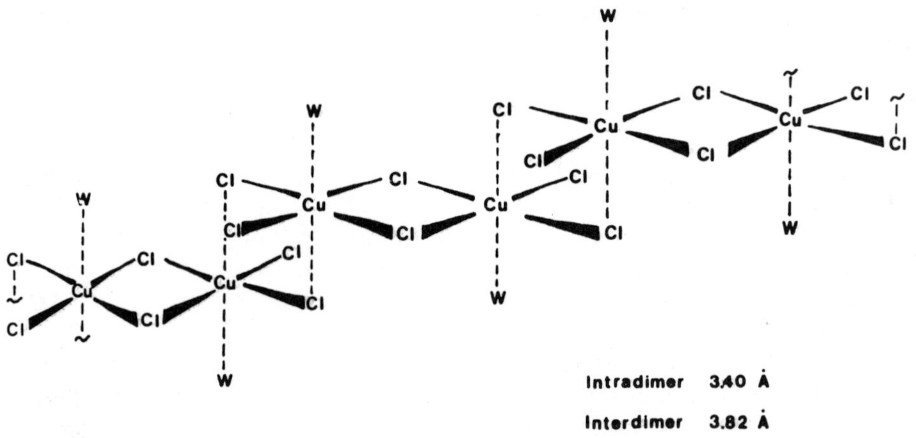

Intradimer   3.40 Å

Interdimer   3.82 Å

Figure 3. Structure of the alternating chain in LiCuCl$_3$·2H$_2$O. The chain structure in (IPA)CuCl$_3$ is identical, except that the copper(II) ions are only five coordinate.

Structural Descriptions

The crystal structure of $LiCuCl_3 \cdot 2H_2O$ (14) and (IPA)$CuCl_3$ (6) have been determined previously. In both compounds, the nearly planar $Cu_2Cl_6^{2-}$ dimeric anion is the fundamental structural unit used to form alternatingly-spaced linear chains as shown in Figure 3. Long Cu-Cl bonds between these dimeric units link the dimers into the alternatingly-spaced, bibridged chain structures. In the case of $LiCuCl_3 \cdot 2H_2O$, the sixth position of the copper(II) ion coordination sphere is filled by a coordinated water molecule. In (IPA)$CuCl_3$, each copper(II) ion is surrounded by five chlorides in a near perfect, square pyramidal coordination site.

Exchange Coupling

There is now a considerable body of data for exchange coupled, ligand bridged copper(II) systems which reveals that the experimentally observed exchange coupling energy is a function of the angle at the ligand bridge, ϕ, and the length of the long copper-ligand bond, R_o (26). A relatively smooth correlation of 2J with the quotient ϕ/R_o exists for chloro-bridged copper(II) complexes.

The chloro-bridges which occur in $LiCuCl_3 \cdot 2H_2O$ and (IPA)$CuCl_3$ are of two major types. Type I is the intradimer symmetrical bridging unit composed only of the short Cu-Cl bonds (ca. 2.3 A) and occurs in the structural $Cu_2Cl_6^{2-}$ dimeric units. Type II is the unsymmetrical Cu_2Cl_2 bridging unit which links the structural $Cu_2Cl_6^{2-}$ dimeric units into alternatingly-spaced chains. Both long and short Cu-Cl bonds are involved in this bridge, and it is this type of bridge for which magnetostructural correlations exist.

The intradimer structural features are essentially the same for both $LiCuCl_3 \cdot 2H_2O$ and (IPA)$CuCl_3$. The difference between the ϕ/R values for example, is negligible when attempting to correlate magnetic properties. Hence, it not expected that the exchange coupling constants corresponding to the type I bridges will be substantially different from one another in the two compounds. The data analysis confirms this conclusion since each of the compounds exhibit at least one exchange coupling constant which is on the order of -4 cm^{-1}.

The structural features which correspond to the interdimer bridging pathways are distinctly different in the two compounds. The ϕ/R_o values of 32.2 deg/A for $LiCuCl_3 \cdot 2H_2O$, and 33.1 deg/A for (IPA)$CuCl_3$ suggest that the exchange coupling constants corresponding to these type II bridges should be different, and that both should be antiferromagnetic. Indeed, the alternating Heisenberg chain analysis of the (IPA)$CuCl_3$ data indicates that one of the two exchange coupling constants is -13.7 cm^{-1} and hence larger than either of the two exchange coupling constants in $LiCuCl_3 \cdot 2H_2O$. The larger magnitude of this exchange constant is also in qualitative agreement with the 0.3 A decrease in interdimer Cu-Cu separation on going from $LiCuCl_3 \cdot 2H_2O$ to (IPA)$CuCl_3$.

Phase transition in LiCuCl$_3$·2H$_2$O

The phase transition that appears at 4.4 K in LiCuCl$_3$·2H$_2$O is of interest. The susceptibiltiy data taken in an external applied magnetic field of 100 Oe tends to a susceptibility value at T = 0 K which corresponds to ca. 66% of the susceptibility value at the transition temperature. This result suggests that the transition temperature corresponds to a transition to a long range, antiferromagnetically ordered phase (LRO), in agreement with previous work (27).

Unlike uniformly-spaced Heisenberg chains, alternating Heisenberg chains have a singlet ground state which is separated from the band of excited triplet states by an energy gap, ΔE. To a first approximation, ΔE/2J is proportional to the quantity 1-α (24). The consequence is that alternating-chains are not expected to exhibit LRO in zero field when interchain exchange interactions are present, whereas uniform-chains may do so. However, alternating-chains can show complex LRO regions in their phase diagrams between specific critical fields, and these LRO regions are a function of the alternation parameter and interchain magnetic coupling (25). This has been found true in the studies on Cu(NO$_3$)$_2$·2.5H$_2$O (2).

Catena-3-Ethoxy-2-oxobutyraldehyde-bis(thiosemicarbazonato)copper(II), Cu-KTS, and its Dimethylformamide Adduct

Cu-KTS is one of three compounds in Table I which is structurally characterized, (15) and which has an alternatingly-spaced structure. In view of the interest in the properties of Cu-KTS in particular, and, the general interest in alternating-chains and magnetostructural correlations, we have determined the magnetic properties of Cu-KTS and Cu-KTS•DMF, and, present an analysis of the data in terms of the alternatingly-spaced structures.

We have isolated a sufficient amount of the triclinic phase of Cu-KTS for determination of magnetic properties by allowing crystals to grow over a three hour period at approximately 65-70°C in a 50/50 ethanol/water solution, and then filtering the hot solution through a Büchner funnel to remove the product. The similar morphology of all of the triclinic crystals and X-ray powder diffraction data confirmed that the product used for bulk magnetic measurements was the triclinic phase of Cu-KTS. Recrystallization of the triclinic phase of Cu-KTS from DMF led to the production of a 1:1 solvate Cu-KTS•DMF.

Magnetic Properties of Cu-KTS

Magnetic susceptibility data for Cu-KTS exhibit a maximum in the susceptibility at 8.0 K, which provides strong evidence for antiferromagnetic exchange interactions. These interactions occur along the chain structure composed of alternatingly-spaced copper(II) ions. At T = 1.9 K, the data for Cu-KTS exhibit a discontinuity with spike-like characteristics. At larger field strengths the discontinuity becomes obscured, as is often the case for magnetic phase transitions. Below the discontinuity, the magnetic susceptibility decreases as the temperature is lowered. Only the susceptibility data in the paramagnetic temperature regime (T > 2.2 K) were considered in the fitting. The best fit of Equation 1.4 to the data yielded J = −4.53 cm^{-1} and α = 0.98(2) with the EPR g-value of 2.08 being held constant. Below T = 4.5 K, the experimental data deviate from the theoretical prediction.

The magnetic susceptibility data for Cu-KTS·DMF exhibit a maximum near 4.4 K which is indicative of an antiferromagnetic interaction. The best fit of Equation 1.4 to the data was obtained using the EPR g-value of 2.071 and yielded J = −2.6 cm^{-1} and α = 0.55.

Structure of Cu-KTS

Planar Cu-KTS molecular units stack to form an alternatingly spaced linear chain (15). The coordination of the copper(II) ions is "4+1+1" with the unequal axial copper-sulfur bond distances being 3.102(2) and 3.312(2) A. The exchange coupled units are planar Cu_2S_2 units composed of two short and two long copper-sulfur bond distances. The important feature of the Cu-KTS structure for this study is the alternating copper-sulfur out-of-plane bond distances.

Exchange Coupling in Cu-KTS and Cu-KTS DMF

A smooth correlation of J with the quotient ϕ/R_o exists for sulfur-bridged dimers and chains (26). The ϕ/R_o parameters for the exchange coupled Cu_2S_2 units in Cu-KTS are 29.0 and 26.1 deg/A. Based on the correlations, these values of ϕ/R_o suggest that antiferromagnetic interactions should occur in both of the exchange coupled units. However, the observed magnitude of the exchange coupling constants for the two Cu_2S_2 units in Cu-KTS are smaller than predicted from the correlation given by other sulfur-bridged systems (26,28). The departure of the data for Cu-KTS from the magnetostructural correlation may be understood in terms of the structure of the chain. Adjacent Cu_2S_2 units lie in planes which are nearly mutually perpendicular. It is proposed that the angle between adjacent planes is important in determining the alternating exchange. Adjacent planes are also mutually perpendicular in the alternatingly-bridged chain compound Cu(3,6-DTO)Cl$_2$ (13), for which the observed exchange coupling constants were smaller than expected. Collection of additional data on other compounds with this structural feature will permit a confirmation of this proposal.

The analysis of the magnetic susceptibility data for Cu-KTS·DMF suggests that this compound is also an alternatingly-spaced linear chain. The decreased magnitude of the exchange coupling constant in Cu-KTS·DMF relative to the magnitude observed in Cu-KTS signals that the incorporation of the DMF solvate molecule significantly alters the structural parameters associated with the Cu_2S_2 superexchange bridges. The increase in degree of alternation in Cu-KTS·DMF (α = 0.55) relative to Cu-KTS (α = 0.98) indicates that the two superexchange paths in the chain structure are also unequally affected by the addition of the DMF molecule to the lattice. As in the case of Cu-OTS and Cu-HTS, structural characterization of Cu-KTS·DMS is highly desirable so that these postulations can be verified.

Alternating-Next-Nearest-Neighbor Exchange-Coupling in the Linear Chain Compound Aquaphthalatocopper(II)

Here we report an analysis of magnetic susceptibility data which indicates that $Cu(H_2O)(pht)$ is an alternating-next-nearest-neighbor (ALNNN) linear chain system.

Structural Properties

As shown in Figure 4, two types of copper(II) ions, Cu1 and Cu2, occur in the structure of $Cu(H_2O)(pht)$ (29). The sequence -Cu1-Cu2-Cu1-Cu2-Cu1- forms the magnetic chain direction. Both types of copper(II) ion are coordinated by two water molecules which form bridges to nearest neighbors in the chain. The four

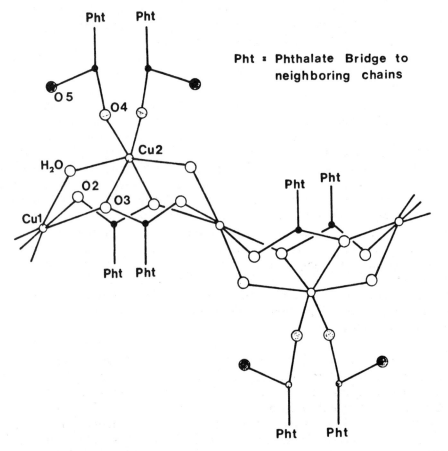

Figure 4. Structure of the $Cu(H_2O)(pht)$ chain structure. Note the phthalate (Pht) groups which bind neighboring chains into a complex sheet polymer.

remaining coordination positions of both types of copper(II) ion are filled by the oxygens of the carboxy groups from four different phthalate molecules. Each phthalate group is bound to four different copper(II) ions through three of its oxygen atoms. The result is a complex sheet polymer in the bc-plane which is composed of chains linked together through phthalate bridging groups. The fundamental units in the chains are constructed of the different Cu1 and Cu2 ions with superexchange transmitted through bridges between Cu1 and Cu2, and, also between Cu1 and Cu1′. The phthalate groups which allow for the carboxy bridges within the chains, also tie the neighboring chains together to form the sheet polymer.

The Hamiltonian for the ALNNN chain can be written as

$$\mathbf{H} = -2J\sum_{i=1}^{N-1} \hat{S}_i \cdot \hat{S}_{i+1} - 2J \sum_{i=1}^{N/2-1} \alpha \hat{S}_{2i-1} \cdot \hat{S}_{2i+1} \tag{1.5}$$

The exchange integral J occurs between each spin and its two nearest neighbors. The exchange integral αJ occurs alternatingly between every other spin and its two next-nearest-neighbors. In the limit of $\alpha = 0$, the ALNNN model approaches the uniform chain limit. When α is very large (i.e. $\alpha J \gg J$) the limiting behavior is that of a uniform chain for half of the ions in the structural chain, whereas the other half would behave as paramagnetic sites with Curie-type magnetism.

Magnetic Properties

Magnetic susceptibility data for $Cu(H_2O)(pht)$ were collected in the temperature range 1.8 K to 100 K. The maximum that occurs in the susceptibility at 21.5 K provides strong evidence for antiferromagnetic exchange interactions. In view of the structure of $Cu(H_2O)(pht)$, these interactions occur through the superexchange pathways identified above. Isothermal magnetization data have been collected at 1.8 K.

The Bonner-Fisher model for the uniform linear chain accounts for the temperature dependence of the magnetic susceptibility reasonably well, and the fit of the model to the data verifies the predominant 1-D character of $Cu(H_2O)(pht)$. The "best fit" uniform chain model analysis yields a solid line which goes through most of the experimental data. The best fit parameter is $J = -12.35$ cm^{-1} using g = 2.19.

However, there is a discrepancy between the experimental susceptibility data and the best fit uniform-chain curve in the temperature region of the maximum. The discrepancy is important since susceptibility data near the region of maximum susceptibility are most sensitive to the specific characteristics of a magnetic model system. The important characteristics associated with the magnetic susceptibility maximum of $Cu(H_2O)(pht)$ are given in Table II for both the experimental values and the values predicted by the uniform-chain analysis. The temperature at which the maximum is located, T_{max}, is experimentally 1.3 K below the theoretical value obtained from the uniform-chain analysis. Likewise, the observed value of χ_{max} is slightly higher than the value predicted by uniform chain theory. The failure of the

Table II

Parameters associated with the magnetic susceptibility maximum of next-nearest neighbor chains

	α	T_{max}	$\dfrac{kT_{max}}{\lvert J\rvert}$	χ_{max}	$\dfrac{\chi_{max}\lvert J\rvert}{N_A g^2 \beta^2}$
Experimental		21.5	1.210	0.0747	0.07398
	−0.5		1.625		0.0740
	−0.4		1.565		0.0738
	−0.3		1.500		0.0736
	−0.2		1.450		0.0735
	−0.1		1.385		0.07345
(Uniform chain)	0.0	22.8	1.283	0.0742	0.07346
	0.1		1.150		0.0736
	0.2		1.025		0.0739
	0.3		0.820		0.075
	0.4		0.580		0.076
	0.5		0.550		0.076

uniform-chain model to fit the data precisely is a consequence of the second superexchange pathway in the ALNNN structure.

The experimental data were compared to the theoretical results of Ananthakrishna, et al. (30) for the NNN linear chain. Ananthakrishna has provided theoretical χ_{max} and T_{max} values for the NNN chain as a function of the neighbor-interaction parameter, α, the ratio of the NNN interaction to the NN interaction. These results are summarized in Table II. From a comparison of the experimental location of the magnetic susceptibility maximum for $Cu(H_2O)(pht)$ with the predicted value in Table II, a neighbor-interaction parameter in the range of 0.05 to 0.20 is appropriate since the experimental maximum is shifted to lower temperatures and higher susceptibility values relative to the uniform-chain limit. The best fit for α is 0.12 (7).

Acknowledgement

This research was supported by the National Science Foundation (grant no. CHE 83 08129).

References and Footnotes

1. W.E. Hatfield, W. E. Estes, W. E. Marsh, M. W. Pickens, L. W. ter Haar and R. R. Weller in *Extended Linear Chain Compounds,* J. S. Miller Ed., Plenum Press: New York, *vol. 3,* Chapter 3, 1982, and references therein.
2. J. C. Bonner, S. A. Friedberg, H. Kobayashi and D. L. Meier, H. W. Blöte, *Phys. Rev. B, 27,* 248 (1983), and references therein.
3. B. Morosin, *Acta Crystallogr., Sect B, B26,* 1203 (1970).
4. J. S. Valentine, A. J. Silverstein and Z. G. Soos, *J. Amer. Chem. Soc., 96,* 97 (1974).
5. B. Chiari, W. E. Hatfield, O. Piovesana, T. Tarantelli, L. W. ter Haar and P. F. Zanazzi, *Inorg. Chem., 22,* 1468 (1983).

6. S. A. Roberts, D. R. Bloomquist, R. D. Willett and H. W. Dodgen, *J. Amer. Chem. Soc., 103,* 2603 (1981).

7. W. Hiller, J. Strähle, A. Datz, M. Hanack, W. E. Hatfield, L. W. ter Haar and P. Gütlich, *J. Amer. Chem. Soc., 106,* 329 (1984).

8. J. J. Smit, L. J. de Jongh, J. A. C. van Ooijen, J. Reedijk and J. C. Bonner, *Physica B+C, 97,* 229 (1979).

9. J. C. Jansen, H. van Koningsveld and J. A. C. van Ooijen, *Cryst. Struct. Commun,. 7,* 637 (1978).

10. V. H. Crawford and W. E. Hatfield, *Inorg. Chem., 16,* 1336 (1977).

11. W. E. Marsh, E. J. Valente and D. J. Hodgson, *Inorg. Chim. Acta, 51,* 49 (1981).

12. H. J. M. de Groot, L. J. de Jongh, R. D. Willett and J. Reedijk, J., *J. Appl. Phys., 53,* 8038 (1982).

13. M. M. Olmstead, W. K. Musker, L. E. ter Haar and W. E. Hatfield, *J. Amer. Chem. Soc., 104,* 6627 (1982).

14. P. H. Vossos, D. R. Fitzwater and R. E. Rundle, *Acta Crystallogr., 16,* 1037 (1963).

15. M. R. Taylor, J. P. Glusker, E. J. Gabe and J. A. Minkin, *Bioinorg. Chem., 3,* 189 (1974).

16. L. W. ter Haar and W. E. Hatfield, to be published.

17. J. C. Bonner and M. E. Fisher, *Phys. Rev. A, 135,* 640 (1964).

18. J. C. Bonner, B. Sutherland and P. M. Richards in *Magnetism and Magnetic Materials—1974, Proceedings of the 20th Annual Conference on Magnetism and Magnetic Materials,* C. D. Graham, G. H. Lander and J. J. Rhyne, Eds., AIP: New York, p. 335 (1965).

19. G. Müller, H. Beck and J. C. Bonner, *Phys. Rev. Lett., 43,* 75 (1979).

20. J. W. Hall, Ph.D. Dissertation, University of North Carolina, Chapel Hill, 1977.

21. W. Duffy and K. P. Barr, *Phys. Rev., 165* 647 (1968).

22. J. W. Hall, W. E. Marsh, R. R. Weller and W. E. Hatfield, *Inorg. Chem., 20,* 1033 (1981)

23. J. C. Bonner, H. W. J. Blöte, J. W. Bray and I. S. Jacobs, *J. Appl. Phys., 50,* 1810 (1979).

24. J.C. Bonner and H. W. J. Blöte, *Phys. Rev. B, 25,* 6959 (1982).

25. J. W. Bray, L. V. Interrante, I. S. Jacobs and J. C. Bonner, in *Extended Linear Chain Compounds,* J. S. Miller Ed., Plenum Press: New York, *vol. 3* (1983).

26. W. E. Hatfield, *Comments Inorg. Chem., 1,* 105 (1981).

27. J. W. Metselaar and D. de Klerk, *Physica B, 69,* 499 (1973).

28. W. E. Hatfield, *J. Appl. Phys., 52,* 1985 (1981).

29. C. K. Prout, J. R. Carruthers and F. J. C. Rossotti, *J. Chem. Soc. (A),* 3550 (1971).

30. G. Ananthakrishna, L. F. Weiss, D. C. Foyt and D. J. Klein, *Physica, 81B,* 275 (1976).

Biological & Inorganic Copper Chemistry,
ISBN 0-940030-11-X, Eds., K. D. Karlin & J. Zubieta, Adenine Press, ©Adenine Press, 1985

Interaction Between Copper(II) Ions through Azido and Cyanato Bridges; Spin Polarization Effects

Olivier Kahn and Marie-Laure Boillot

Laboratoire de Spectrochimie des Eléments de Transition
ERA 672, Université de Paris Sud
91405 Orsay, France

Abstract

This paper deals with the structure-magnetic properties correlations in azido and cyanato bridged copper(II) binuclear complexes. The structures of several new compounds of this kind are described, as well as their magnetic properties and their EPR spectra. From this investigation it emerges that: (i) when N_3^- bridges in a symmetrical end-to-end fashion, the interaction is strongly antiferromagnetic; (ii) when N_3^- or NCO^- bridges in an end-on fashion, this favors a ferromagnetic interaction. In the case where there is another bridge in addition to the end-on azido or cyanato bridge, the ground state can however be the singlet pair state if this other bridge exerts a strong antiferromagnetic stabilization. The mechanism of the interaction through the azido bridge is discussed. It is emphasized that a spin polarization effect due to the nature of the π_g highest occupied molecular orbitals of N_3^- adds to the antiferro- and ferromagnetic contributions arising from the interaction of the magnetic orbitals.

Introduction

The investigation of azido bridged copper(II) polymetallic complexes lies at the meeting point of two apparently widely separated scientific areas, namely bioinorganic chemistry and molecular magnetism. The role of the azido ligand in the study of the protein binuclear copper centers is now well documented. For instance azido may be present in met-hemocyanin and met-tyrosinase (1-2). There has been recently a great deal of synthetic effort to prepare binuclear copper(II) complexes with an endogenous oxygen bridging ligand and an exogenous azido bridging ligand. These complexes have been considered as models of azido bridged met-hemocyanin protein (3-5). However, the nature of the interaction between the metal centers has not always been investigated in detail by the bioinorganic chemists and it has not been fully realized that the azido bridged copper(II) polymetallic complexes have quite peculiar electronic properties. Likely, it was the duty of the specialists in molecular magnetism to detect and to try to rationalize these properties (6). This is the subject of this paper.

It has been known for a long time that azido can bridge two copper(II) ions either in an end-to-end fashion or in an end-on fashion:

end-to-end   end-on

It has also been realized in 1978 that N_3^- can bridge in a dissymmetrical end-to-end fashion with a short $Cu-N_\alpha$ bond and a long $Cu-N_\beta$ bond (7). Such a situation is expected for di-μ-azido copper(II) dimers where each metal ion is fivefold coordinated with three coordination sites belonging to terminal ligands, the other positions being occupied by the N_α atom of an azido group and the N_β atom of the other azido group as shown below.

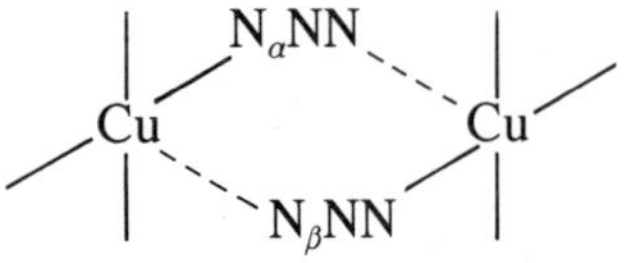

Likely the most fascinating aspect of the properties of these different μ-azido complexes is the versatility of their magnetic behavior (6). When N_3^- bridges in an end-to-end fashion, the interaction between the metal centers is strongly antiferro-magnetic. When N_3^- bridges in an end-on fashion, the ferromagnetic interaction is favored. When two copper(II) ions are bridged by an end-on azido and another ligand X, the sign and the magnitude of the interaction, of course, depends also on the nature of X. However, in all complexes found to date, the

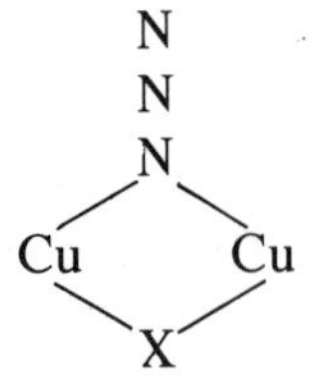

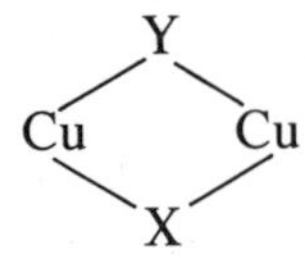

networks exhibits a less antiferromagnetic, or more ferromagnetic interaction than any other network if the other ligands remain unchanged. Finally, in complexes with dissymmetrical end-to-end azido bridges, the interaction is either negligible when the geometry around the metal is square pyramidal, or very weakly antiferromagnetic when this geometry tends towards the trigonal bipyramid.

In the next section, we shall present some of the newest experimental results in the field of the μ-azido copper(II) complexes, then we shall propose an interpretation of the magnetic properties of these systems by introducing the concept of spin polarization effect.

Structural and magnetic data

End-to-end azido bridges

The first structurally characterized copper(II) binuclear complex with symmetrical end-to-end azido bridge was described by Agnus et al (8). It contains the planar

$$
\begin{array}{c}
\text{NNN} \\
\diagup \qquad \diagdown \\
\text{Cu} \qquad\qquad \text{Cu} \\
\diagdown \qquad \diagup \\
\text{NNN}
\end{array}
$$

network inside a cryptate cavity. The two metal ions are separated by 5.145 Å. In spite of this large separation, the metal ions are so strongly coupled in an antiferromagnetic fashion that the compound is diamagnetic. The singlet state is very stabilized with regard to the excited triplet state, so that even at room temperature the magnetic state is totally depopulated. A similar situation as for the electronic structure was found in two complexes containing the nearly planar

$$
\begin{array}{c}
\text{NNN} \\
\diagup \qquad \diagdown \\
\text{Cu} \qquad\qquad \text{Cu} \\
\diagdown \qquad \diagup \\
\text{O}
\end{array}
$$

network. In one of them, the oxygen atom belongs to an alkoxide group (4); the Cu...Cu separation is then 3.615 Å. In the other one, the oxygen atom belongs to a phenolato group and the Cu...Cu separation is 3.678 Å. In this latter compound (5), the singlet-triplet (S-T) energy gap, deduced from accurate magnetic measurements, was found larger than 1200 cm^{-1} in absolute value. McKee et al. suggested that the most efficient pathway in their μ-alkoxide μ-azido compound was through

the oxygen atom of the alkoxide group(4). If it is true that the $\text{Cu} \diagup^{\text{O}}\diagdown \text{Cu}$ linkage with large bridging angle favors an antiferromagnetic interaction, the result of Agnus et al. (8) clearly shows that the end-to-end azido bridge is at least as efficient as the oxygen bridge in this respect.

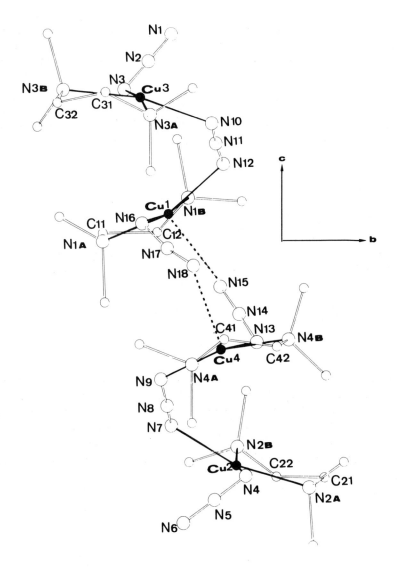

Figure 1. Asymmetric unit for $[Cu_2(tmen)_2(N_3)_3](PF_6)$, *1*, showing the association of two binuclear cations.

The first complex with a single symmetrical end-to-end azido bridge is $[Cu_2(tmen)_2(N_3)_3](PF_6)$,*1*, with tmen=N,N,N′,N′-tetramethylethylenediamine (9). Its structure consists of zig zag chains of binuclear cations $[Cu_2(tmen)_2(N_3)_3]^+$ and non coordinated PF_6^- anions as shown in Fig. 1. Within the binuclear unit, of which a perspective view is given in Fig. 2, the copper atoms are bridged by the end-to-end azido with a Cu...Cu distance of 4.44 Å. The binuclear units are linked to each other by a double dissymmetrical end-to-end azido bridge with a Cu...Cu separation of 5.13 Å. The short and long Cu−N bond lengths of the double dissymmetrical

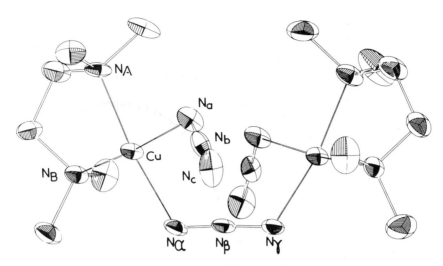

Figure 2. Perspective view of the binuclear cation $[Cu_2(tmen)_2(N_3)_3]^+$.

bridge are equal to 2.00 Å and 2.32 Å respectively. Each copper atom is surrounded by five nitrogen atoms, two from tmen and three from the azido groups, occupying the vertices of a slightly distorted square-based pyramid. The two basal planes within a binuclear unit make a dihedral angle of 46°. In spite of the polymeric nature of the compound, its magnetic properties shown in Fig. 3 very closely follow what is expected for an antiferromagnetically coupled copper (II) binuclear complex with a S-T energy gap J = −308.6 cm⁻¹. The interaction through the dissymmetrical bridges is negligible with regard to the interaction through the symmetrical bridge and cannot be determined by the magnetic technique. The polymeric structure of the compound is however apparent in EPR. The spectrum associated with the excited state is poorly resolved. It exhibits only a very large resonance centered at g = 2.09, which vanishes at low temperature. This aspect of the spectrum arises from exchange broadening due to the interdimer interactions.

The non efficiency of the dissymmetrical end-to-end azido bridge to transmit the electronic effects between copper(II) ions is clearly demonstrated by the study of the complex $[Cu(tmen)(N_3)_2]_2$, **2** (10). Its structure shown in Fig. 4 consists of discrete dimeric units. Each copper atom is surrounded by five nitrogen atoms, two from tmen and three from azido groups, occupying the vertices of a slightly distorted square based pyramid. Two azido groups bridge in an end-to-end fashion between the apical position of one copper atom and the basal plane of the adjacent copper atom. The short and long Cu−N bond lengths in the bridges are equal to 1.979 Å and 2.456 Å respectively and the Cu...Cu separation is 5.004 Å. The magnetic and EPR properties of **2** have been investigated. In the whole temperature range 4.2 ≤ T/K < 300, the molar magnetic susceptibility χ_M follows the Curie law expected for two noncoupled copper(II) ions with $\chi_M T = 0.85 \pm 0.02$

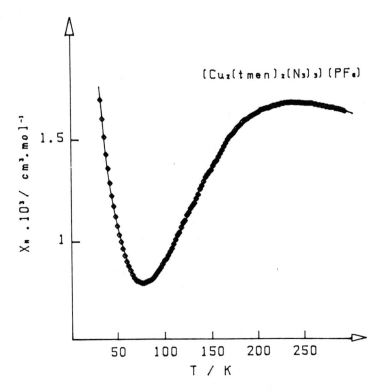

Figure 3. Experimental (◊) and theoretical (——) temperature dependences of the molar magnetic susceptibility of [Cu$_2$(tmen)$_2$(N$_3$)$_3$](PF$_6$), *1*.

cm^{3}mol^{-1}K (see Fig. 12). In the same way, the EPR spectrum is typical of an noncoupled copper(II) ion in an elongated tetragonal environment with g$_{||}$ = 2.19 and g$_{\perp}$ = 2.06.

reported by Felthouse et al. (7), [Cu$_2$(Me$_5$dien)$_2$(N$_3$)$_2$](BPh$_4$)$_2$ where Me$_5$dien is 1,1,4,7,7-pentamethyldiethylenetriamine. The fivefold geometry about each copper atom is intermediate between square pyramidal and trigonal bipyramidal. The Cu−N bond lengths of the bridges are equal to 1.985 Å et 2.252 Å. Owing to the trigonal bipyramidal character of the CuN$_5$ chromophore, there is a non zero spin density on the nitrogen atom located at 2.252 Å from the copper atom. This allows a very weak antiferromagnetic interaction with a S-T gap J = −6.2 cm^{-1}. The EPR spectrum is also typical of a triplet state.

End-on azido bridges

Till now, only two di-μ-end-on azido bridged copper(II) complexes have already been synthesized and structurally characterized. The first one is Cu$_2$(N$_3$)$_4$⊂(C$_{16}$H$_{34}$N$_2$O$_6$),

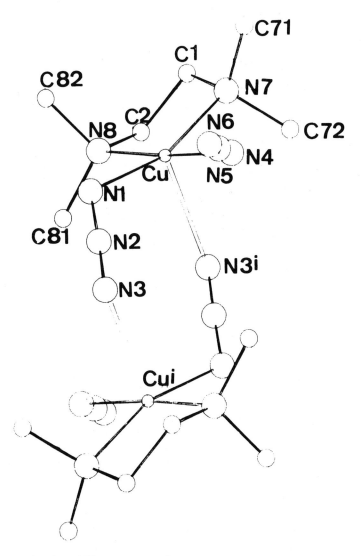

Figure 4. Perspective view of [Cu(tmen)(N$_3$)$_2$]$_2$, **2**.

3 (11). Its structure is given in Fig. 5. The planar Cu(N$_3$)$_2$Cu network is located inside a cryptate cavity with a Cu...Cu separation of 3.162 Å and an average value of the bridging angle equal to 103.6°. The second one is |Cu$_2$(t-bupy)$_4$(N$_3$)$_2$|(ClO$_4$)$_2$, **4** where t-bupy is 4-terbutylpyridine (12). **4** consists of dimeric cations and noncoordinated perchlorate anions. The structure of the cation is given in Fig. 6. The copper atoms are fourfold coordinated with coplanar surroundings. The Cu...Cu distance is 3.045 Å and the bridging angle is equal to 100.5°. Both **3** and **4** exhibit an intramolecular ferromagnetic interaction. Since the space is limited, we shall

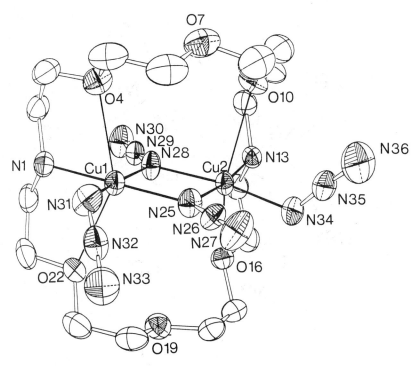

Figure 5. Perspective view of $Cu_2(N_3)_4 \subset (C_{16}H_{34}N_2O_6)$, *3*.

only discuss the results concerning *4*, for which very accurate magnetic and EPR investigations have been carried out. The magnetic behavior of *4* is shown in Fig. 7 in the form of the $\chi_M T$ versus T plot. At room temperature, $\chi_M T$ is equal to 0.95 $cm^3mol.^{-1}K$, which is a value already higher than what is expected for two noncoupled copper(II) ions, increases upon cooling and reaches a plateau below 60 K with $\chi_M T$ = 1.15 ± 0.02 $cm^3mol^{-1}K$ (13). This behavior is actually characteristic of a ferromagnetic interaction with a triplet ground state very separated in energy from the excited singlet state. In the low temperature range, where $\chi_M T$ is constant, only the triplet ground state is significantly populated. The S-T energy gap may be deduced in principle from the magnetic data. However, it has already been pointed out that the larger the stabilization of the triplet state, the less accurate the determination of J is (11,12,15). In the present case, we found J = 105 ± 20cm^{-1}.

The powder EPR spectrum of *4* at 4.2 K is given in Fig. 8. Both its shape and its temperature dependence confirm that the ground state is a triplet state with a relatively large axial zero field splitting parameter. In order to analyse in detail the zero field splitting on the triplet state, a single crystal EPR investigation has been carried out at X-band frequency, at 4.2 K (14). The principal values and the orientations of the *g* (Zeeman) and *D*(zero field splitting) tensors have been determined from the angular variation of the resonant fields in three orthogonal planes shown in Fig. 9. The axial and rhombic zero field splitting parameters were

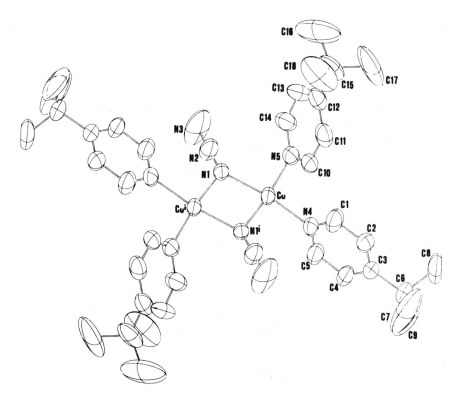

Figure 6. Perspective view of the binuclear cation [Cu$_2$(t-bupy)$_4$(N$_3$)$_2$]$^{2+}$ in **4**.

found as $|D| = 0.43$ cm^{-1} and $|E| = 0.026$ cm^{-1}. D is oriented in such a way that D$_{zz}$ is close to the normal to the plane containing the Cu(N$_3$)$_2$Cu network and D$_{xx}$ close to the Cu...Cu direction, as shown in Fig. 10. D was decomposed into a dipolar contribution and an anisotropic exchange contribution, this latter being by far predominant. This anisotropic exchange contribution is due to the combined effect of the local spin orbit coupling and of the interaction between the ground state of an ion and the excited states of the other.

Several copper(II) complexes with the

$$
\begin{array}{c}
\text{N} \\
\text{N} \\
\text{N} \\
\text{Cu} \quad \quad \text{Cu} \\
\text{O}
\end{array}
$$

network have been reported. In many cases, the sign and the magnitude of the intramolecular interaction have been determined. The first reported compound of

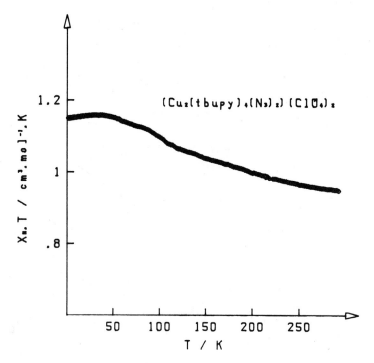

Figure 7. Temperature dependence of $\chi_M T$ for $[Cu_2(t\text{-bupy})_4(N_3)_2](ClO_4)_2$, **4**.

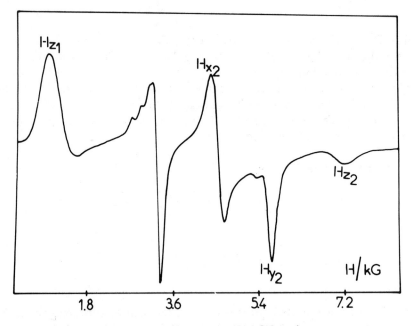

Figure 8. X-band powder EPR spectrum of $[Cu_2(t\text{-bupy})_4(N_3)_2](ClO_4)_2$, **4**.

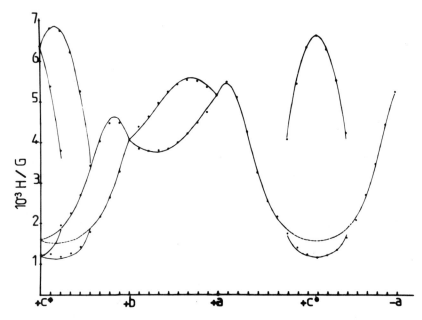

Figure 9. Experimental (●) and calculated (——) angular variations of the resonant fields for [Cu_2(t-bupy)$_4$(N_3)$_2$](ClO$_4$)$_2$, **4**.

this kind is [Cu_2(tmen)$_2$(N_3)(OH)](ClO$_4$)$_2$, **5** (15). The structure of the binuclear cation is shown in Fig. 11. The two copper atoms are bridged by an azido and an hydroxo groups. The bridging network is disordered so that only the values of the Cu—X distance (1.960 Å) and of the Cu—X—Cu angle (99.4°) are known accurately, X being the $N_{0.5}O_{0.5}$ composite bridging atom. The magnetic properties of **5** are represented in Fig. 12. At first view, they are not spectacular. In fact, they reveal quite a peculiar situation. $\chi_M T$ is equal to 1.02 cm^{3}mol^{-1}K at room temperature, then very smoothly increases upon cooling down and reaches a plateau around 150 K down to very low temperature. This quasi Curie law corresponds to a triplet ground state with a singlet excited state so high in energy that it is only weakly populated, even at room temperature. The S-T energy gap is too large to be deduced from the magnetic data. It is estimated to be larger than 200 cm^{-1}. In Fig. 12, we compared the magnetic behavior of **5** to the Curie law corresponding to the two noncoupled copper(II) ions of [Cutmen(N_3)$_2$]$_2$, **2**. This comparison emphasizes that a Curie law for a copper(II) binuclear complex does not mean necessarily that there is no interaction. Only an accurate determination of the Curie constant allows to conclude, as also the aspect of the EPR spectrum.

The complex [Cu_2(tmen)$_2$(NCO)(OH)](ClO$_4$)$_2$, **6**, with NCO$^-$ instead of N_3^- was also investigated. It is isomorphous to **5** and also exhibits a strong ferromagnetic interaction.

Recently, we have synthesized several binuclear copper(II) complexes with the binucleating ligand obtained by condensation of two moles of 1,1-dimethylethylenediamine on one mole of 2,6-diformyl 4-methylphenol, and an exogenous ligand X. Three of these complexes may be schematized as:

with $X^- = N_3^-$,   7
         NCO^-, 8
         OH^-,   9

For the three complexes, we obtained extremely thin single crystals, unsuitable for X ray investigation. However, it is most likely that the metal ions are in planar surroundings (or nearly planar if a perchlorato ion is weakly bound to each metal atom in apical position). It follows that the magnetic orbitals have the xy symmetry, refering to the referentiel axes shown above. The S-T energy gaps for **7**, **8** and **9** were deduced from the magnetic behaviors of the compounds and found as $J = -86.5 \text{ cm}^{-1}$ for **7**, -4.1 cm^{-1} for **8** and -366.8 cm^{-1} for **9**. The magnetic curve for **7** is given in Fig. 13. One immediately sees that the hydroxo bridged complex **9** is much more antiferromagnetically coupled than the azido and cyanato ones **7** and **8**. In di-μ-phenolato copper(II) complexes, J was found of the order of -600 cm^{-1}. Since, in copper(II) complexes, the contributions along each $Cu-X-Cu$ linkage are expected to be roughly additive, in contrast to what happens in heterobimetallic complexes like Cu(II)VO(II) (16), the contribution to the measured interaction from the phenolato bridge may be estimated as about -300cm^{-1} (17). We can therefore deduce that, while the hydroxo bridge exerts an additional antiferromagnetic contribution, the azido and the cyanato bridges exert a ferromagnetic stabilization strong enough to lower the magnitude of the antiferromagnetic interactions to the values that are observed. We can also mention that the three complexes, including **8** for which J is close to zero, exhibit a triplet state EPR spectrum.

With the same binucleating ligand, we obtained two other compounds, one with an end-on azido bridge, **10**, the other one with an end-on cyanato bridge **11**. In addition, both have an acetato bridge located in a plane perpendicular to the plane of the binucleating ligand. In **10** and **11**, the copper environments are dissymmetrical and

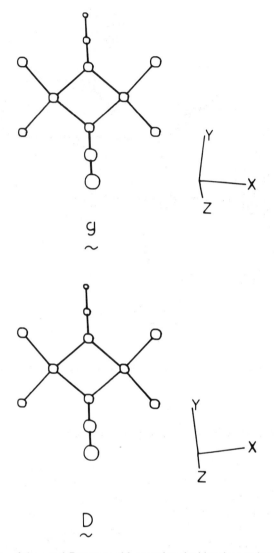

Figure 10. Orientations of the g and D tensors with regard to the binuclear cation for *4*.

highly distorted, between square based pyramids and trigonal bipyramids, the dissymmetry being more pronounced in *11*. The structure of *10* is shown in Fig. 14. A striking difference between the two compounds is the geometry of the bridging nitrogen atom. It is pyramidal for the azido compound and planar for the cyanato compound. The sum of the angles around this bridging nitrogen atom is 321.5° and 357° respectively. This difference is visualized in Fig. 15. The magnetic properties of *10* and *11* are compared in Fig. 16. The S-T energy gap were found equal to $-17.4\,\text{cm}^{-1}$ for *10* and $-6.3\,\text{cm}^{-1}$ for *11*, confirming that the end-on N_3^- and NCO^- bridges have a contribution to the measured interaction which oppose the contribution of the phenolato and acetato bridges.

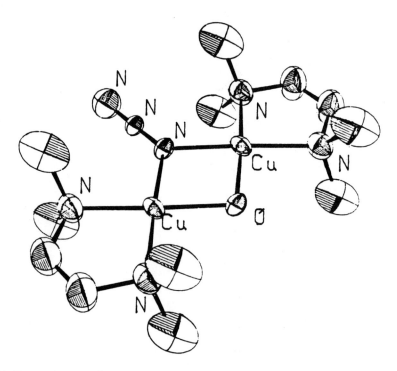

Figure 11. Perspective view of the binuclear cation $[Cu_2(tmen)_2(N_3)(OH)]^{2+}$ in **5**.

Interaction through the azido bridge: spin polarization effect

In the last decade, we developed a model to describe the exchange interaction, grounded on the concepts of magnetic orbitals and of overlap densities between pairs of magnetic orbitals (6,18). In this model, it is implicitly assumed that the magnetic orbitals are much higher in energy than the highest occupied molecular orbitals (h.o.m.o.'s) of the ligands. This so-called active electron approximation loses its validity when this above condition is not filled up any longer. More exactly, in the expression of the S-T energy gap, the h.o.m.o.'s of the ligands close in energy to the magnetic orbitals bring an additional contribution which can add to or oppose the contribution arising from the interaction between the magnetic orbitals. This is the case for azido bridged systems. The ab initio calculation of the electronic structure of N_3^- has shown that in the $^1\Sigma_g$ ground state, the non bonding h.o.m.o.'s $(\pi_g)^4$ are high in energy and very separated (6.7eV) from the level located immediately below (19). Thus, the π_g molecular orbital in the plane of the bridging network plays a dominant role in the interaction between the copper(II) ions through the azido bridge. The interaction between π_g and the d_{xy} metal orbitals gives rise to: (i) an antibonding m.o. φ_A^*, antisymmetric regarding the mirror plane perpendicular to the azido bridge in the end-to-end (EE) case and containing the azido bridge in the end-on (EO) case. This m.o. is destabilized by an energy Δ with

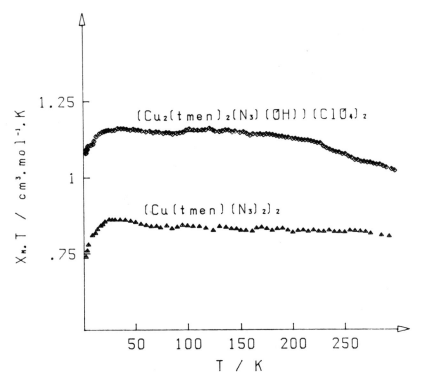

Figure 12. Temperature dependences of $\chi_M T$ for [Cutmen(N$_3$)$_2$]$_2$, **2** and [Cu$_2$(tmen)$_2$(N$_3$)(OH)](ClO$_4$)$_2$, **5**.

regard to the non bonding xy-type m.o. φ_S symmetric regarding the same mirror plane; (ii) a bonding m.o. φ_A, again antisymmetric regarding the mirror plane.

In the active electron approximation, the S-T energy gap has a negative (antiferromagnetic) contribution proportional to Δ^2 and a positive (ferromagnetic) contribution equal to 2j, j being the self repulsion of the overlap density between natural magnetic orbitals (6,18). In both the EE and the EO situations, Δ is expected to the large owing to the strong $\langle d_{xy}|\pi_g \rangle$ antibonding overlaps in φ_A^*. As far as j is concerned, its magnitude is expected to be larger in the EO case. Indeed, a strong extremum of the overlap density is then localized on the single nitrogen bridging atom, which authorizes an important value for the j integral (6). In contrast, in the EE case, as in the other cases with extended bridging ligands (20), each magnetic orbital is delocalized on all the bridging atoms, so that there is no region of strong overlap density. Let us summarize the situation at this level of approximation; the interaction is expected to be strongly antiferromagnetic through the EE bridge and more weakly antiferromagnetic through the EO bridge. Moreover, in this latter case, as in the planar μ-hydroxo and μ-halogeno copper(II) binuclear complexes, when the bridging angle increases, the $\langle d_{xy}|\pi_g \rangle$ overlaps increase, as well as Δ, so that the singlet state is more stabilized (21). It is clear that in this active electron

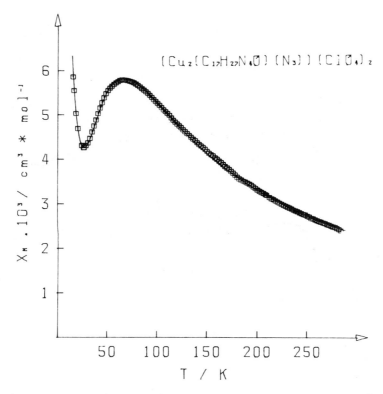

Figure 13. Experimental (□) and theoretical (——) temperature dependences of χ_M for [Cu$_2$(C$_{17}$H$_{27}$N$_4$O)(N$_3$)](ClO$_4$)$_2$, **7**.

approximation, we do not account for all the experimental data, in particular the ferromagnetic interaction found in the compounds **3**, **4** and **5**. We have to examine now the role of the bonding m.o. φ_A. In the π_g m.o. of N$_3^-$, at a given instant, an electron with the α spin is localized around one of the terminal nitrogen atoms and the other electron with the β spin is localized around the other terminal atom. When N$_3^-$ bridges in an EE fashion, the α electron is partially delocalized in φ_A towards a d$_{xy}$ metal orbital and the β electron is symmetrically delocalized towards the d$_{xy}$ orbital centered on the other metal ion. Therefore, in φ_A, we have an instantaneous density of α spin in a d$_{xy}$ orbital and of β spin in the other d$_{xy}$ orbital. To respect locally the Pauli principle, the unpaired electrons occupying the magnetic orbitals will have a probability of β spin larger than ½ around the former metal center and of α spin larger than ½ around the latter metal center, which favors the singlet state and increases the magnitude of the antiferromagnetic interaction. When N$_3^-$ bridges in an EO fashion, the electron on the bridging nitrogen atom, say with the α spin, is partially delocalized in φ_A towards the two d$_{xy}$ metal orbitals. This gives an instantaneous density of α spin on the two metal centers. Therefore each unpaired electron occupying its magnetic orbital will have a probability of β spin larger than ½, which favors the triplet state, hence increases the ferromagnetic contribution. This role of φ_A is defined as a spin polarization effect,

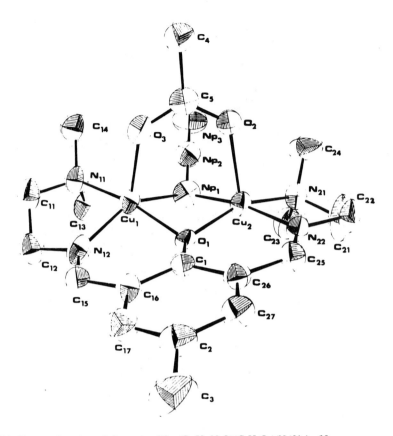

Figure 14. Perspective view of the cation $[Cu_2(C_{17}H_{27}N_4O)(C_2H_3O_2)(N_3)]^+$ in *10*.

which is apparently predominant for the EO complexes. The whole discussion on the mechanism of the interaction through the azido ligand is tentatively schematized in Figs. 17 and 18.

The last point remaining to be discussed is the absence or the very weak interaction through dissymmetrical end-to-end bridges. For that we define the referencial axes for each chromophore, where the apical position is occupied by the terminal atom of a semibridging azido group. Each magnetic orbital is of a d_{xy} type with a very small admixture of d_{z^2}. It follows that the two magnetic orbitals are essentially localized in parallel planes separated by more than 5 Å, which is particularly

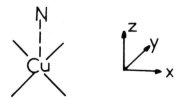

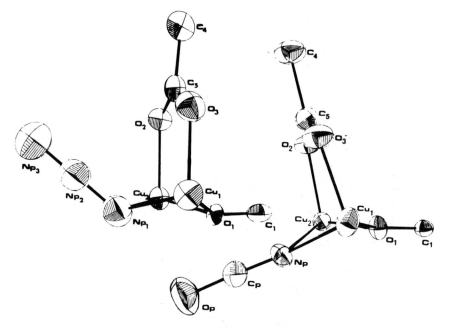

Figure 15. Perspective view of the three bridges arrangement between copper atoms for the compounds *10* and *11*.

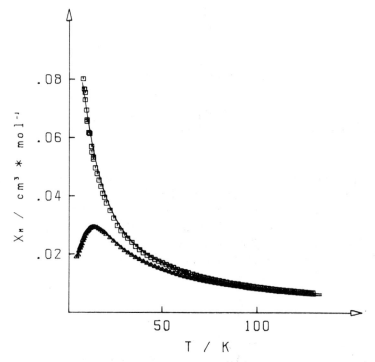

Figure 16. Experimental (△ for *10* and □ for *11*) and calculated (——) temperature dependences of χ_M for the compounds *10* and *11*.

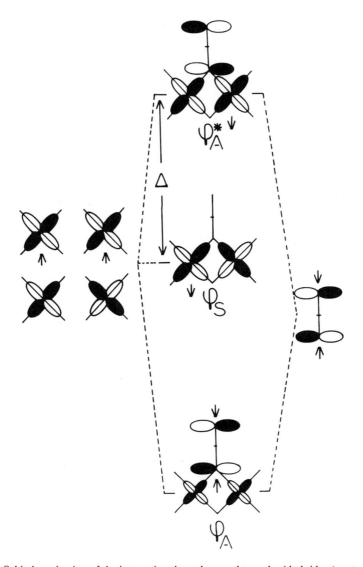

Figure 17. Orbital mechanism of the interaction through an end-to-end azido bridge (see text).

unfavorable for their interaction. Indeed, the overlap density between the magnetic orbitals is then negligible in any point of the space. When the chromophore acquires some trigonal bipyramidal character, the spin density along the z direction and on the apical site is enhanced and a weak antiferromagnetic interaction may be observed.

Conclusion

Two strongly related points emerge from this work. The first one is experimental and might be of great interest for the bioinorganic chemists. It deals with the

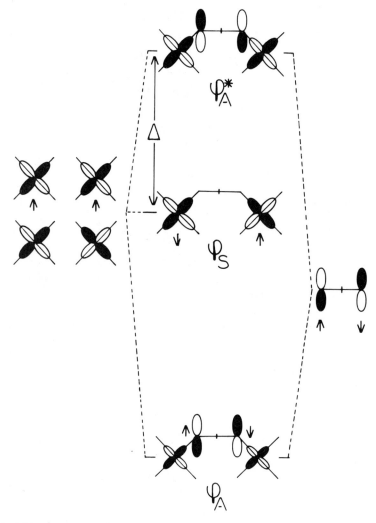

Figure 18. Orbital mechanism of the interaction through an end-on azido bridge (see text).

striking differences of the magnetic properties associated with the CuN_3Cu linkage. In case of symmetrical end-to-end bridge, the compound exhibits a very strong antiferromagnetic interaction. It can even appear diamagnetic and without detectable EPR spectrum. When there are two end-on azido bridges, the compound is ferromagnetically coupled with a triplet state EPR spectrum visible at very low temperature. When there are one end-on azido bridge and another bridge, the nature of the interaction depends on the eventual antiferromagnetic stabilization exerted by the other bridge, but in any case the compound exhibits a triplet state EPR spectrum. Finally, when N_3^- semi bridges two copper(II) ions in a dissymmetrical end-to-end fashion, the interaction ranges from zero with an EPR spectrum corresponding to a doublet local state, to a very weak stabilization of the singlet pair state and a triplet state EPR spectrum.

The second point emerging from this work is theoretical. It concerns the mechanism of the interaction, particularly in the case of strong stabilization of the triplet state due to N_3^- bridging in an end-on manner. This mechanism can be understood only when going beyond the active electron approximation. The key role is played by the h.o.m.o. π_g of N_3^- in the plane of the bridging network, which polarizes the spins of the magnetic (active) electrons. To specify the theoretical status of this spin polarization effect, we are performing ab initio calculations with extended bases and large Configuration Interaction on model systems like $|Be_2(N_3)|^+$.

Acknowledgements

We are most grateful to our colleagues who participated to this work, particularly I. Bkouche-Waksman, J. Gouteron, S. Jeannin, Y. Jeannin, Y. Journaux, I. Morgenstern-Badarau and S. Sikorav. We also thank C.J. O'Connor for very helpful discussions.

References and Footnotes

1. E.I. Solomon in *Metal Ions in Biology III,* Ed. T.G. Spiro, Wiley-Interscience, New York, p. 41 (1981).
2. (a) R.S. Himmelwright, N.C. Eickman, C.D. Lubien and E.I. Solomon, *J. Am. Chem. Soc., 102,* 5378 (1980); (b) R.S. Himmelwright, N.C. Eickman, C.D. Lubien, K. Lerch and E.I. Solomon, *J. Am. Chem. Soc., 102,* 7339 (1980); (c) M.E. Winkler, K. Lerch and E.I. Solomon, *J. Am. Chem. Soc., 103,* 7001 (1981).
3. (a) K.D. Karlin, J.C. Hayes, Y. Gultneh, R.W. Cruse, J.W. MacKown, J.P. Hutchinson and J. Zubieta, *J. Am. Chem. Soc., 106,* 2121 (1984); (b) K.D. Karlin, J.C. Hayes, J.P. Hutchinson and J. Zubieta, *J. Chem. Soc., Chem. Comm., 376* (1983).
4. V. McKee, J.V. Dadgegian, R. Bau and C.A. Reed, *J. Am. Chem. Soc., 103, 7001* (1981).
5. T.N. Sorrell, C.J. O'Connor, O.P. Anderson and J.H. Reibenspies, submitted for publication.
6. O. Kahn in *Magneto Structural Correlations in Exchange Coupled Systems,* Eds., R.D. Willett, D. Gatteschi and O. Kahn, D. Reidel Publishing Company, Dordrecht (1984).
7. T.R. Felthouse and D.N. Hendrickson, *Inorg. Chem., 17,* 444 (1978).
8. (a) Y. Agnus, R. Louis and R. Weiss, *J. Am. Chem. Soc., 101,* 3381 (1979); (b) Y. Agnus, R. Louis, J.P. Gisselbrecht and R. Weiss, *J. Am. Chem. Soc., 106,* 93 (1984).
9. I. Bkouche-Waksman, M.L. Boillot, O. Kahn and S. Sikorav, *Inorg. Chem. 23,* 4454 (1984).
10. I. Bkouche-Waksman, S. Sikorav and O. Kahn, *J. Crystallogr. Spectrosc. Res., 13,* 303 (1983).
11. J. Comarmond, P. Plumere, J.M. Lehn, Y. Agnus, R. Louis, R. Weiss, O. Kahn and I. Morgenstern-Badarau, *J. Am. Chem. Soc., 104,* 6330 (1982).
12. S. Sikorav, I. Bkouche-Waksman and O. Kahn, *Inorg. Chem., 23,* 490 (1984).
13. In a first investigation (12), a slight decrease of $\chi_M T$ was observed below 18 K. This decrease was in fact due to a shift (0.3 K) of the zero of the thermometer. R. Carlin has shown that the compound followed a Curie law down to 1.2 K.
14. M.L. Boillot, Y. Journaux, A. Bencini, D. Gatteschi and O. Kahn, *Inorg. Chem. 24,* 267 (1985).
15. O. Kahn, S. Sikorav, J. Gouteron, S. Jeannin and Y. Jeannin, *Inorg. Chem., 22,* 2877 (1983).
16. O. Kahn, J. Galy, Y. Journaux, J. Jaud and I. Morgenstern-Badarau, *J. Am. Chem. Soc., 104,* 2165 (1982).
17. T.J. Smith, E.N. Duester, R.R. Gagné and D.N. Hendrickson, *Inorg. Chem., 20,* 1229 (1981).
18. O. Kahn and M.F. Charlot, *Nouv. J. Chim., 4,* 567 (1980).
19. J.F. Wyatt, I.H. Hillier, V.R. Saunders, J.A. Connor and M. Barber, *J. Chem. Phys., 54,* 5311 (1971).
20. M. Julve, M. Verdaguer, A. Gleizes, M. Philloche-Levisalle and O. Kahn; *Inorg. Chem. 23,* 3808 (1984).
21. P.J. Hay, J.C. Thibeault and R. Hoffmann, *J. Am. Chem. Soc., 97,* 4884 (1975).

Biological & Inorganic Copper Chemistry,
ISBN 0-940030-11-X, Eds., K. D. Karlin & J. Zubieta, Adenine Press, ©Adenine Press, 1985

EPR of Copper Clusters in Molecular Metal Oxides

G. Kokoszka and F. Padula
Dept. of Chemistry
SUNY Plattsburgh, NY 12901, USA

A.R. Siedle
3M Central Research Laboratories
St. Paul, MN 55144, USA

Abstract

There has been a continuing interest in characterizing oligomeric metal ion clusters. The dimeric copper complexes studied by EPR have provided remarkable insight into the nature of the exchange coupling between the metal centers. Moreover, one and two dimensional polymeric systems and magnetically concentrated three-dimensional copper compounds have also been characterized and reviewed. Some EPR information on higher order clusters of copper(II) complexes has been available for over a decade. These copper oligomers lie midway between the (a) monomers and dimers and (b) the 1,2 or 3 dimensional polymers in terms of spacial or geometrical complexity but are far less understood from an EPR viewpoint. These are a major subject of this review. In particular, we focus on trinuclear copper(II) clusters. These trimers, whose study presents many of the experimental difficulties associated with tetramers and higher order clusters will be treated in detail because of recent advances in our knowledge of their spin exchange behavior by several groups. We also refer to selected EPR studies of monomers, dimers, other oligomers and polymers where insight into the copper(II) EPR aspects is useful.

Introduction

There has been a continuing interest in characterizing oligomeric metal ion clusters. The dimeric copper complexes studied by EPR have provided remarkable insight into the nature of the exchange coupling between the metal centers. Moreover, one and two dimensional polymeric systems and magnetically concentrated three-dimensional copper compounds have also been characterized and reviewed (1-14). EPR information on higher order clusters of copper(II) complexes has been available (15-26) but a detailed description of their full EPR behavior is still in a developing stage. In terms of spacial or geometrical complexity these copper oligomers lie midway between the (a) monomers and dimers and (b) the 1,2 or 3 dimensional polymers but are far less understood from an EPR viewpoint. They are a major subject of this review and in particular, we will focus on trinuclear clusters. These trimers, whose study presents many of the experimental difficulties associated with tetramers and higher order clusters, will be treated in detail because of recent advances of our knowledge of their spin exchange behavior. We will also refer to selected EPR studies of monomers, dimers, other oligomers and polymers where insight into the copper(II) EPR aspects is useful.

EPR studies have been hindered by a lack of well characterized trimers in which (a) the magnetic parameters of the individual species were available, (b) the full crystal structure information was known and (c) the intermolecular exchange was effectively suppressed. Of these three features the third is the most significant. A small intermolecular spin coupling can significantly alter the EPR spectra and remove or modify detailed spectral features. Experimentally, the suppression of the intra-molecular exchange pathways has proven to be successful in (a) solutions (27-29), (b) donor clusters in semiconductors (30-32), (c) organic triradicals (33-36), (d) highly doped paramagnetic metal ions in diamagnetic host lattices (37-40), (e) matrix isolated clusters (41-44) and (f) certain molecular metal oxide lattices (15). In the latter case, the other two conditions listed above also can be met and, as a result, these materials have provided the major impetus for our studies. The inter-pretation of our results are closely connected with the other studies and these will be reviewed as noted earlier. The molecular metal oxide clusters which are discussed in greater detail include a weakly coupled Cu(II) dimer (Figure 1), a triangular trimer (Figure 2) and a nearly planar tetramer (Figure 3) (45-48).

Figure 1. Dimeric metal ion complex based on Ref. 45.

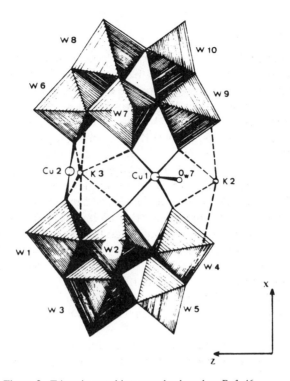

Figure 2. Trimeric metal ion complex based on Ref. 46.

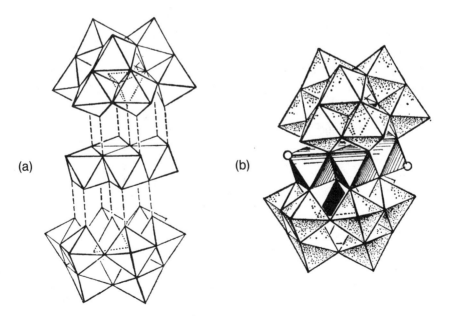

Figure 3. Tetrameric metal ion complex based on Ref. 48.

Dimers

The study of dimers has a history almost as long as that of isolated monomers (1). The cases of computer simulation of EPR spectra of systems with non-collinear tensors in single crystals and polycrystalline materials have been considered (49,50). Work on $S=\frac{1}{2}$ exchange coupled dimers with medium exchange ($J<30K$) and non-parallel axes (51) has been reviewed by two major contributors to our knowledge in this area (8). Weak exchange, about 0.1K, has been measured from the extra lines of Cu(II) in $K_2(Cu_{0.05}Zn_{0.95})SO_4 \cdot 6H_{20}$ (52). In single crystals of $Na_6Cu(P_2O_7)_2 \cdot 16H_2O$, EPR has been observed including the dipolar and hyperfine structure (53). In the polycrystalline spectra of 1:1 dioxane adducts of Cu(II) chelates with para-substituted benzoylpivaloymethanates (54), the same sort of weak coupling, were successfully simulated. In other copper containing monomers and dimers the utility of low frequency (S-band) spectra have been noted (55). The effects of intradimer effects on the EPR in Cu(II) dimers may be important and a recent study of $[M(en)_3]_2[Cu_2Cl_8]Cl_2 \cdot 2H_2O$ with M = Co, Rh, Ir, demonstrates how these may obscure the interdimer interactions (56). Fluoride-bridged Cu(II) dimers (24) with small J show $\Delta M=1$ and 2 lines (57) and weakly coupled dimers have recently been reported in the work of Wilcox, Long and Solomon (58).

In Figure 4 we show the EPR spectrum at X-band of a polycrystalline sample of the copper(II) analogue of ammonium dicobalto(II)-40-tungstotetraarsenate(III) (45):

$$(NH_4)_{23}(NH_4As_4W_{40}O_{140}Co_2(H_2O)_2) \cdot nH_2O \quad 18<n<20$$

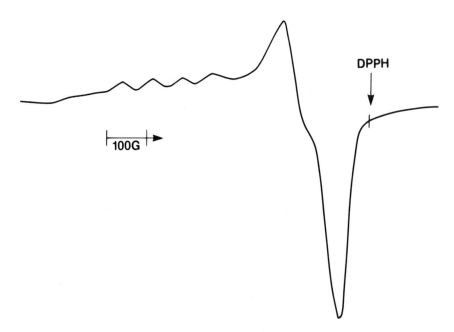

Figure 4. X-band EPR spectrum of dimer.

The low field components (parallel) are indicative of dipolar interactions but the overall placement of the absorptions in the field between about 2800 to 3300 gauss is indicative of a very small J. In fact, the separation between these two copper centers is about 10A as inferred from the X-ray structure of the Co(II) analogue and they are related by a center of symmetry. The magnetic z axis is inclined at an angle of 17.9 to the internuclear copper-copper vector and the effects of this lack of alignment are indicated qualitatively by the lack of an even spacing in the low field portion of the spectrum as well as the splitting in the high field portion. The magnetic exchange interaction, J, would have to propagate through at least four individual WO_6 octahedra, including both edge and corner sharing configurations (see Figure 1) and it is therefore quite reasonable that it should be less than or of the order of the dipolar EPR effects. The spectrum of the Co(II) dimer will be discussed elsewhere. This material is of interest here because it demonstrates the usefulness of these molecular metal oxides for isolating oligomers of copper and at the same time in this case, setting a rough upper bound for the distance over which identifiable electronic effects may be transmitted (59).

Trimers

Harris and Owen (37) studied the exchange coupling of the three $S=\frac{1}{2}$ Ir(IV) ions in various geometrical trimeric configurations in the K_2PtCl_4 and $(NH_4)_2PtCl_4$ lattices. Their investigations and the related studies of the relaxation effects provide the first experimental basis for our present knowledge of the EPR of trimeric metal ion systems (38-40). These studies include (a) a description of the relative energies of the two doublets and one quartet state which may be observed in six different configurations, (b) an analysis of the large pseudodipolar contributions to the zero field splitting and (c) the first discussion of the phonon modulation of exchange as a mechanism for explaining the interesting and sometimes puzzling EPR behavior of the quartet and doublet states vis-a-vis the monomer or dimeric species in related environments.

Shimizu (30) and Marho (31) investigated theoretical aspects of the EPR spectra associated with donor clusters in silicon with emphasis on the unique EPR features of trimers and these studies have been confirmed by the recent work of New and Castner (32). Relaxation effects, cluster-cluster interactions, a distribution of J values, and hyperfine patterns provide a variety of insights into the EPR behavior of trimers. These studies contain a range of ideas which extend well beyond semiconductor aplications.

The first observation of a zero field splitting in an organic radical with a quartet ground state was made just over a decade ago. The radical was made by dehalogenation of 1,3,5-tris-[(di-bi-phenyl-4-yl)chloromethyl)]-benzene with Ag powder in toluene. Brinkman and Kothe (33) were able to analyze the $\Delta M=1$ and 2 transition regions in great detail in this important paper. The observation and analysis of the relative intensities of the $\Delta M=1$, 2 and 3 transitions in an organic radical occurred soon thereafter (34). Moreover, Kothe and coworkers have extended these studies to slowly tumbling triradicals (35). Factors affecting the appearance of EPR spectra of organic triradicals, especially the distribution of hyperfine intensities, in fluid solutions were discussed by Hudson and Luckhurst (36).

The EPR spectra of $Na_6(VO)_3(P_2O_7)_3 \cdot 18H_2O$ in an acidic solution at pH 5 showed a twenty-two line hyperfine pattern associated with the first trimeric transition metal ion complex studied in solution (27). Hasagawa (28) also observed this vanadyl trimer and analyzed the hyperfine splitting employing methods earlier applied to nitroxide free radicals (36). The cyanurate- and trithiocyanurate bridged trimeric titanium(III) methylcyclo-pentadienyl complex was the first metal ion complex to exhibit $\Delta M=1$ as well as $\Delta M=2$ and 3 signals. The low field spectral features in these trimers are reminiscent of that observed in organic triradicals due to the small g-value anisotropy of the titanium ion. These features were observed in frozen toluene/benzene glass at 77K (29) thereby ensuring magnetic dilution.

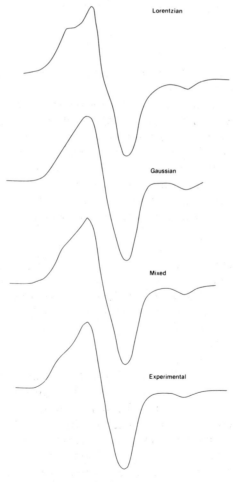

Figure 5. Set of computer simulated (upper three) and experimental X-band trimeric spectra (see text).

The magnetically isolated trimer copper(II) cluster in a molecular metal oxide which we have studied in detail by EPR spectroscopy is shown in Figure 2. The empirical formula of the diaquatricuprooctadecatungsto-diarsenate(III) anion is:

$$W_{18}As_2O_{66}Cu_3(H_2O)_2{}^{12-}$$

There are two coppers of type Cu(1) related by symmetry and one labeled Cu(2) which form the nearly equilateral triangle with an average Cu-Cu distance of 4.68A. The copper(II) cations have their molecular z and y axes in the trimeric plane while the x axes are along a crystallographic axis labeled x in Figure 2. Thus, to a first approximation, the effective trimeric g values in the quartet state should be the exchange coupled average of the isolated cation's g value.

$$g_\perp = \frac{g_z + g_y}{2}$$

$$g_\parallel = g_x$$

where the parallel designation is along the axis normal to the plane. Moreover, although the three copper(II) ions are not exactly equivalent, the four oxygens coordinated to each of them in their individual xy planes allow them to be treated as nearly equivalent. We will make this assumption here. Then, the molecular g values are found to be $g_z = 2.411$ and $g_x = g_y = 2.075$ from the quartet state trimeric g values: 2.075 and 2.243 (15). The J value, as determined by magnetic susceptibility measurements is about $-2K$ and is small enough so that the effects of neither the anisotropic nor the antisymmetrical exchange should be small compared to the dipolar splitting (1,8-10,13). In Figure 5 a set of spectra corresponding to the $\Delta M=1$ transition region at 9GHz is shown. The lower curve is the experimental curve and the one immediately above it is the best fit with the g values as listed above and a D value of about 190 gauss. The Hamiltonian is:

$$H=\beta \overline{S}:g:\overline{H} + D(S_z{}^2-(S)(S+1)/3) + E(S_x{}^2-S_y{}^2)$$

The highest field spectral feature in Figure 5 is one of the three parallel components but the curves are quite convoluted at X-band. At V-band (55GHz) the parallel and perpendicular regions are quite well separated and the higher field parallel region shows three features with a separation of about twice that of the three more intense low field perpendicular peaks. In Figure 6 the experimental V-band curve is compared with the computer simulated curve obtained using the magnetic parameters derived from X-band results. The agreement between the two curves is quite good. At 35GHz, the separation into a clear parallel and perpendicular region was just achieved.

From the $\Delta M=2$ and 3 regions, a great deal of information can be obtained. The anisotropic appearance of the $\Delta M=2$ curve is largely associated with the g value anisotropy and the parallel component is at higher field. This result is in marked

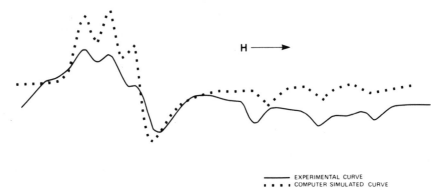

Figure 6. V-band experimental (solid line) and computer simulated (dotted line) spectra.

contrast with the more symmetrical shapes obtained in organic free radicals (33) or in transition metal ion trimers with smaller g anisotropy (29). In Figure 7 we show a computer simulation of this curve for 35GHz. This frequency was chosen because the X-band data are already in the literature (15) and because the anisotropy is more pronounced. Of course, the actual intensity is much lower at these frequencies and may not be experimentally detected. The details of the intensity distribution follows from the mathematical form of the dipolar Hamiltonian (33) but the g anisotropy of the copper(II) ion plays a central role in determining the appearance of this spectral feature. A pattern in the $\Delta M=2$ region with the smaller peak downfield from the larger peak has been obtained by Reedijk and coworkers and a detailed analysis is in progress (24). It would appear that such a result would be more indicative of a linear arrangement. Indeed it should be possible to deduce the approximate molecular geometry based on the shape of the $\Delta M=2$ region. Moreover, in favorable cases, this spectral region may well produce more reliable magnetic parameters and greater insight into stereochemical subtleties from the more intense (but convoluted) $\Delta M=1$ region.

The $\Delta M=3$ line shows a slight anisotropy but this is difficult, though not impossible, to detect at 9GHz. The main reason for showing this simulation at 35GHz is to point out the slight anisotropy in the $\Delta M=3$ line which has a sin(theta) to the fourth power intensity dependence (Figure 8). This was first noted experimentally in a study of the two dimensional material $K_2Mn_xM_{(1-x)}F_4$ when M = Mg, Zn or Cd (60,7) and has a firm theoretical foundation in the form of the dipolar Hamiltonian (1). The position of this line is a value in determining the perpendicular components of the g tensor.

In addition to the quartet there are two doublet states expected in a copper trimer. For the case of an equilateral triangle these should be degenerate. Thus an interesting question arises as to the location of the doublet spectra in the EPR spectrum of this copper(II) trimer. Relaxation effects and unusual g value relationships may play a role in determining the position and intensity of these transitions (2,16,40). In the

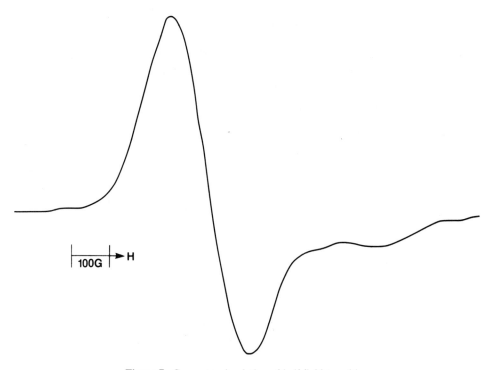

Figure 7. Computer simulation of half-field transition.

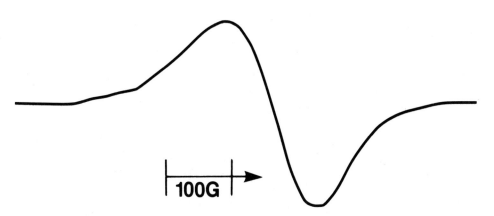

Figure 8. Computer simulation of one-third field transition.

triangular Cu(II) trimer we have noted a broad line in the EPR spectrum below 120K. This line narrows somewhat with decreasing temperature to 77K but its g value is difficult to determine with accuracy due to the long tail on the low field side. It is significantly more intense than the $\Delta M=3$ at 77K (see Figure 9). Moreover, the line is present in the same relative intensity to the $S=3/2$ spectral features in several samples so it seems to be characteristic of the trimer, not some impurity.

The $\Delta M=2$ and 3 line decrease with increasing field (frequency) as second and fourth power of (D/H). We have found this additional line at 55GHz and at 77K where the forbidden transitions cannot be observed. The g value is about 9.7 in reasonable agreement with the value estimated from the X-band data. For the present we associate this line with the doublet states but we offer no detailed interpretation of neither the g factor nor the structure which appears at the higher frequency.

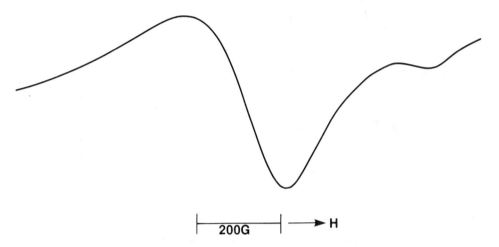

Figure 9. X-band spectrum of extra absorption found in trimer and 1/3 field line.

Tetramers

Interest in the magnetic properties of tetranuclear copper(II) complexes has a long history with emphasis on magnetic susceptibility studies (16-20,61-65) and much of the activity has centered around molecules with a Cu_4O_4 core. A variety of interactions including antisymmetrical exchange, intratetramer interactions, non-equivalent coupling and dynamical modulation of the intramolecular exchange interactions have all been used with some degree of success to account for the observed experimental results. By comparison, there has been a paucity of EPR results on tetrameric complexes. The first observation of an EPR due to a four-ion copper(II) aggregate seems to be the work of Stankowski (66) which was followed by increasingly improved theoretical treatments of the interpretation of the S=2 EPR powder pattern (21-23). The period of recent inactivity has been broken by the observation of Black and co-workers (16) of the variable temperature EPR at liquid helium temperatures of the S=2 manifold in $Cu_4OCl_6(Ph_3PO)_4$. In a very careful and important study, these workers not only characterized the placement of the S=2 state as being about 20K above the ground state but noted explicitly the absence of the spectral features from the S=1 manifolds. A variety of explanations can be used to account for this observation. It does seem worth noting, however, that the highest spin state in trimers as well as tetramers is easiest to observe by EPR of copper compounds.

The tetramer we have studied is one which has lower symmetry than the Cu_4O_4 type and is shown in Figure 3. This is the copper analogue of 18-tungstatetra-cobalto(II)diphosphate:

$$P_2Co_4(H_2O)_2W_{18}O_{68}{}^{10-}$$

These have an intramolecular exchange interaction which should be very nearly zero. In fact the molecular metal oxide caps are larger in the tetramer (47,48) than in the trimer (46) and in the latter case there were no experimentally observed intermolecular effects. Moreover, the magnetic susceptibility data (67) suggest that there is an intermolecular coupling of about 1K, but the data over the 2K to 250K range are not fully understood. We have observed an X-band EPR which can be fit with an S=2 Hamiltonian. The spectrum is shown in Figure 10. The high field feature above DPPH is the only well resolved parallel feature and the zero field splitting is roughly that expected for dipolar interactions. As in the case of the Cu(II) trimer in the molecular metal oxide, the anisotropic or antisymmetric exchange terms are not expected to play a major role. There is little change in the X-band spectral appearance down to 2K, again suggesting that the highest spin value is most easily observed. At 35GHz, a greater resolution of the parallel and perpendicular regions has been achieved confirming that the S=2 state is the state observed by EPR.

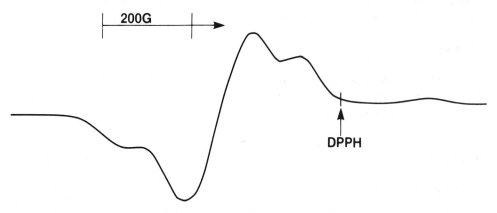

Figure 10. X-band spectrum of tetramer.

Low Dimensional Systems

No discussion of copper EPR can be complete without a brief review of the progress in our understanding of low dimensional systems. Drumheller's recent review (6) with some emphasis on 1d and 2d compounds which exhibit long range order, provides an excellent summary of work through 1982 with a balanced overview of copper compounds. This work also includes brief sections on very current topics such as Random Exchange Heisenberg Antiferromagnetic Chains and linewidth changes as the critical temperature is approached from above. One of the more important studies of 2d systems is that of K_2CuF_4 by Yamada and coworkers (7). They summarize earlier results on this ferromagnet and emphasize the EPR behavior in the temperature region near the critical temperature. The paper includes a discussion of the lineshape and the intensity in the $\Delta M=2$ (half-field) region and the appearance of a $\Delta M=3$ (one-third field) absorption. However, the angular dependence of the line at one-third field does not follow the dependency as expected both from the earlier theoretical and experimental results (60). A systematic study of eclipsed layered copper compounds provides a vehicle for a discussion of the diffusive and non-diffusive spin interactions (68). The antisymmetrical term is explicitly treated in this paper. Earlier work on the broadening effects and temperature dependencies produced by a phononmodulation of the antisymmetric exchange term are also reviewed. In this connection, a correlation between linewidth and the high temperature effective Curie-Weiss constant in the EPR of polycrystalline copper compounds found by Hyde and his collaborators (69) follows the theory of Soos and coworkers (70).

Among the one dimensional copper compounds, two interesting examples: The metamagnetic behavior of $(C_6H_{11}NH_3)CuCl_3$ (71) and the alternately bridged and alternately spaced linear chain compound (12) are especially noteworthy. Finally, an important NMR study on the temperature variation of the exchange interaction in $K_2CuCl_4 \cdot 2H_2O$ has been found to complement earlier EPR results (73). This material has been found to exhibit a g-shift and a 10/3 effect which is experimentally detectable in poly-crystalline substances (74).

Acknowledgements

Acknowledgement is made to the donors of the Petroleum Research Fund, administered by the American Chemical Society for partial support of this work (GK) and to the 3M Corporation, General Offices, St. Paul, MN for partial support (FP, GK).

References and Footnotes

1. A. Abragam, and B. Bleaney, *Electron Paramagnetic Resonance of Transition Ions.* Clarendon Press (1970).
2. *Magneto Structural Correlations in Exchange Coupled Systems,* Ed. R.D. Willett, O. Kahn, D. Gatteschi, D. Reidel, NATO-ASI (1984).
3. W.E. Hatfield, *Inorg. Chem. 22,* 833 (1983).
4. R. Gaura, R. Adams, D. D'Avignon, G. Kokoszka, P. Szydlik, *J. Mag. Res. 25,* 299 (1977).
5. R.L. Carlin and A.J. van Duyneveldt, *Magnetic Properties of Transition Metal Compounds,* Springer Verlag, NY (1978).
6. J.E. Drumheller, *Mag. Res. Rev. 7,* 123 (1982).
7. I. Yamada, I. Morishita and T. Tokuyama, *Physica, 115B,* 179.
8. T.D. Smith and T.R. Pilbrow, *Coor. Chem. Rev. 13,* 173 (1974).
9. G.F. Kokoszka and G. Gordon in *Transition Metal Chemistry, 5,* 181, Ed. R.L. Carlin, Dekker, NY (1969).
10. D. Gatteschi, *J. Mol. Cat. 23,* 145 (1984).
11. R.P. Scaringe, J.D. Hodgson and W.E. Hatfield, *Mol. Phys. 35,* 701 (1978).
12. M.M. Olmstead, W.K. Musker, L.W. Ter Haar and W.E. Hatfield, *J. Am. Chem. Soc. 104,* 6627 (1982).

13. G.F. Kokoszka and R.W. Duerst, *Coor. Chem. Rev. 5,* 209 (1970).
14. Low Dimensional Phenomena, Ed. H.J. Keller, *Plenum Press* (1975).
15. A.R. Siedle, F. Padula, J. Baranowski, C. Goldstein, M. DeAngelo, G. Kokoszka, L. Azevedo and L. Venturini, *J. Am. Chem. Soc. 105,* 7447 (1983).
16. T.D. Black, R.S. Rubins, O.K. De, R.C. Dickinson and W.A. Baker, Jr., *J. Chem. Phys. 80,* 4620 (1984).
17. J. A. Barnes, G.W. Inman and W.E. Hatfield, *Inorg. Chem. 10,* 1725 (1971).
18. M.E. Lines, A.P. Ginsberg, R.L. Martin and R.C. Sherwood, *J. Chem. Phys. 57,* 1 (1972).
19. D.H. Jones, J.R. Sams and R.C. Thompson, *J. Chem. Phys. 79,* 3877 (1983).
20. W. Haase, *J. Mol. Cat. 23,* 334 (1984).
21. R.D. Dowsing, *J. Mag. Res. 2,* 332 (1970).
22. M. Mackowiak, and M. Kurzynski, *Phys. Stat. Sol. 51(b),* 841 (1972).
23. J. Baranowski, T. Cukierda, B. Jezowska-Trzebiatowska and H. Kozlowski, *J. Mag. Res 33,* 585 (1979).
24. R.J. Reitmeijer, R.A.G. de Graaff, A.J. den Hartog and J. Reedijk, private communication and presented at NATO-ASI, Tuscany, Italy (1983).
25. L. Banci, A. Bencini, A. Dei and D. Gatteschi, *Inorg. Chem, 22,* 4018 (1983).
26. J. Hulliger, private communication.
27. C.C. Parker, R.R. Reeder, L.B. Richards, and P.H. Reiger, *J. Am. Chem. Soc. 92,* 5230 (1970).
28. A. Hasegawa, *J. Chem. Phys. 55,* 3101 (1971).
29. L.C. Francesconi, D.R. Corbin, D.N. Hendrickson and G.D. Stucky, *Inorg. Chem. 18,* 3074 (1979).
30. T. Shimizu, *J. Phys. Soc. Japan, 25,* 1021 (1968).
31. J.R. Marko, *Phys. Lett. 27A,* 119 (1968).
32. D.New and T.G. Castner, *Phys. Rev. 29,* 2077 (1984).
33. J. Brinkmann and G. Kothe, *J. Chem. Phys. 59,* 2807 (1973).
34. S.I. Weissman and G. Kothe, *J. Am. Chem. Soc. 97,* 2537 (1975).
35. G. Kothe, K.H. Wassmer, A. Naujok, E. Ohmes, J. Rieser and K. Wallenfels, *J. Mag. Res. 36,* 425 (1979).
36. A. Hudson and G. Luckhurst, *Mol. Phys. 13,* 409 (1967).
37. E.A. Harris and J. Owen, *Proc. Roy. Soc. 289,* 122 (1965).
38. E.A. Harris, M.E. Lines and J. Owen, *Electron Paramagnetic Resonance* Ed. W. Low, Vol. 2, 552 (1970).
39. E.A. Harris and K.S. Yngvesson, *Phys. Lett. 21A,* 252 (1966).
40. R.G. Gengbland and K.S. Yngvesson, *Phys. Lett. 25A,* 437 (1967).
41. G.A. Thompson and D.M. Lindsay, *J. Chem. Phys. 74,* 959 (1981).
42. D.M. Lindsay and G.A. Thompson, *J. Chem. Phys. 77,* 1114 (1982).
43. R.J. Van Zee, C.M. Brown, K.J. Zerinque and W. Weltner, *Acc. Chem. Res. 13,* 237 (1980).
44. W. Weltner, *Magnetic Atom and Molecules,* Van Nostrand-Reinhold (1983).
45. F. Robert, M. Leyrie, G. Herve, A. Teze and Y. Jeannin, *Inorg. Chem. 19,* 1746 (1980).
46. R. Robert, M. Leyrie, and G. Herve, *Acta Crystallogr, B38,* 358 (1982).
47. R.G. Finke and M.W. Droege, *Inorg. Chem. 22,* 1006 (1983).
48. T.J.R. Weakley, H.T. Evans, Jr., J.S. Showell, G.F. Tourne and C.M.J. Tourne, *J. Chem. Soc. Chem. Commun.* 139 (1973).
49. R.M. Golding and W.C. Tennant, *Mol. Phys. 25,* 1163 (1973).
50. M. Iwasaki, *J. Mag. Res. 16,* 417 (1974).
51. S.G. Carr, T.D. Smith and T.R. Pilbrow, *J. Chem. Soc.* Fara II, 497 (1974).
52. D.I. Meredith and J.C. Gill, *Phys. Lett. 25A,* 429 (1967).
53. H. So, G.J. Haight, Jr. and R.L. Belford, Private Communication.
54. E. Kwiatkowski, Z. Peplinski and J. Baranowski, *J. Trans. Met. Chem. 5,* 337 (1980).
55. C.E. Brown, W.E. Antholine and W. Froncisz, *J. Chem. Soc. Dalton,* 590 (1980).
56. S.K. Hoffmann and W.E. Hatfield, *J. Mag. Res. 53,* 341 (1983).
57. F.J. Rietmeyer, R.A. deGraff and J. Reedijk, *Inorg. Chem. 23,* 151 (1984).
58. D.E. Wilcox, J.R. Long and E.I. Solomon, *J. Am. Chem. Soc. 106,* 2186 (1984).
59. D.N. Hendrickson in Ref. (2).
60. I. Yokozawa and M. Tanimoto, *J. Phys. Soc. Japan, 44,* 1741 (1978).
61. W.E. Hatfield and G.W. Inmann, *Inorg. Chem. 8,* 1376 (1969).
62. H. Wong, H. tom Dieck, C.J. O'Connor and E. Sinn, *J. Chem. Soc. Dalton* Trans. 875 (1980).
63. D.H. Jones, J.R. Sams and R.C. Thompson, *Inorg. Chem. 22,* 1399 (1983).

64. W.J. Jones, S. Gupta, L.J. Theriot, F.T. Helm and W.A. Baker, *Inorg. Chem. 16,* 1572 (1977).
65. L. Walz, H. Paulus, W. Haase, H. Longhof and F. Nepveu, *J. Chem. Soc. Dalton,* 657 (1983).
66. J. Stankowski, *Phys. Stat. Sol. 24,* 451 (1967).
67. L. Azevedo and E. Venturini, private communication (1984).
68. T. Kite, J. Drumheller and K. Emerson, *J. Mag. Res. 48,* 20 (1982).
69. M. Lynch, K.E. Hyde, P.L. Bocko and G. Kokoszka, *Inorg. Chem. 16,* 562 (1977).
70. Z.G. Soos, K.T. McGregor, T. Chung and A.J. Silversteon, *Phys. Rev. 16B,* 3036 (1977).
71. R.D. Willett, C.P. Landee, R.M. Gaura, D.D. Swank, A. Groenendijk and A.J. van Duyeveldt, *J. Mag. Mat. 15-18,* 1055 (1980).
72. M.M. Olmstead, W.K. Musker, L.W. Ter Haar, and W.E. Hatfield, *J. Am. Chem. Soc. 104,* 6627 (1982).
73. S.H. Choh, T.J. Han, N.D. Moon, K.H. Lee, *Phys. Lett. 99A,* 193 (1983).
74. L. Mauriello, R. Scaringe and G. Kokoszka, *J. Inorg. Nucl. Chem. 36,* 1565 (1974).

Biological & Inorganic Copper Chemistry,
ISBN 0-940030-11-X, Eds., K. D. Karlin & J. Zubieta, Adenine Press, ©Adenine Press, 1985

Electron Transfer in Binuclear
Mixed-Valence Copper(II)-Copper(I) Complexes

David N. Hendrickson*, Russell C. Long,
Yeong Tsyr Hwang, and Hsiu-Rong Chang
School of Chemical Sciences
University of Illinois
Urbana, Illinois 61801

Abstract

Twelve mixed-valence binuclear copper(II)-copper(I) complexes of macrocyclic ligands have been prepared to study systematically the factors affecting intramolecular electron transfer. Six of the complexes have both copper sites equivalent, whereas, the other six complexes are constructed such that the two copper coordination sites are not equivalent. Except in the case of two complexes, all of the binuclear copper(II) complexes employed to prepare the mixed valence complexes exhibit two quasi-reversible one-electron reduction waves, i.e., $Cu_2^{II} \rightleftharpoons Cu^{II}Cu^I \rightleftharpoons Cu_2^I$. Variable-temperature EPR data, taken for acetone solutions of the mixed-valence complexes from room to liquid-nitrogen temperature, are presented. The factors that control intramolecular electron transfer are discussed. Magnetic susceptibility data from 6.0 to 375 K are presented for several of the Cu_2^{II} complexes.

Introduction

The study of electron transfer in mixed-valence transition metal complexes can give insight about electron transfer in oxidation-reduction, electrochemical and biological processes (1,2). Until recently, only two mixed-valence binuclear $Cu^{II}Cu^I$ complexes have been reported (3,4). The importance of work on $Cu^{II}Cu^I$ complexes comes, in part, from the fact that Solomon and coworkers (5) found the mixed-valence $Cu^{II}Cu^I$ form of certain copper proteins to be the most informative form of the binuclear site. Interesting EPR signals and intervalence transfer electronic transitions have been seen for these $Cu^{II}Cu^I$ protein sites.

Very recently we reported the preparation and physical properties of seven new $Cu^{II}Cu^I$ Complexes (6). The basic structural unit of these seven complexes is illustrated in Figure 1, where it can be seen that BF_4^- is the counterion and two diamines, NH_2-R_1-NH_2 and NH_2-R_2-NH_2, are incorporated into the ligand. For these seven complexes (complexes I-VII), the R_1 and R_2 moieties are as follows:

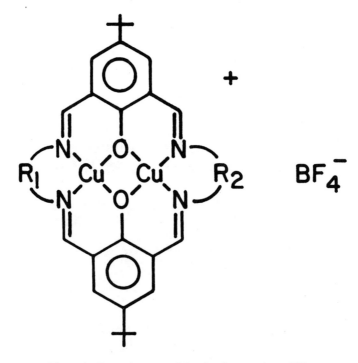

Figure 1. General structural drawing for complexes I-XI.

I	$R_1 = R_2$ = propylene
II	$R_1 = R_2$ = 2,2'-dimethylpropylene
III	$R_1 = R_2$ = butylene
IV	$R_1 = R_2$ = 2,2'-biphenylene
V	R_1 = propylene; R_2 = 2,2'-dimethylpropylene
VI	R_1 = propylene; R_2 = 2,2'-biphenylene
VII	R_1 = propylene; R_2 = butylene

Five new variations of this type of $Cu^{II}Cu^{I}$ complex have been prepared where the following diamine linkages are found in four of the complexes:

VIII	$R_1 = R_2$ = 2-hydroxypropylene
IX	$R_1 = R_2$ = 1,3-cyclohexylene
X	R_1 = propylene; R_2 = 1,8-naphthalene
XI	R_1 = propylene; R_2 = 2-hydroxypropylene

Mixed-valence complex XII, which is pictured in Figure 2, was obtained by chemically reducing the four C=N bonds in complex III. In this paper the physical data for all twelve $Cu^{II}Cu^{I}$ complexes will be summarized. Particular attention will be payed to describing the status of our knowledge of the electron transfer process in these complexes. It will be seen that many fundamental questions remain to be answered.

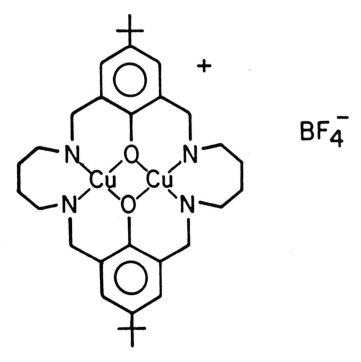

Figure 2. Complex XII.

Materials and Methods

Compounds Preparation. Samples of $Cu^{II}Cu^{I}$ complexes VIII-XI, as BF_4^- salts, were prepared as described previously (6) for complexes I-VII. These complexes were prepared by chemical reduction of the analogous Cu_2^{II} complex with sodium dithionite. The mixed-valence complex XII (see Figure 2) was prepared by first reducing the four C=N bonds in the Cu_2^{II} analog of complex III in the following manner. An eight-fold excess of $NaBH_4$ was added to a solution containing 1.2 g of Cu_2^{II} analog of complex III dissolved in 100 ml of dry THF. The stirred solution was lightly heated under argon for 7h. Copper metal and other insoluble residues were filtered out of solution employing Schlenkware techniques. 1.2 g of $Cu(BF_4)_2 \cdot 6H_2O$ and 1 g of triethylamine were then added to the filtrate. This solution was concentrated in air until a crude precipitate formed. The precipitate was recrystallized from H_2O to give an analytically pure Cu_2^{II} complex which was then reduced by sodium dithionite to the $Cu^{II}Cu^{I}$ complex XII. Good analytical results were obtained for complexes I-XII (7).

Physical Measurements. Eletrochemical, and EPR, electronic absorption and IR spectroscopic experiments were carried out as described previously (6). Variable-temperature magnetic susceptibility data were obtained with a S.H.E. model 300 Squid Susceptometer.

Results and Discussion

Electrochemistry. Cyclic voltammetry and differential pulse polarographic measurements (DMF solvent) have been carried out for all twelve Cu_2^{II} analogs of complexes I-XII. The results are given in Table I. Each of the twelve Cu_2^{II} complexes exhibit two one-electron reduction waves and, except for two complexes (X and XII), the waves can be judged to be reversible when compared to the oxidation wave for ferrocene. Previous publications (6,7) should be consulted to see illustrations of typical data. In the case of complex X the more negative wave which corresponds to the process $Cu^{II}Cu^I \Rightarrow Cu_2^I$ is not very reversible on a Pt electrode. The E_{ox}-E_{red} separation for this wave in the cyclic voltammogram is 0.150 V. As can be seen in Figure 3, the two one-electron waves for the Cu_2^{II} complex XII are quite

Table I

Comparison of Parameters for Series of Complexes

Complex	K_{con}	$E_{1/2}^{1a}$ Volts	$E_{1/2}^{2a}$ Volts	$A_{iso}^{b,d}$ $\times 10^{-4}$ cm^{-1}	$A_{\parallel}^{b,d}$ cm^{-1}	$\nu IT^{(\epsilon)b,c}$ kK(cm^{-1}M^{-1})	$T_{\circ K}^{f}$
I	4.3×10^6	-0.534	-0.927	41	193	10.5(401)	~200
II	3.7×10^6	-0.556	-0.945	41	194	10.5(355)	~230
III	1.2×10^8	-0.334	-0.810	37	184	13.5(303)	~250
IV	9.0×10^6	-0.236	-0.646	64	174	10.7(378)	>390
V	5.2×10^6	-0.542	-0.939	41	194	10.5(363)	~230
VI	4.0×10^7	-0.378	-0.838	78	187	12.1(176)	>390
VII	7.1×10^8	-0.404	-0.926	82	191	12.6(218)	>390
VIII	1.2×10^7	-0.546	-0.946	41	193	10.9(218)	~225
IX	4.1×10^7	-0.471	-0.827	77	191		>390
X	3.1×10^5	-0.501	-0.827	80	187		>390
XI	5.0×10^6	-0.559	-0.955	41	193	10.4(401)	~215
XII	1.1×10^7	-0.748	-1.160	84	177	e	>390

(a) Average of potentials obtained from cyclic voltammetry and differential pulse polarography measurements carried out on Cu_2^{II} complexes in DMF.
(b) Obtained from mixed-valence complex.
(c) Acetone solvent.
(d) Acetone/toluene solvent mixture.
(e) No apparent IT band.
(f) Temperature at which the seven-line EPR spectrum converts to four-line spectrum for acetone solution of mixed-valence complex.

irreversible. To some degree this was expected for a complex of such a saturated amine ligand. The two redox potentials (-0.75 and -1.16V vs. normal hydrogen electrode) for this complex are considerably more negative than those for the other eleven complexes. Examination of the data in Table I leads to the following additional observations:

   1. A comparison of the reduction potentials for complexes I, II, V, VIII, and XI shows that the addition of either CH_3^- or HO^- substituents on the central

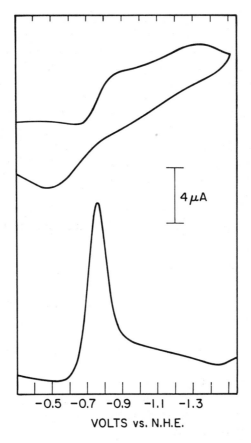

Figure 3. The cyclic voltammogram and differential-pulse polarogram of complex XII in DMF run at 10 mV/s and 2 mV/s scan rates, respectively.

carbon atom of the propylene linkage does not have much of an effect on the reduction potentials. The HO⁻ substituent does make the potentials somewhat more negative.

2. The ease of reduction of the Cu_2^{II} complexes decreases in the order IV > III > IX > I. This is largely a manifestation of the steric constraints provided by the different linkages in the complexes. The Cu_2^{II} precursor of complex IV is the easiest to reduce because the copper coordination geometry in this complex is known from monomeric analogs (6) to be intermediate between square planar and tetrahedral, that is, intermediate between the coordination geometry preferences of Cu^{II} and Cu^{I}.

3. Complexes VI, VII, and X each have two quite different coordination sites. Unfortunately, it was not possible to prepare the complex with $R_1 = R_2 = $ 1,8-naphthalene. In the cases of complexes VI and VII, it is interesting that the reduction potentials are generally intermediate between those for the

corresponding symmetric complexes. For example, the first wave for Cu_2^{II} complex VII falls at -0.404 V, whereas the first waves for Cu_2^{II} complexes I and II are at -0.534 and -0.334 V, respectively. This could be the result of steric interactions between the two different linkages in Cu_2^{II} complex VII. The propylene and butylene linkages indirectly affect the conformation of each other. On the other hand, the potentials for complexes VI and VII could reflect the fact that the electronic manifolds of the two Cu^{II} ions in these Cu_2^{II} complexes are strongly coupled. Molecular orbitals encompassing both halves of the binuclear Cu_2^{II} complex are present. Thus, the electron added to the Cu_2^{II} complex VII goes into a molecular orbital that consists of appreciable contributions from atomic orbitals centered on both Cu^{II} ions.

In Table I are listed the conproportionation constants for the twelve complexes. Conproportionation constants are calculated for the equilibrium

$$Cu^{II}Cu^{II}L^{2+} + Cu^ICu^IL \overset{K_{con}}{\rightleftharpoons} 2Cu^{II}Cu^IL^+$$

where L is the macrocyclic ligand and the equilibrium constant is calculated from the following equation:

$$E_{\frac{1}{2}}^1 - E_{\frac{1}{2}}^2 = 0.0591 \log(K_{con})$$

In this series of complexes K_{con} varies from 3.1×10^5 to 7.1×10^8. From previous studies (3,8) it can be said that the magnitudes of the K_{con} values seen for these complexes indicate moderately strong electronic coupling between Cu^{II} and Cu^I ions in the mixed-valence complexes.

Magnetic Exchange Interactions for Cu_2^{II} Complexes. The electrochemistry results indicated that there are appreciable interactions between the two metal ions in both the Cu_2^{II} complexes (reduction potentials) and the $Cu^{II}Cu^I$ complexes (K_{con} values). A determination of the temperature dependence of the magnetic susceptibility for a Cu_2^{II} complex can give a quantitative analysis of the interaction between the two Cu^{II} ions. The so-called magnetic exchange interaction in a binuclear complex is an electrostatic interaction between two unpaired electron manifolds, one centered at each of the two metal ions. This interaction can be characterized by the spin Hamiltonian $\hat{H} = -2J\hat{S}_1 \cdot \hat{S}_2$, where S_1 and S_2 are the spin operators on the two metal centers and J is the exchange interaction parameter that characterizes the magnitude of the interaction. Variable-temperature (6.0-375K) magnetic susceptibility data are collected for the Cu_2^{II} complexes I, III, IV and VII (BF_4^- salts). Plots of effective magnetic moment per copper ion (μ_{eff}/Cu) are shown in Figure 4. The molar paramagnetic susceptibilities of the binuclear Cu_2^{II} complexes were least-squares fit to the following equation:

$$\chi = \frac{Ng^2\beta^2}{kT} \left[\frac{2}{3 + \exp(-2J/kT)} \right] + \frac{C}{T} + TIP$$

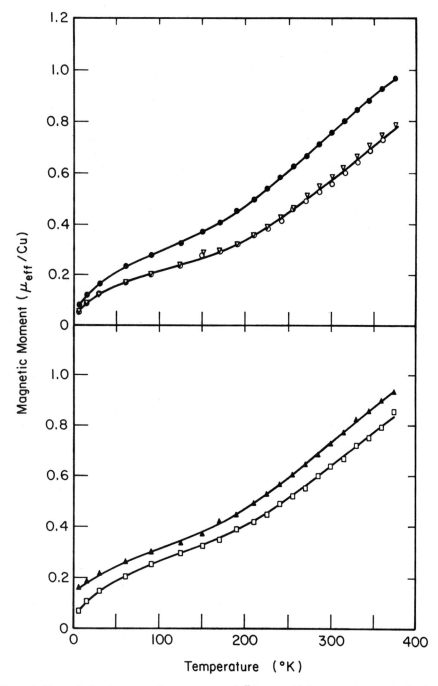

Figure 4. Plots of effective magnetic moment per Cu^{II} ion (μ_{eff}/Cu) versus temperature for the Cu_2^{II} complexes: I, •; III, $\triangledown$ and $\bigcirc$; IV, ▲; and VI, □. Two independent data sets were collected for Cu_2^{II} complex III. The solid lines result from a least-squares fit of the susceptibility data to the theoretical equation given in the text; see Table II for fitting parameters.

In this equation N, g, β, and k have their usual meanings; C/T gauges small amounts of paramagnetic impurities and TIP is the temperature-independent paramagnetism. In Table II are given the four best parameters (J, g, C and TIP) found to fit the data for each compound. As can be seen in Figure 4, the fits of the data are very good. Special care was exercized to secure accurate susceptibility data for these compounds on a SQUID susceptometer. The reproducibility of background correction (empty cell) was checked. Data were collected for two different samples of Cu_2^{II} complex III and it is evident in Figure 4 that the two data sets are very similar. First, it should be said that reasonable variations in C or TIP do not affect appreciably the value of J for a compound. However, the values of g and J are correlated. In summary, our careful analysis tells us that, barring any systematic errors, the estimated standard deviation on the J values for these complexes is $\pm 20 cm^{-1}$.

Table II

Parameters Resultant from Least-Squares Fitting of Magnetic Suceptibility Data

Cu_2^{II} Complex[a]	J,cm^{-1}	g	C($\times 10^4$)[b]	TIP($\times 10^4$)[b]
I	−386	2.12	2.82	2.15
III[c]	−440	2.20	1.60	1.13
	−449	2.20	1.60	1.13
IV	−403	2.15	51.0	2.00
VI	−445	2.20	1.85	1.76

(a) Each of the Cu_2^{II} complexes is a BF_4^- salt.
(b) In c.g.s. units.
(c) Measurements were carried out for two different samples of this complex.

As expected, the two bridging phenoxide oxygen atoms lead to a moderately strong exchange interaction between the two Cu^{II} ions in each of these complexes. The weakest interaction (J = −386 cm^{-1}) is found for the $R_1 = R_2$ = propylene complex, the complex that probably has a Cu^{II} coordination geometry that is closest to being square pyramidal. It is interesting that the strongest exchange interaction (J = −445 cm^{-1}) is found for the Cu_2^{II} complex VII. Perhaps Cu^{II} coordination geometries distorted from square pyramidal are responsible for this interaction. The exchange interaction (J = −440 cm^{-1}) in the Cu_2^{II} complex III is not much weaker. It is probably fortuitous that the magnitude of these exchange interactions qualitatively correlate with the conproportionation constants. The main conclusion in this susceptibility work is that moderately strong interactions do exist in these complexes, and, furthermore, there are not dramatic changes in the interaction from one complex to another.

Electronic Absorbtion Spectra. In our previous paper (6) we reported the electronic absorption transitions seen in the near-IR and visible regions for mixed-valence complexes I-VII dissolved in acetone. Intervalence transfer (IT) bands, which are most characteristic of mixed-valence complexes, were seen in the near-IR region.

IT bands were also observed for complexes VIII and XI, as summarized in Table I. As with the electrochemical results, complexes VIII and XI, which are the same as complex I except for the addition of hydroxyl substituents on one or both of the propylene linkages, have electronic absorption spectra that are very similar to that observed for complex I. It is also found that the intensity of the IT band for asymmetric complexes such as VI and VII is low compared to the intensities of IT bands of the corresponding symmetric complexes. Finally, it does not seem that there is any simple correspondence of energy and intensity of the IT band for a given $Cu^{II}Cu^{I}$ complex with the electron transfer rate deduced from the EPR data for the same complex.

EPR for $Cu^{II}Cu^{I}$ Complexes. In previous studies (3,6) of $Cu^{II}Cu^{I}$ macrocyclic complexes, EPR spectroscopy was found to give the most direct and useful comment on the rate of electron transfer in a given $Cu^{II}Cu^{I}$ complex. Room-temperature X-band EPR spectra were run for acetone (other solvents were used also) solutions of all twelve $Cu^{II}Cu^{I}$ complexes. Complexes IV, VI, VII, IX, X, and XII give room-temperature solution spectra that show four-line copper hyperfine patterns; the spectrum for complex XII is illustrated in Figure 5. This type of spectrum is characteristic of the situation where the single unpaired electron of the mixed-valence complex is localized on one copper center on the timescale of the EPR technique. On the other hand, complexes I, II, III, V, VIII, and XI give room-temperature solution X-band spectra with seven-line copper hyperfine patterns (see Figure 5). In these complexes the electron transfer is faster than the inverse of the EPR timescale. In Table I, the isotropic copper hyperfine splittings, A_{iso}, observed in the room-temperature solution spectra for the twelve $Cu^{II}Cu^{I}$ complexes are given.

In a frozen (~ 105 K) glass of acetone-toluene (2:3) all twelve mixed-valence complexes exhibit "axial" spectra with the $g_{\parallel}$ signal split into four copper hyperfine lines ($A_{\parallel}$). Under these conditions, the single unpaired electron is localized on one copper ion. Values of $A_{\parallel}$ are given in Table I. Complex IV has the smallest $A_{\parallel}$ value, in keeping with the idea that the copper coordination geometry in this complex is the most distorted from square pyramidal toward tetrahedral as a result of the sterically hindered 2,2'-biphenylene linkages. One other fact can be gleaned from the $A_{\parallel}$ values in Table I. For the asymmetric complexes VI and VII, the $A_{\parallel}$ values are somewhere between the $A_{\parallel}$ values for the corresponding symmetric complexes (compare data for complexes I, III, and VII). As before, this indicates that, either as a result of conformation interplay between the two different linkages in complexes VI and VII or as a result of strong electronic coupling between the two copper centers, the copper centers in these asymmetric complexes have been changed from what is found in the symmetric complexes.

One most amazing fact surfaces in the above analysis. Complex VII is localized on the EPR timescale at room temperature, whereas complexes I and III are delocalized. The interplay of the butylene and propylene linkages in complex VII is enough to give an EPR-localized species, which remains localized in solution up to temperatures of ~ 390 K.

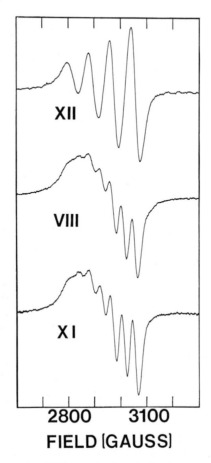

Figure 5. Ambient temperature x-band EPR spectra for mixed-valence complexes VIII, XI, and XII in acetonitrile.

An examination of the above EPR data leads to the conclusion that the single most important factor controlling the electron transfer rate in these mixed-valence complexes is the steric nature of the ligand. The 2,2'-biphenylene, 1,3-cyclohexylene, and 1,3-naphthalene linkages are apparently too bulky to permit the adjustments in coordination geometries that are required for an electron to transfer from the Cu^I ion to the Cu^{II} ion.

The payload in all of this work comes, however, in the study of the temperature dependence of the solution EPR spectra of these mixed-valence complexes. Of particular interest are the temperature dependencies seen for the six complexes that show seven-line copper hyperfine patterns in their room-temperature EPR spectra. In our previous paper (6) EPR solution spectra were reported at several temperatures for complexes I, II, III, and V. For comparison purposes, variable-temperature EPR spectra were also reported (6) for complex VII which is EPR-localized at room temperature.

Figures 6 and 7 illustrate the temperature dependence of the solution EPR spectra of complexes VIII and XI, respectively. The temperature dependencies are similar. In the case of either complex, the room-temperature spectrum has seven copper hyperfine lines (see Figure 5). It is understandable that the linewidths of the seven lines are not equal. The $Cu^{II}Cu^{I}$ complexes are not tumbling fast enough to give a completely averaged (A-and g-tensors) isotropic spectrum. In each case, as the solution temperature is lowered the "seven-line pattern" disappears and a pattern that is characteristic of the axial anisotropic pattern (randomly distributed non-tumbling complexes) of an EPR-localized complex grows in intensity. This latter pattern (see Figure 4 in ref. 6) consists of four copper hyperfine lines on $g_{\parallel}$ and a $g_{\perp}$ signal which can be structured. Following Gagné and co-workers' lead (3) and the analysis in our last paper (6) we can identify the temperature at which the last signs of the delocalized seven-line pattern disappear. Examination of the spectra in Figure 7 shows that for complex XI the transformation from EPR-delocalized to EPR-localized occurs at ~215 K. If this temperature is really the approximate transformation temperature required to activate thermally the complex so that it transfers over a potential energy barrier at a rate faster than sensed by the EPR technique, then a thermal activation energy ($E_{th}^{\ddagger}$) can be calculated from the following expression:

$$k_{th} = \frac{kT}{h} e^{-E_{th}^{\ddagger}/RT}$$

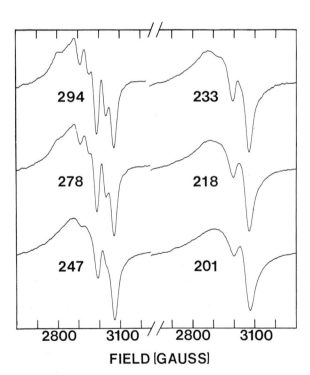

Figure 6. Variable-temperature EPR spectra for mixed-valence complex VIII in acetone.

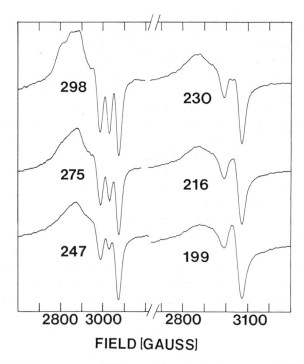

Figure 7. Variable-temperature EPR spectra for mixed-valence complex XI in acetone.

The value of k_{th} is taken as $5.5 \times 10^8 s^{-1}$ at the transformation temperature; this value of k_{th} is determined by a consideration of the process whereby the hyperfine splitting and g-tensor anisotropy of a EPR-delocalized species is averaged to get to the spectrum of a EPR-localized species. It must be emphasized that this value of k_{th} and this type of analysis only gives a very approximate value for $E_{th}^{\ddagger}$. It would be necessary to simulate the lineshape of the spectra at each temperature (9). Needless to say, this is a next-to-impossible task, for it is necessary to know the effects of the molecular tumbling upon the appearance of the spectrum at any temperature.

Electrochemical data, the values of $A_{\parallel}(Cu)$ from the frozen-glass EPR spectra (see Table I), and structural results from analogous Cu^{II} complexes (see ref. 7) strongly suggest the planarity of the Cu^{II} coordination geometry decreases in the series I>III>IV. Of various four-coordination geometries, the Cu^{II} ion prefers square planar. This indicates that the ligand inflexibility increases in the series I<III<IV. It is somewhat satisfying then that the above EPR analysis indicates at room temperature the rate of intramolecular electron transfer decreases in the series I>III>IV. The least flexible ligand (complex IV) exhibits the slowest rate in this series.

It would perhaps be foolhardy to suggest at this time that there may be something wrong with the above analysis. Nevertheless, lengthy study of the temperature dependence of the EPR spectra for complexes I, II, III, V, VIII, and XI leads us to suggest that a simple thermal activation process is not all that is involved. It is implicit in the above analysis that the symmetric binuclear mixed-valence complex has a constant potential energy barrier in the symmetric, double-minima potential energy curve for the ground state (see right hand diagram in Figure 8). The po-

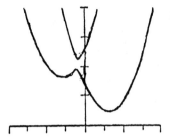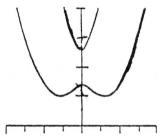

Figure 8. Two different plots of potential energy for the binuclear mixed-valence complex as a function of the nuclear coordinate changes required for the electron transfer process. The diagram on the right is for the case of a symmetric binuclear mixed-valence complex which also has no asymmetry in its environment. The diagram on the left is for the case where a zero-point energy difference is introduced either as a result of a difference in coordination geometries or as a result of asymmetry in the environment.

tential barrier is assumed to be constant. At higher thermal energies more of the complexes have enough energy to be thermally activated over the barrier (or tunnel through it). Under these conditions we would expect (perhaps naively!) that lowering the solution temperature and the seven-line isotropic copper hyperfine pattern (1:2:3:4:3:2:1 intensities) would gradually convert into a four-line isotropic copper hyperfine pattern, as indicated in Figure 9. Further cooling of the solution to a point where molecules are effectively not tumbling fast relative to the EPR timescale and the localized, anisotropic (frozen solution) spectrum would be obtained (see Figure 4 in ref. 6). It is not clear that this is what is seen. Instead, it appears that the intensity of the "isotropic" seven-line pattern just decreases without any signs of line broadening and the intensity of the anisotropic EPR-localized pattern increases when the temperature of the solution is decreased. It is possible that the potential energy diagram for such a binuclear mixed-valence copper complex is changing with temperature. At low temperatures in solution (and in the solid state most likely) the two copper ions in the complex are in different coordination environments. There is not enough thermal energy at low temperatures in solution for the solvent structure to adjust very rapidly around the mixed-valence cation. It is also possible that the mixed-valence cation is ion paired with the BF_4^- anion and the BF_4^- anion is closer to one copper ion than the other. Furthermore, there might not be enough energy for the mixed-valence cation to change its molecular conformation. This all could result in the potential energy diagram for the mixed-valence cation being assymetric as pictured in the left hand side of Figure 8. In this situation the mixed-valence complex is clearly valence localized with a relatively high potential energy barrier.

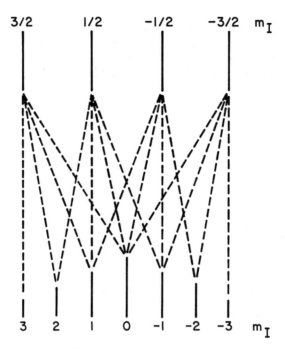

Figure 9. Interrelationships between the components of an isotropic seven-line copper hyperfine pattern for an "EPR-delocalized" binuclear copper complex and the components of an isotropic four-line copper hyperfine pattern for an "EPR-localized" complex.

At higher temperatures the solvent structure would be more dynamic around each mixed-valence cation. In addition, any ion pairing of the BF_4^- anion with the mixed-valence cation could be modified. As well there will be more thermal energy for the mixed-valence cation to interconvert between higher energy molecular conformations. All of this could lead to the situation where the potential energy diagram of the mixed-valence cation is now symmetric as pictured on the right hand side of Figure 8. If this is the case, the intramolecular electron transfer rate would be considerably larger at high temperature than at low because the effective barrier for electron transfer has been reduced. Whether or not any line broadening or coalescing of features in the EPR spectrum would be expected as the solution temperature is changed depends on the frequency with which the "environment" around the mixed-valence cation adjusts compared to the frequency difference needed to average EPR signals.

Analogous observations of the influence of the dynamics of the environment upon the rate of intramolecular electron transfer in mixed-valence complexes in the solid state have been made. The oxo-centered, trinuclear complexes of general formula $[Fe_3O(O_2CCH_3)_6(pyridine)_3](solvate)$ formally have two Fe^{III} ions and one Fe^{II} ion. In very recent work (10) we have found that for a given mixed-valence complex, $[Fe_3O(O_2CCH_3)_6(pyridine)_3]$, changing the solvate molecule dramatically affects the electron-transfer rate in the solid state. More importantly, we found that for Fe_3O complexes which show a change from two doublets at low temperature to one at high temperature there is no evidence of line broadening in the Mössbauer signals. Through detailed variable-temperature single-crystal x-ray structural work and Mössbauer spectroscopy it has been established that the intramolecular electron-transfer rate in these Fe_3O complexes in the solid state are determined by dynamic disorder of coordinated ligands or solvate molecules. At low temperature in the solid state certain ligands and/or solvate molecules are statically disordered and the environment around a given Fe_3O complex is asymmetric. At higher temperatures these ligands and/or solvate molecules begin to move between two positions. This dynamic disorder tends to symmetrize the environment about the Fe_3O complex and the rate of electron transfer increases. We have also found evidence that a similar phenomenon is occurring for mixed-valence biferrocenes in the solid state (11). In this case, because the mixed-valence complex is a cation, the anion must be involved in a dynamic disorder in the solid state.

Acknowledgements

We thank the National Institutes of Health for support through grant HL13652. We also thank Dr. Bernard A. Goodman for discussions about the EPR data.

References and Footnotes

1. *Mixed-Valence Compounds, Theory and Applications in Chemistry, Physics, Geology, and Biology,"* D. B. Brown, Ed.; Reidel Publishing Co.: Boston, 1980.
2. P. Day, Int. Rev. *Phys. Chem. 1,* 149 (1981).
3. R. R. Gagné, C. A. Koval, T. J. Smith and M. C. Cimolino, *J. Am. Chem. Soc. 101,* 4571 (1979); R. R. Gagné, L. M. Henling and T. J. Kistenmacher, *Inorg. Chem. 19,* 1226 (1980).
4. A. W. Addison, *Inorg. Nucl. Chem. Letters 12,* 899 (1976).
5. E. I. Solomon, chapter 2 in *Copper Proteins,* T. G. Spiro, Ed.; Wiley: New York, 1981, and references therein.
6. R.C. Long and D. N. Hendrickson, *J. Am. Chem. Soc. 105,* 1513 (1983).
7. R. C. Long, Ph.D. Thesis, University of Illinois, 1984.
8. H. Taube, *Ann. N. Y. Acad. Sci. 313,* 481 (1978); R. W. Callahan, F. R. Keene, R. J. Meyer and D. J. Salmon, *J. Am. Chem. Soc. 99,* 1064 (1982).
9. J. H. Freed, *J. Phys. Chem. 84,* 2668 (1980).
10. S. M. Oh, D. N. Hendrickson, K. L. Hassett and R. E. Davis, *J. Am. Chem. Soc. 106,* 7984 (1984).
11. T.-Y. Dong, M. J. Cohn, M. F. Moore, and D. N. Hendrickson, unpublished work.

Biological & Inorganic Copper Chemistry,
ISBN 0-940030-11-X, Eds., K. D. Karlin & J. Zubieta, Adenine Press, ©Adenine Press, 1985

Sensitivity Analysis in Multifrequency EPR Spectroscopy

James S. Hyde and William E. Antholine

Department of Radiology, National Biomedical ESR Center,
Medical College of Wisconsin, Milwaukee, Wisconsin, 53226 U.S.A.

and

Riccardo Basosi

Department of Chemistry,
University of Siena, Siena, Italy

Abstract

The concept of sensitivity analysis introduced by R. Basosi, W.E. Antholine and J.S. Hyde, *J. Chem. Phys.* (in press) is further developed and illustrated by application to Cu(II) spectra in liquids and in powders. A least squares (termed "goodness of fit", Gof) between two simulated spectra is calculated: the minimum detectable Gof occurs when one of the spectra is a best fit to an experimental spectrum and one has one input parameter varied until a discernable difference is seen in comparison to the experimental spectrum. Sensitivity analysis shows in a quantitative manner how use of a number of the microwave frequencies (multifrequency EPR spectroscopy) improves the overall quality of the data. The paper contributes to the field of computer aided EPR spectroscopy.

Introduction

Multifrequency EPR spectroscopy in its most ideal form is the acquisition of spectra at a number of microwave frequencies, coupled with the successful simulation of all of the spectra where the only input parameter that is varied is the frequency itself. Spectra in this ideal spectroscopy should be obtained on the same identical sample at the same temperature. It is implicitly assumed that all spectrometers are of equal sensitivity and all microwave resonators have negligible background contamination. Thus the only possible reason for the observed differences in spectra is the microwave frequency.

In our laboratory we have in recent years had some success in approaching this ideal, and we continue to work on the methodology of multifrequency EPR spectroscopy. Froncisz et al (1) using a 2-4 GHz spectrometer built at the National Biomedical ESR Center obtained improved resolution in the spectra of the so-called visible copper of cytochrome *c* oxidase, compared with X-band. It became apparent that there were microwave frequency dependent line broadening effects, and Froncisz and Hyde studied these effects in spectra of immobilized non-blue copper complexes (2). They were due to an interplay of g-strain and A-strain; by their inclusion, improved agreement between simulated and experimental spectra over a range of microwave frequencies was obtained.

Pasenkiewicz et al (3) made careful simulations of EPR spectra of nitroxide radical spin-labels in a second derivative display at both X and Q-band. Although the goal of simulation at both frequencies with no change in input parameters was achieved, in fact, the best fit that could be obtained at one frequency required slightly different input paramenters than for the other frequency. This suggests that the assumption of co-linear zeeman and hyperfine tensors is invalid. It was also noted that the simulations of second derivative spectra seemed better than for first derivative spectra, which suggests that the lineshape function that was used was not quite appropriate.

Liczwek et al (4) required data at 3.7 and 9.5 GHz in order to obtain accurate spin-Hamiltonian input parameters for bis(diethyldithiocarbamato)-copper (II). These workers were interested in the effect of this coordination on copper quadrupole couplings.

Basosi et al (5) in a paper that will be heavily referenced here, obtained spectra at 5 widely varying frequencies from 1 to 35 GHz of a low molecular weight copper complex in solution. They achieved very good agreement between their simulated and experimental spectra using a surprisingly large number of simplifying assumptions: Brownian isotropic rotational diffusion, axial zeeman tensor, axial hyperfine tensor, and colinearity of the principle axes of these tensors.

Lessons to be learned from these examples are: (1) the dependence on microwave frequency of linewidths is an important aspect of multifrequency EPR spectroscopy; (2) the assumptions made in the simulation procedure may be either too complex or too simple and objective criteria are needed; (3) least squares analysis leads to slightly different optimum parameters in a first derivative display compared with a second derivative display and (4) simultaneous fits at two or more frequencies may be required to determine the spin Hamiltonian parameters.

By the words "sensitivity analysis" we mean the analysis by computer of the sensitivity of a simulated spectra to each of the input parameters in the program. Let $Y_F(n)$ be a good simulation of a spectrum at frequency F, where Y is the intensity at the nth value of the magnetic field, and let $Y_F^B(n)$ be a spectrum simulated at frequency F where all of the input parameters are unchanged compared with $Y_F(n)$ except for the Bth parameter, which is allowed to vary slightly. Then we define a goodness-of-fit, Gof,

$$\text{Gof(goodness of fit)}_F^B = \frac{1}{N}\sum_{n=1}^{N}[Y_F^B(n) - Y_F(n)]^2. \tag{1}$$

This computed least squares number is a measure of the sensitivity of the spectrum to input parameter B. If the maximum derivative peak-to-peak signal height is normalized to one and the amount of baseline at the extrema of the spectrum is restricted, the Gof values obtained on different samples or by different laboratories are comparable. To repeat, sensitivity analysis does not in itself involve any actual experimental spectra. It is an analysis using a computer of the sensitivity of a spectrum to changes in an input parameter. It is like a partial derivative of the spectrum with respect to the input parameter.

The use of multifrequency EPR has received considerable impetus by the development of the loop-gap resonator of Froncisz and Hyde (6). This lumped element resonator can be configured to accept a normal X-band 3 mm i.d. sample tube at microwave frequencies from 1 to 10 GHz with nearly unity filling factor. Thus one ideal of multifrequency EPR is approached: namely the ability to collect data on the same sample. Another recent development has been octave bandwidth microwave bridges. At the National Biomedical ESR Center, 1-2 and 2-4 GHz bridges are in active use and 0.5-1 and 4-8 are being constructed. The wide availability of coaxial microwave components makes these bridges possible. Q-band (35 GHz) has long been commercially available and several workers are making plans to construct bridges at still higher frequencies. In our laboratory we soon hope to be able to operate from 0.5 to 70 GHz. Probably two sizes of sample tubes will be required to span the entire range.

Materials and Methods

Liquid phase spectra were simulated by the program of Basosi et al (5). This program uses the Kivelson formulation of liquid phase ESR spectra (7-10) with the addition of dynamic second order frequency shifts as given by Bruno et al (11). See Hyde and Froncisz for more details on the theoretical basis of the program (12).

Solid phase powder spectra were simulated using the program of Pilbrow and Winfield (13).

All simulations were performed on a PDP11-34 computer.

Results and Discussion

Let B be the value of an input parameter and B' be a slightly different value. Then

$$\Delta B = B - B' \tag{2}$$

If we plot $-\text{Log(Gof)}$ versus ΔB, then as $\Delta B \Rightarrow 0$, a divergence to $+ \infty$ will be found. But the nature of the approach to this pole will depend on choice of microwave frequency and, of course, on the other input parameters.

The input parameters that we have used for liquid phase simulations of copper spectra are given in the first column of Table I for bis(dimethyldithiocarbamato)

Copper(II), ^{65}Cu(dtc)$_2$, as determined by Basosi et al (5). Figure 1 shows such a plot for $\Delta g = g_{\parallel} - g_{\perp}$. The pole is observed at $\Delta g = 0.087$, which was the value that yielded the best fit between simulated and experimental spectra.

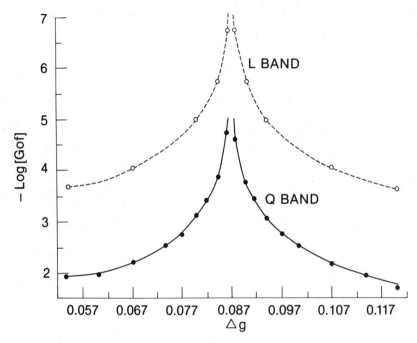

Figure 1. The "goodness-of-fit," Gof, versus Δg in the liquid phase. L-band is less sensitive to variations in Δg as expected. The change in the Gof with change in Δg is much greater for Q-band than L-band as Δg approaches its exact value.

This figure shows in general that Q-band is very much superior to L-band for determination of zeeman interactions, which is not surprising.

Least squares fitting between experimental and simulated spectra is in our experience a difficult matter using a computer. Baselines are seldom perfect and broad underlying background contamination is common. Mostly we have used a light table and visual comparison by a trained observer which is a logical procedure in the presence of systematic error.

If finally we have what is considered a best fit, call it simulation I, then we can systematically vary an input parameter and create new simulations. Label one of these as simulation II, which gives a just discernable difference between simulated and experimental spectra. Then Gof can be calculated between I and II, and this is the minimum detectable Gof for that particular input parameter at that particular microwave frequency. We assume that the minimum detectable Gof is the same for each input parameter at that particular frequency, an assumption that lies behind

Eq. 1 and that seems experimentally to be valid. It is further assumed in the analysis below that all of the spectrometers used to obtain the multifrequency spectra are of comparable quality, so that there exists a minimum detectable Gof that is characteristic of the sample and of the simulation procedure, but that is independent of input parameter and microwave frequency.

Referring now to Figure 1, if the minimum detectable Gof were 10^{-3} and we were at L-band, then we practically could not determine Δg. If the minimum detectable value were 10^{-4} then Δg could be determined at L-band with an error of about ± 0.02.

At Q-band, a minimum detectable Gof of 10^{-3} corresponds to an error in Δg of ± 0.008 and for 10^{-4}, ± 0.002. Sensitivity analysis has led us in a quantitative manner to the result that high frequencies are better than low frequencies for determining zeeman interactions, which of course is well known qualitatively.

Basosi et al (5) in their study of $^{65}Cu(dtc)_2$ at $2 \times 10^{-3}M$ in toluidine in the liquid phase at 1.1, 2.5, 3.4, 9.1 and 35.4 GHz obtained a minimum detectable Gof of 1.0×10^{-3}, and used this value to determine the errors in the spin-hamiltonian parameters. The procedure can be illustrated by considering, as an example, the isotropic g value, which was found to be 2.0440 ± 0.0003. With this error, the Gof at 35.4 GHz was calculated to be 1×10^{-3}. At all other frequencies it was much less than 1×10^{-3}—that is, less than the minimum detectable Gof, and therefore not detectable. An error of ± 0.0003 is just detectable at 35.4 GHz, but cannot be detected at any other of the five frequencies.

Table I
Magnetic Parameters of $^{65}Cu(dtc)_2$ as Determined in the Liquid Phase

	298°K Data	Error from Gof Analysis	Best Frequency (GHz)
g_{iso}	2.0440	± 0.0003	35.4
$g_\perp$	2.015	± 0.003	35.4
$g_\parallel$	2.102	± 0.006	35.4
Δg	0.087	± 0.008	35.4
a_{iso}	-229.0 MHz	± 2 MHz	9.1
$A_\perp$	-90.3 MHz	± 12 MHz	1.1
$A_\parallel$	-506.3 MHz	± 24 MHz	1.1
ΔA	-416.0 MHz	± 36 MHz	1.1
τ_R	75 ps	± 15 ps	1.1

For each input parameter, errors were systematically varied until at one of the five frequencies, the Gof was 1×10^{-3}, it being less at the other frequencies. Errors determined in this manner are given in Table I. The best microwave frequency is also given. By requiring fits of equal quality at all microwave frequencies, the overall quality of the data is substantially better than would be possible at a single frequency.

Figures 2 and 3 illustrate other aspects of sensitivity analysis in EPR spectroscopy and were obtained using the same type of approach that Basosi et al (5) used for liquid phase spectra, applied to powder Cu(II) spectra. The simulation program was that of Pilbrow and Winfield (13).

A problem of interest to us is the determination of in-plane magnetic parameters of Cu(II) spectra for small departures from tetragonal symmetry. Reported here are initial studies to determine the optimum microwave frequency using sensitivity analysis. Magnetic parameters were taken from Rist and Hyde (14): $g_1 = 2.039$, $g_2 = 2.078$, $g_3 = 2.246$, $A_{||} = 212 \times 10^{-4} cm^{-1}$, $A_{\perp} = 30 \times 10^{-4} cm^{-1}$, linewidth = 4.0G.

Figure 2 shows $-\log$ Gof for g_2 at 1.2, 3.4 and 9.1 GHz. As for Fig. 1, the maximum peak-to-peak was set to one, and the calculation terminated a few linewidths on either side of the spectrum. It was gratifying that Eq. 1, the Gof equation, gave similar results as for the liquid phase, which supports the universality of the equation. As before, the highest frequency available was best for determining the zeeman interaction. But this conclusion is premature. Thus far no analysis of strain broadening effects in the $g_{\perp}$ region of the spectrum in analogy to that of Froncisz and Hyde (2)

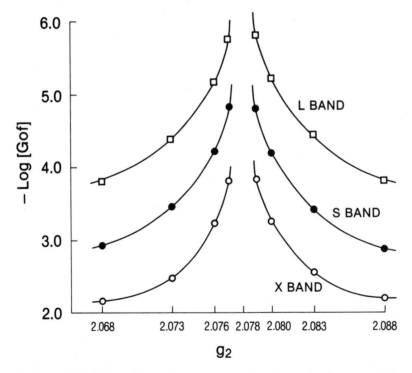

Figure 2. Gof versus g_2 for a Cu(II) powder spectrum: $g_1 = 2.039$, $g_2 = 2.078$, $g_3 = 2.246$, $A_{||} = 212 \times 10^{-4} cm^{-1}$, $A_{\perp} = 30 \times 10^{-4} cm^{-1}$, linewidth = 4.0G. Values taken from reference 14. L-Band 1.2 GHz, S-Band 3.4 GHz, X-Band 9.1 GHz.

for the $g_{||}$ region has been carried out. The linewidth will certainly exhibit an increase as the magnetic field is increased, and there seems little doubt but that an optimum microwave frequency will exist for determination of g_1 and g_2.

Sensitivity analysis need not be carried out in only one dimension (i.e. only one spin-hamiltonian input parameter.) A multidimensional space exists in which Gof is determined for all input parameters. Figure 3 illustrates a plot of Gof for two input parameters, calculated for powder Cu(II) spectra assuming axially symmetric colinear magnetic tensors: $g_{||} = 2.206$, $g_{\perp} = 2.039$, $A_{||} = 212 \times 10^{-4} cm^{-1}$, $A_{\perp} = 30 \times 10^{-4} cm^{-1}$, and linewidth = 4G. This figure shows that $A_{\perp}$ can be obtained with somewhat less error (but greater percentage error) than $A_{||}$, which is an interesting result. $A_{||}$ features are separated, well resolved, and rather weak; $A_{\perp}$ features are much more intense but poorly resolved.

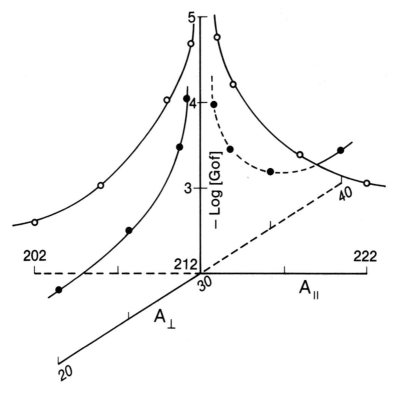

Figure 3. Two parameter Gof plot for $A_{||}$ and $A_{\perp}$ for Cu(II) at 3.4 GHz, $g_{||} = 2.206$, $g_{\perp} = 2.039$, $A_{||} = 212 \times 10^{-4} cm^{-1}$, $A_{\perp} = 30 \times 10^{-4} cm^{-1}$.

It is our judgment that sensitivity analysis using the least squares approach of Eq. 1 should be a routine procedure of computer-aided EPR spectroscopy.

Acknowledgment

This work was supported by Grants GM-27665 and RR-01008 from the National Institutes of Health.

References and Footnotes

1. W. Froncisz, C.P. Scholes, J.S. Hyde, Y.-H. Wei, T.E. King, R.W. Shaw, and H. Beinert, *J. Biol. Chem. 254,* 7482 (1979).
2. W. Froncisz and J.S. Hyde, *J. Chem. Phys. 73,* 3123 (1980).
3. M. Pasenkiewicz-Gierula, J.S. Hyde, and J.R. Pilbrow, *J. Magn. Reson. 55,* 255 (1983).
4. D.L. Liczwek, R.L. Belford, J.R. Pilbrow, and J.S. Hyde, *J. Phys. Chem. 87,* 2509-2512 (1983).
5. R. Basosi, W.E. Antholine, W. Froncisz, and J. S. Hyde, *J. Chem. Phys. 81(11),* 4849-4857 (1984).
6. W. Froncisz and J.S. Hyde, *J. Magn. Reson. 47,* 515 (1982).
7. D. Kivelson, *J. Chem. Phys. 27,* 1987 (1957).
8. D. Kivelson, *J. Chem. Phys. 33,* 1094 (1960).
9. D. Kivelson, *J. Chem. Phys. 41,* 1904 (1964).
10. R. Wilson and D. Kivelson, *J. Chem. Phys. 44,* 154 (1966).
11. G.V. Bruno, J.K. Harrington, and M.P. Eastman, *J. Phys. Chem. 81,* 1111 (1977).
12. J.S. Hyde and W. Froncisz, *Ann. Rev. Biophys. Bioeng. 11,* 391 (1981).
13. J.R. Pilbrow and M.E. Winfield, *Mol. Phys. 25,* 1073 (1973).
14. G.H. Rist and J.S. Hyde, *J. Chem. Phys. 50,* 4532 (1969).

Biological & Inorganic Copper Chemistry,
ISBN 0-940030-11-X, Eds., K. D. Karlin & J. Zubieta, Adenine Press, ©Adenine Press, 1985

5- and 6-coordinated Cu²⁺-complexes with Terpyridine Ligands—Cases of Dynamic Static and Cooperative Jahn-Teller Interactions

D. Reinen
Fachbereich Chemie der Philipps-Universität
and Sonderforschungsbereich 127,
Hans-Meerwein-Strasse, D-3550 Marburg (G.F.R.)

Abstract

Pseudo-octahedral terpyridine complexes $Cu(terpy)_2X_2 \cdot nH_2O$ undergo strong first-order Jahn-Teller interactions, which dominate the distortion components due to rigid ligand effects. Phase transitions from dynamic to static distortion geometries, induced by cooperative-elastic forces, are frequently observed. 5-coordinate complexes Cu terpy $X_2 \cdot nH_2O$ are subject of vibronic couplings of the pseudo Jahn-Teller type, which stabilize the elongated square pyramid with respect to the compressed trigonal bipyramid. Structural and spectroscopic results are reported.

Introduction

5- and 6-coordinate Cu^{2+} complexes with 2,2′,2″-terpyridine as a ligand are interesting examples for studying various aspects of vibronic coupling and the Jahn-Teller effect. The structure of compounds $Cu(terpy)_2X_2 \cdot nH_2O$ is characterized by pseudo octahedral CuN_6-polyhedra (Figure 1), while complexes Cu terpy $X_2 \cdot nH_2O$ contain CuN_3L_2 (L=X,O) entities of varying geometry (Figure 4). While Cu^{2+} in octahedral coordination possesses a ^2E_g ground state and undergoes first order Jahn-Teller distortions (1,2),5-coordinate Cu^{2+} may be subject to a pseudo-Jahn-Teller effect (2).

Results

A. Cu(terpy)₂X₂·nH₂O [X: NO₃⁻, Cl⁻, Br⁻, PF₆⁻ etc]

The compound with $X=NO_3^-$, $n=0$ crystallizes in space group $I4_1/a$ [Z=8], with the Cu−N bond lengths given in Table I (3). The comparison with data of the complex $Ni(terpy)_2(NO_3)_2 \cdot 3 H_2O$ (4) reveals a significant difference in geometry, because octahedral Ni^{2+} has a non-degenerate $^3A_{2g}$ ground state and is Jahn-Teller stable in contrast to Cu^{2+}. Though the rigid ligand induces a pronounced compression of the $M-N_{11(21)}$ spacings already for Ni^{2+}, the Cu^{2+} polyhedra show a very strong anisotropy of the $Cu-N_{12}$ and $Cu-N_{22}$ bond lengths in addition as the consequence

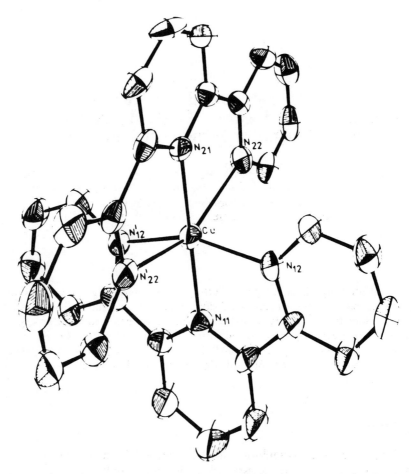

Figure 1. Molecular structure of $Cu(terpy)_2^{2+}$ in $Cu(terpy)_2(NO_3)_2$.

of a Jahn-Teller effect [$E \otimes \epsilon$ vibronic interaction] (5). The Cu^{2+}-polyhedra may then be considered as elongated along the $Cu-N_{22}$ direction, with a small o-rhombic component superimposed. Neighboured CuN_6 entities in the unit cell have their long axes oriented perpendicular to each other, the cooperative order pattern is antiferrodistortive (Figure 2). While this compound does not show a phase transition to a dynamic structure up to the decomposition temperature, a dynamic Jahn-Teller effect is present in the complex $Cu(terpy)_2(PF_6)_2$ already at 298 K (Table I) (6). The geometry of the CuN_6 polyhedron reflects only the steric ligand effect, as is also obvious by comparison with the corresponding data for the Ni^{2+} compound. We could deduce from single crystal EPR data, however, that a transition to a low-temperature phase occurs below 77 K (7). The structure of this phase is presumably identical with the one of $Cu(terpy)_2 (NO_3)_2$.

The Cu^{2+} complex with $X=Br^-$, $n=3$ crystallizes in space group $P\bar{1}$ [$Z=2$] (4). The unit cell can be transformed into a pseudotetragonal cell, which is similar to the

Table I
Bond length data (Å) for complexes $M(terpy)_2X_2 \cdot nH_2O$
[compare Figure 1]

M^{2+}	X	n	$M-N_{11(21)}$	$M-N_{12}$		$M-N_{22}$
Cu	NO_3^-	0	1.99_5	2.08_5		2.29
Ni	NO_3^-	3	2.00		2.13	
Cu	PF_6^-	0	1.98		2.18	
Ni	PF_6^-	0	2.01_5		2.13_5	
Cu	Br^-	3	1.97	2.15		2.20

one of $Cu(terpy)_2(NO_3)_2$. The Cu$-$N bonds perpendicular to Cu$-N_{11(21)}$ are only slightly different (Table I). Single crystal EPR results indicate, however, that the anisotropy in these spacings becomes more pronounced at lower temperature (4). Obviously the transition from the dynamic to the static Jahn-Teller effect covers a wide range of temperature in this case. The reduction of the water content from n=3 to n=1 and n=0 transforms the triclinic into tetragonal unit cells with similar

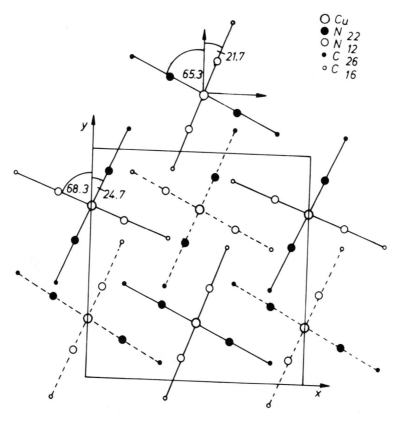

Figure 2. Projection of the CuN_6 polyhedra ($z \simeq \frac{1}{8}, \frac{3}{8}$—full and broken lines) into the (001)-plane [$Cu(terpy)_2(NO_3)_2$; space group $I4_1/a$].

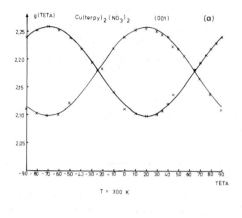

T = 300 K

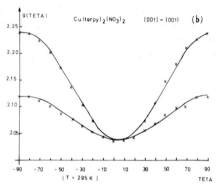

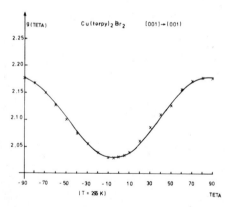

Figure 3. Angular dependence of the g-tensor of the "low-temperature" structure: (a) (001) plane, (b) [001] direction ⇒ (001) plane and of the "high-temperature" structure: [001] direction ⇒ (001) plane [no angular dependence in (001) plane].

dimensions as the one of $Cu(terpy)_2(NO_3)_2$ (4). The temperature dependence of the g-tensor is analogous to the one of $Cu(terpy)_2(PF_6)_2$, with a dynamic ⇔ static phase transition above 80 K (8).

The temperature dependencies of the g-tensor for the "low-temperature" structure (static Jahn-Teller effect) and for the "high-temperature" phase (dynamic Jahn-Teller effect) of the discussed tetragonal compounds $Cu(terpy)_2X_2 \cdot nH_2O$ are shown in Figure 3 (compare Figure 2).

Similar compounds to Cu^{2+} and Ni^{2+} can be prepared with Co^{2+} (9). They exhibit high-spin low-spin equilibria, which are temperature dependent (10,11). The interesting feature is, that complexes $Co(terpy)_2X_2 \cdot nH_2O$ may show similar dynamic $\Leftrightarrow$ static phase transitions as Cu^{2+} (11), because low-spin Co^{2+} in octahedral coordination also possesses a strongly Jahn-Teller unstable E_g ground state (1). Hence the Jahn-Teller stabilisation energy stabilizes the low-spin with respect to the high-spin state.

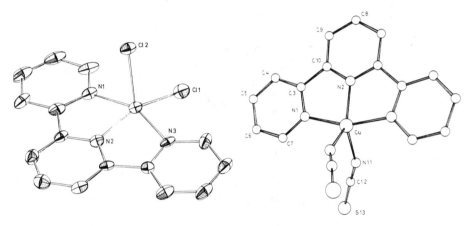

Figure 4. Molecular structure of $Cu(terpy)X_2$ polyhedra in compounds $Cu(terpy)X_2 \cdot nH_2O$: $X=Cl^-$, $n=1$ and 0 [left]; $X=NCS^-$ or Br^-, $n=0$ [right].

B. $Cu(terpy)X_2 \cdot nH_2O$ [2X: 2 Cl$^-$; 2 Br$^-$; 2 NCS$^-$; CN$^-$, NO$_3^-$; 2 NO$_2^-$; NO$_2^-$, NO$_3^-$ etc]

In the unit cell of the complexes with $X=Cl^- - n=0$ (12) and $n=1$ (12,13); $2X=CN^-$, $NO_3^- - n=1$ (14); $X=NO_2^- - n=1$ (15) and $2X=NO_2^-$, $NO_3^- - n=1$ (16) always—somewhat distorted—tetragonal square pyramids are found, which are strongly elongated along the apical bond direction. The terpyridine ring is located in the equatorial plane (Figure 4). We have demonstrated, that this geometry is stabilized with respect to the (compressed) trigonal bipyramid by the pseudo-Jahn Teller effect (17). Strain effects by the rigid ligand are not deciding for the choice of coordination geometry in 5-coordinate terpyridine complexes, because the terpyridine molecule can equally adapt to a (distorted) tetragonal pyramid or trigonal bipyramid (12,17). Surprisingly the compounds with $X=NCS^-$ and Br^- contain CuN_3X_2-polyhedra, which resemble trigonal bipyramids at the first sight (18) (Figure 4). A closer look at the bond angles and bond lengths reveals, however, that they are rather intermediates between two tetragonal pyramids, which are elongated along one of the Cu—X bonds, than trigonal bipyramids (7). While the apparent trigonal bipyramid of $CuCl_5^{3-}$ in $M^{III}(NH_3)_6 CuCl_5$ (M=Cr,Co) is the average of three square pyramids (17) (Figure 5), only two conformations are averaged in this case. The presence of just two ligands (X^-), which can adapt to a long bond distance, is the obvious reason.

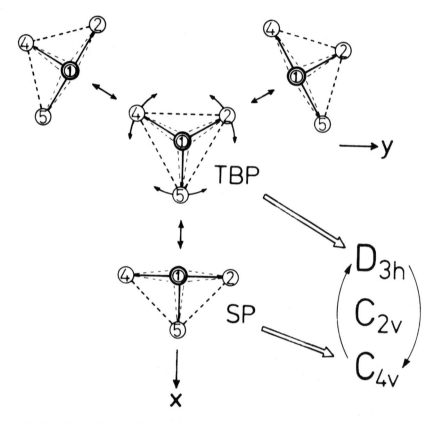

Figure 5. The trigonal bipyramid as the dynamic average of three square pyramidal conformations in the high-temperature phase of $[Co(NH_3)_6]CuCl_5$ (17).

Conclusion

Concluding one may state, that the geometry of 5- and 6-coordinate terpyridine complexes of Cu^{2+} is strongly influenced by vibronic interactions of the Jahn-Teller type. Though the rigid tridentate ligand imposes already significant deformations on the Cu^{2+}-polyhedra, the additional Jahn-Teller forces are much more pronounced and lead to various dynamic, static and cooperative effects including phase transitions.

References and Footnotes

1. D. Reinen and C. Friebel, *Structure Bond. 37,* 1 (1979).
2. D. Reinen, *Comments Inorg. Chem. 2,* 227 (1983).
3. R. Allman, W. Henke and D. Reinen, *Inorg. Chem. 17,* 378 (1978) M. Mathew and G. J. Palenik, *Coord Chem, 1,* 243 (1971).
4. W. Henke, Thesis Marburg/GFR (1980) W. Henke, R. Allmann and D. Reinen, to be published.
5. Because the degeneracy of the E_g ground state is already lifted by the angular and radial distortions imposed on the cation by the terpyridine ligands, a pseudo-Jahn-Teller effect is operating in a strict sense.
6. M. I. Arriortua, T. Rojo, J. M. Amigo, G. Germain and J.P. Declercq, *Acta Cryst, B38,* 1323 (1982).
7. D. Reinen, T. Rojo, H. Stratemeier et al., to be published.
8. W. Henke and D. Reinen, *Z. anorg. allg. Chem. 436,* 187 (1977) [Error; for $X=Br^-$: n=1 instead of n=2]
9. B.N. Figgis, E.S. Kucharski and A. H. White, *Aust. J. Chem. 36,* 1537 (1983).
10. D.L. Williams, D.W. Smith and R.C. Stoufer, *Inorg. Chem. 6,* 590 (1967) J.S. Judge and W.A. Baker, *Inorg. Chim. Acta 1,* 68 (1968).
11. S. Kremer, W. Henke and D. Reinen, *Inorg. Chem. 21,* 3013 (1982) R. Allman, S. Kremer and D. Kucharzcyk, *Inorg. Chim. Acta 85,* 57 (1984).
12. W. Henke, S. Kremer and D. Reinen, *Inorg. Chem. 22,* 2858 (1983).
13. T. Rojo, M. Vlasse and D. Beltran-Porter, *Acta Cryst. C39,* 194 (1983).
14. O.P. Anderson, A.B. Packard and M. Wicholas, *Inorg. Chem. 15,* 1613 (1976).
15. R. Allmann, S. Kremer and D. Kucharzcyk, *Inorg. Chim. Acta 85,* L19 (1984).
16. J. M. Savariault, T. Rojo, M.I. Arriortua et J. Galy, *C.R. 297 Serie II,* 895 (1983).
17. D. Reinen and C. Friebel, *Inorg. Chem. 23,* 791 (1984).
18. D. Beltran-Porter, T. Rojo et al., unpublished results.

Biological & Inorganic Copper Chemistry,
ISBN 0-940030-11-X, Eds., K. D. Karlin & J. Zubieta, Adenine Press, ©Adenine Press, 1985

Use of UV/VIS and EPR Spectroscopy for the Determination of Stabilities and Structures of Cupric Complexes in Solution

Harald Gampp, Charles J. Meyer, Marcel Maeder
and Andreas D. Zuberbühler
Institut für Anorganische Chemie
Universität Basel
Spitalstrasse 51
CH-4056 Basel, Switzerland

Abstract

The pH-dependent equilibria between copper(II) and the ligands 4,7,10-triazatridecanediamide (AMIDE) and 4,7,10-triazatridecane-1,13-diamine (AMINE), respectively, have been studied by UV/VIS spectrophotometry and by EPR spectroscopy.

For these rather complicated equilibrium systems, the spectroscopic measurements not only give reliable stability constants (comparing favorably with those obtained by potentiometry) but also yield the spectra of the complexes, which contain valuable structural information.

The detailed analysis of spectroscopic data from multicomponent systems has become possible by using an algorithm, the basic features of which are (i) data reduction by matrix rank analysis and (ii) an elimination procedure, where only the stability constants have to be refined iteratively and where no information with regard to the spectra of the complexes is needed.

The two equilibrium systems chosen, illustrate the advantages of spectroscopic studies over potentiometric ones:

— The results of the Cu(II)-AMIDE system demonstrate that spectrophotometry is superior with respect to discrimination between two different chemical models.

— The Cu(II)-AMINE system shows that the spectra even of species which occur only to a minor extent are easily obtained and that the spectral information allows the assignment of the structures.

Introduction

Potentiometry still is the standard method for the determination of equilibrium constants. This method, however, has the disadvantages that it does not give structural information and that it cannot be used in strongly acidic or basic solutions, where

255

the buffering capacity of H_3O^+ or OH^- obscures any complexation equilibria.

These restrictions do not apply to spectroscopic methods such as UV/VIS or EPR spectroscopy, which thus should be ideal for the elucidation of complicated solution equilibria.

Quite frequently the solution spectra are rather broad (e.g. in the case of cupric complexes) and extensive overlapping occurs in the respective mixtures. As in most cases the spectra of the individual complexes are unknown, useful information can only be obtained if complete spectra are evaluated. The necessarily large number of spectral data to be handled and of parameters to be refined prevent a straightforward data evaluation.

A comprehensive, reliable and user-friendly program SPECFIT (written in standard FORTRAN 77) has been developed to overcome these difficulties (1). By elimination of the molar absorptivities from the iterative refinement of the nonlinear parameters, the number of unknowns is reduced to the number of equilibrium constants, i.e. the same as in corresponding potentiometric titrations (2). Principal component analysis reduces the amount of raw data typically by a factor of 5-10 (3). The use of analytical instead of numerical derivatives increases both speed and numerical safety (4).

By using this algorithm, spectroscopy becomes a powerful tool for investigating complicated complex equilibria. This is shown in the present paper for the pH-dependent equilibria between copper(II) and the ligands 4,7,10-triazatridecanediamide (AMIDE) and 4,7,10-triazatridecane-1,13-diamine (AMINE), respectively.

The first example (AMIDE) demonstrates that spectrophotometry is superior to potentiometry with respect to discrimination between two different chemical models. The second example (AMINE) shows that stabilities and spectra even of species which occur only to a minor extent are easily obtained and that the spectral information (VIS and EPR) allows the assignment of the structures.

Experimental

Materials. NaOH, HCl (Merck, Titrisol), KCl and $CuSO_4 \cdot 5H_2O$ (Merck, p.A.) were used without further purification. The synthesis of the ligands 4,7,10-triazatridecane-diamide (AMIDE) and 4,7,10-triazatridecane-1,13-diamine (AMINE) has been described in ref. 5.

Instrumentation. Spectrophotometric titrations were done on a CARY 118C with a fully automatic setup (6,7). The EPR titration was done on a VARIAN E3 (9.5 GHz), the setup has been described in ref. 8.

Measurements. The titrations were done at 25°C in aqueous solution of constant ionic strength (I = 0.5 M, KCl) under N_2. In the spectrophotometric experiments 30 increments of 0.01 ml NaOH were added to 2.3 ml complex solution ($[Cu^{2+}] = 4$ mM, [Lig] = 5 mM, [HCl] = 10 mM). In the EPR titration 30 increments of 0.1 ml NaOH were added to 12 ml complex solution ($[Cu^{2+}] = 19.4$ mM, [AMINE] = 20.4 mM, [HCl] = 20 mM)

Data Reduction. This has been described both for spectrophotometric (5,7) and for EPR titrations (8).

Mathematical Methods

The mathematical methods used for the numerical evaluation of the titration data have been described in detail elsewhere (1-4,8) and will only be shortly summarized in the following.

Given a set of M spectra measured at W discrete wavelengths (UV/VIS) or magnetic field strengths (EPR), the whole data set is written as matrix Y (number of rows = M, number of columns = W).

Using matrix notation, the differences (residuals, R) between calculated and experimental absorbances, Y, are given by eqn. (1)

$$R = C \cdot E - Y \tag{1}$$

(C, $M \times S$-matrix of the concentrations of the S coloured species; E, $S \times W$-matrix of the molar absorptivities)

For a given set of equilibrium constants, the molar absorptivities may be substituted by their least-squares estimates $\hat{E}$ (2), eqn. (2).

$$\hat{E} = (C^t C)^{-1} C^t Y \tag{2}$$

The matrix of residuals thus can be described as a function of the equilibrium constants alone, eqn. (3).

$$R = C(C^t C)^{-1} C^t Y - Y = [C(C^t C)^{-1} C^t - I]Y \tag{3}$$

Factor analysis allows the decomposition of the data matrix Y into eigenvectors $V[S \times W]$ and the corresponding linear coefficients $L[M \times S]$ (3), eqn. (4)

$$Y \approx L \cdot V \tag{4}$$

Without any loss of information the linear coefficients L can be used in place of the much larger original data matrix Y (1,3), eqn. (5).

$$R' = [C(C^t C)^{-1} C^t - I]L \tag{5}$$

In addition, the minimal number of eigenvectors needed in order to represent the spectral data according to eqn. (4) within the limits of experimental error provides an unbiased estimate of the number of absorbing species occuring in the chemical system (3,9).

In SPECFIT, the speed of the calculation and the numerical safety of the algorithm are further improved by using analytical instead of numerical derivatives in the iterative process (1).

Besides the absorbance data, SPECFIT only needs estimates for the unknown equilibrium constants, values for the total concentrations and for the ligand protonation constants, and stoichiometric coefficients of the complex species as further input (10).

Results and Discussion

Cu(II)-AMIDE System. The 31 experimental spectra (measured between 800 and 550 nm at 10 nm intervals) obtained from spectrophotometric titration are given in Fig. 1. Representation in their eigenvector basis reduces the spectral data from 31×26 to 31×4, i.e. by 85%. The eigenvector analysis (1,3,9) indicated 4 absorbing species, and a chemical model including Cu^{2+}, $CuLH^{3+}$, CuL^{2+} and $CuLH^{\pm}_{-1}$ (charges omitted in the following) was chosen for the numerical analysis.

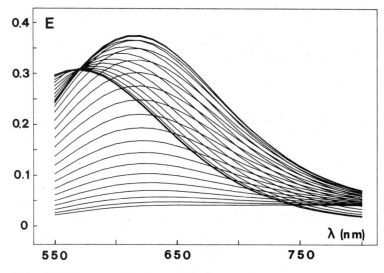

Figure 1. Cu(II)-AMIDE system. Plot of the spectrophotometric data. (5 mM ligand, 4 mM Cu^{2+}, 10 mM HCl)

The task of simultaneously determining the unknown parameters (3 equilibrium constants, 4×26 molar absorptivities) using the complete spectral information is done straightforwardly with the program SPECFIT. Due to the elimination of the molar absorptivities from the iterative refinement process, we need only rough estimates for the 3 equilibrium constants but no information at all with regard to the spectra of the complexes.

The calculated equilibrium constants and visible spectral parameters are summarized in Tables I and II, respectively. The overall standard error of fit is 0.00075 absorbance units (all wavelengths included). From the plot of the residuals (according to eqn. (1)) it is evident that the fit is essentially perfect: The residuals are generally less than twice the overall standard error and do not show any conspicuous peaks (Fig. 2a).

Table I
Stability Constants[a] (with Standard Errors) of the Cu(II) Complexes[b,c]

Ligand		$\log K^H_{CuLH_2}$	$\log K^H_{CuLH}$	$\log K^{Cu}_{CuL}$	$\log K^H_{CuL}$
AMIDE	s	—	2.31 (0.05)	16.28 (0.04)	8.98 (0.02)
	p	—	1.86 (0.07)[d]	16.10 (0.01)	8.83 (0.01)
AMINE	s	3.27 (0.02)	8.97 (0.02)	22.11 (0.09)	—
	p	3.31 (0.03)	8.99 (0.01)	21.65 (0.05)	—
	e	3.20 (0.01)	8.95 (0.01)	21.63 (0.01)	—

[a] $K^H_{CuLH_x} = [CuLH_x]/([CuLH_{x-1}] \cdot [H^+])$; $K^{Cu}_{CuL} = [CuL]/([Cu] \cdot [L])$
[b] Results from spectrophotometric (s), potentiometric (p) (5), and EPR titration (e).
[c] Potentiometrically determined ligand protonation constants from ref. 5 were used.
[d] Species not significant according to F-test for potentiometric data but established spectrophotometrically (see text).

Table II
Spectal Parameters of the Cu(II) Complexes

Complex	λ_{max}^a (nm)	ϵ^a ($M^{-1}cm^{-1}$)	g_{av}^b	A_{av}^b (mK)	$g_{\parallel}^c$	$A_{\parallel}^c$ (mK)	$g_{\perp}^c$
Cu(AMIDE)H^{3+}	632	137					
Cu(AMIDE)$^{2+}$	615	176					
Cu(AMIDE)H$^+_{-1}$	569	150					
Cu(AMINE)H$_2^{4+}$	631	146	2.112	7.49	—[d]	—	—
Cu(AMINE)H^{3+}	573	187	2.102	7.95	2.207	21.64	2.040
Cu(AMINE)$^{2+}$	585	214	2.106	7.77	2.224	19.73	2.050
Cu(DED)$^{2+,e}$	631^f	158^f	2.114^g	7.65^g	2.235	19.30	2.050

[a] From spectrophotometric titration (298 K).
[b] From EPR titration (298 K)
[c] EPR spectra taken from 2 mM solutions in 1:1 DMSO/H$_2$O at 153 K.
[d] Glass spectrum of this minor species was not obtained due to overlapping.
[e] DED = 3,6,9-triazaundecane (5).
[f] From ref. 5.
[g] EPR spectrum taken from a 10 mM aqueous solution at pH 8.30.

The species CuLH is formed around pH 3 and its maximum concentration is less than 10%. Both facts are detrimental to the determination of this species by

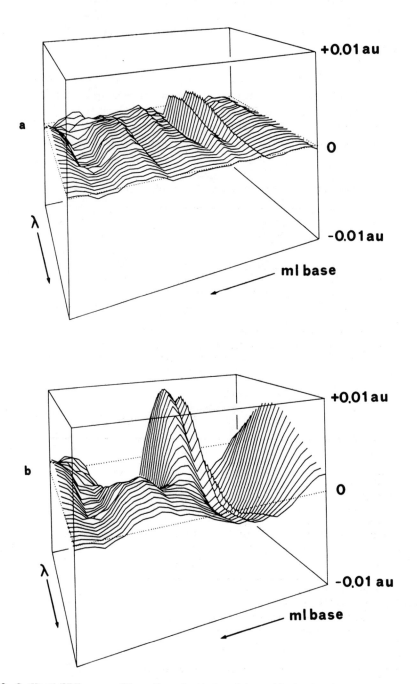

Figure 2. Cu(II)-AMIDE system. Three-dimensional plot of the residuals (absorbance units, au) from spectrophotometric titration (cf. Fig. 1). (a) complete model, including Cu^{2+}, $CuLH^{3+}$, CuL^{2+}, and $CuLH^{+}_{-1}$; overall standard deviation 0.00075 au. (b) same, without $CuLH^{3+}$; standard devation 0.0034 au.

potentiometry. Indeed, the formation of CuLH could not be established on the basis of potentiometric measurements (5): The calculated titration curves with and without inclusion of CuLH were undistinguishable by visual inspection. The standard error of fit decreased from 0.0015 and 0.0011 ml upon inclusion of this species, and the error analysis showed that its formation is not statistically significant (5).

Quite in contrast to the potentiometric results, the formation of CuLH could be clearly established by using the spectrophotometric data. In Fig. 2b the effect of reducing the chemical model to Cu, CuL and $CuLH_{-1}$ is shown. The reduced model is obviously off, with the most prominent deviations at low and medium pH, where CuLH is formed. Subjecting the data to the F-test shows that the formation of this minor species is also statistically highly significant (F = 20).

Cu(II)-AMINE system. This system has been studied by spectrophotometric and EPR titration and also potentiometrically (5). The stability constants obtained by the different methods agree well (Table I) and show that these methods are equally suitable for investigating equilibria.

Before assigning the structures of the complexes based on the calculated spectral parameters (Table II), the results of the EPR titration will be discussed. Although EPR is widely used to study pure paramagnetic compounds (11), it is only rarely applied to complex equilibria in solution (12-14). Recently it was shown that the algorithm used for spectrophotometric data evaluation can be extended to solution EPR data (8). This will be illustrated for the Cu(II) complexes of AMINE.

The data set consisting of 31 spectra measured between 2830 and 3320 G at 10G intervals can be represented by 4 eigenvectors (eqn. (4)). The standard deviation between experimental and represented data is 0.34 au, i.e. less than 1% of the average measured signal. Hence, 4 paramagnetic species occur in agreement with spectrophotometric and potentiometric (5) results.

The eigenvector representation reduces the amount of spectral data to be handled in the numerical analysis from 31×50 to 31×4, i.e. by 92%. No information with regard to the spectra of the complexes is needed since the corresponding 4×50 parameters are eliminated from the iterative refinement of the 3 equilibrium constants.

With the chemical model consisting of Cu^{2+}, $CuLH_2^{4+}$, $CuLH^{3+}$ and CuL^{2+} (charges omitted in the following), the standard error of fit (cf. eqn. (1)) is 0.37 au, i.e. only slightly larger than the one obtained with the model-free eigenvector representation. The calculated EPR titration curves show the excellent fit of the data points and the absence of systematic deviations (Fig. 3).

From the calculated solution spectra (Fig. 4) the strong overlap of the individual spectra is evident. Nevertheless, stability and spectrum even of a minor species like $CuLH_2$ (formed to less than 30% around pH 3.5) are obtained both from EPR and from spectrophotometric titrations.

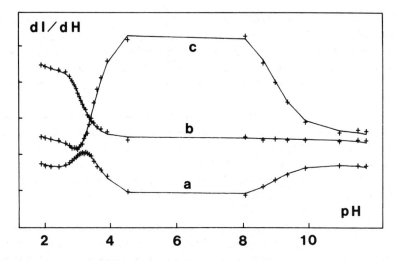

Figure 3. Cu-AMINE system. EPR titration curves at 3120 G (a), 2920 G (b), and 3240 G (c) (experimental points: +; calculated curves: ——).

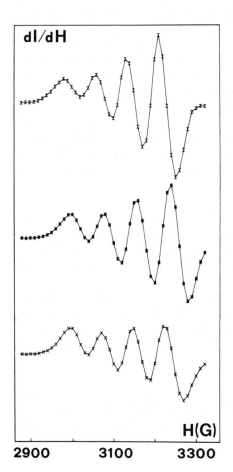

Figure 4. Cu(II)-AMINE system. Calculated solution EPR spectra (I $CuLH_2^{4+}$, * $CuLH^{3+}$, × CuL^{2+}).

Hence, in this case the 3 methods give results of essentially equal reproducibility as far as the equilibrium constants are concerned. The spectroscopic methods, however, yield the spectra of the complexes at no extra cost and this will allow us to assign the structures.

$CuLH_2$ has spectral parameters very similar to the cupric complex of the parent tridentate ligand DED (Table II). Cu(II) will be coordinated to the 3 central nitrogens, whereas the amines in the side arms are protonated and dangling freely in solution.

Deprotonation of $CuLH_2$ results in a decrease of g_{av} and $g_{\parallel}$, in an increase of A_{av} and $A_{\parallel}$ and in a blue shift of the d-d band. This reflects the increased ligand field in CuLH (15,16) and we can expect that the metal is equatorially coordinated by 4 amine groups.

The change of the spectral parameters upon deprotonation of CuLH is explained by an apical interaction of the fifth donor (16,17). The anisotropic EPR spectra of CuLH and CuL display axial symmetry ($g_{\parallel} > g_{\perp}$) and have the usual line shape for mononuclear Cu(II) complexes with a d_{xx-yy} ground state. Hence, tetrahedral distortion or a trigonal-bipyramidal structure can be excluded (16), and the structure of CuL will be essentially tetragonal with the fifth donor only weakly interacting apically.

Conclusion

UV/VIS spectrophotometry and EPR spectroscopy are useful methods for investigating solution equilibria of cupric complexes.

With the algorithm used, the evaluation of the spectroscopic data is straightforward. Only initial estimates for the stability constants are necessary, while no information with regard to the spectra of the complexes is needed.

Spectroscopic measurements are significantly superior to potentiometric ones with respect to discrimination between several models of complexation. This is especially prominent for complexes formed at low or at very high pH.

The numerical analysis of the spectroscopic titrations gives the spectra of the complexes even in cases where strong overlapping occurs and where some complexes are only formed to a minor extent. This spectral information allows the assignment of the solution structures.

Thus, while in no way suggesting abolishment of potentiometric titrations, we are advocating spectroscopic titrations whenever this is feasible. In many cases this will prove to be essential for establishing the correct chemical model.

Acknowledgement

This work was supported by the Swiss National Science Foundation (Grant No. 2.021-0.83).

References and Footnotes

1. H. Gampp, Ch.J. Meyer, M. Maeder and A. D. Zuberbühler, *Talanta 32,* 257 (1985).
2. H. Gampp, M. Maeder and A.D. Zuberbühler, *Talanta 27,* 1037 (1980).
3. M. Maeder and H. Gampp, *Anal. Chim. Acta 122,* 303 (1980).
4. A.D. Zuberbühler and T.A. Kaden, *Talanta 29,* 201 (1982).
5. H. Gampp, D. Haspra, M. Maeder and A.D. Zuberbühler, *Inorg. Chem. 23,* 3274 (1984).
6. G. Hänisch, T.A. Kaden and A.D. Zuberbühler, *Talanta 26,* 563 (1979).
7. A.D. Zuberbühler and T.A. Kaden, *ibid. 26,* 1111 (1979).
8. H. Gampp, *Inorg. Chem. 23,* 1553 (1984).
9. P. Uguagliati, A. Benedetti, S. Enzo and L. Schiffini, *Comp. and Chem.,* in press (1984).
10. SPECFIT has originally been written in HP enhanced BASIC and will shortly be available in standard FORTRAN 77.
11. *Copper Coordination Chemistry: Biochemical and Inorganic Perspectives* Eds., K.D. Karlin, J. Zubieta, Adenine Press, New York (1983).
12. W.S. Kittl and B.M. Rode, *J. Chem. Soc., Dalton Trans.,* 409 (1983).
13. W.S. Kittl and B.M. Rode, *Inorganica Chim. Acta 80,* 39 (1983).
14. See ref. 8 for a survey of applications of EPR to equilibrium studies.
15. J. Peisach and W.E. Blumberg, *Arch. Biochem. Biophys. 165,* 691 (1974).
16. A.W. Addison in ref. 11, p. 109 and further references therein.
17. B.J. Hathaway and D.E. Billing, *Coord. Chem. Rev. 5,* 143 (1970).

Biological & Inorganic Copper Chemistry,
ISBN 0-940030-11-X, Eds., K. D. Karlin & J. Zubieta, Adenine Press, ©Adenine Press, 1985

Magnetic Susceptibility of Di-μ-bromo-bis [bromobis (tetramethylene sulfoxide)copper(II)], Cu$_2$Br$_4$(C$_4$H$_8$SO)$_4$: An Antiferromagnetic Dimer

C.P. Landee and R.E. Greeney,
Department of Physics
Clark University, Worcester, MA 01610

Abstract

As part of a study of the effect of halide substitution on the magnetic exchange and anisotropy within the copper halide sulfoxides, we have undertaken the magnetic study of the title compound (TMSO = tetramethylene sulfoxide). While the crystal structure is not yet complete, x-ray powder patterns show the compound to be isomorphous with the corresponding chloride (1). The chloride structure consists of discrete copper dimers composed of two trans-CuCl$_2$((CH2)$_4$SO)$_2$ monomeric units. One of the chlorine atoms in each monomer interacts with the adjacent copper to form asymmetric bibridged dimers. Antiferromagnetic exchange was observed (J/k = -8.3 cm^{-1}). The magnetic susceptibility of the bromide also shows evidence of antiferromagnetic interactions. The high temperature data was fit to a Curie-Weiss law with parameters C = 0.435 (g = 2.15) and theta = -25 K. The susceptibility reaches a broad maximum near 29 K and then decreases rapidly at lower temperatures. A fit of the date to a S = ½ dimer model yields an exchange constant of J/k = -14.7 cm^{-1} while indicating the presence of antiferromagnetic coupling to adjacent dimers.

1. D.D. Swank, G.F. Needham and R.D. Willett, *Inorg. Chem., 18,* 761 (1979).

Introduction

Interest in the role of ligand-structural characteristics in determining magnetic interactions between metal ions has undergone steady growth. This interest has been spurred by the seminal studies by Hatfield and Hodgson (1) on the planar di-μ-hydroxo complexes [CuL(OH)$_2$]$_2$ in which it was possible to demonstrate a correlation between the isotropic magnetic exchange parameter J and the Cu-O-Cu angle. An explanation of this observed dependence was given by Hoffman and coworkers in terms of molecular orbital theory (2). A similar dependence was observed by Willett et al for the analogous chloride bridged dimers (3). These research efforts have been extended by numerous groups to study the effect upon the exchange strength of changing the coordination geometry and number about the metal ion and by changing the bridging ligands themselves. Substitution of bromide for chloride bridging ions has frequently been observed to increase the magnitude of the exchange interaction by a factor of two (4,5).

An analogous but less understood phenomena is the dependence of magnetic anisotropy upon ligand substitution. In the two-dimensional copper halide salts. $(RNH_3)_2CuX_4$, X=Cl, Br, the magnetic anisotropy causes the moments to remain in the plane for the chlorides and align normal to the plane in the (isostructural) bromides (5). The same variation has been observed in some recently characterized one-dimensional copper halide chains $CHACuX_3$, X=CL, Br, and CHA = cyclohexylammonium (6,7). The magnitudes of the anisotropy energies are typically several percent those of the isotropic exchange interaction. Since the behavior of a magnet in its ordered state is highly sensitive to the amount and type (axial, planar) of anisotropy present, it remains an important question of magnetochemistry to ascertain the origins and structural dependence of this effect.

The copper halide sulfoxides are under study to investigate the topics discussed above. $CuCl_2(DMSO)$, (DMSO = dimethyl sulfoxide) and $CuCl_2(TMSO)$, (TMSO = tetramethylenesulfoxide), have previously been shown to form extended tribridged polymeric chains with ferromagnetic exchange and weak anisotropy (8). The analogous bromides have not yet been synthesized. The structure of the bis form of the DMSO complex, $CuX_2(DMSO)_2$ consists of a monobridged chain for both the chloride (9) and bromide (10) which possesses antiferromagnetic interactions and significant amount of anisotropy (11,12). In addition, there are several other isomers formed between $CuBr_2$ and DMSO which have not yet been characterized (13). The bis form of the TMSO chloride compound $CuCl_2(TMSO)_2$ consists of discrete bibridged dimeric units with an asymmetric bridging geometry consisting of one long Cu-Cl bond (3.02 A), and one short bond (2.27 A), and a bridging angle 88.5° (14). Susceptibility studies (14) showed the exchange to be antiferromagnetic, J = −8.3 cm^{-1}. We report here on the magnetic behavior of the title compound, $[CuBr_2(TMSO)_2]_2$, which is likewise an antiferromagnetic dimer. The complete structural determination of this compound is being carried out elsewhere (15).

Chemical Preparation and Analysis

The sample was prepared with the following procedure. Cupric bromide was prepared by the reaction of hydrobromic acid with copper carbonate. One mole percent of $CuBr_2$ was dissolved in 10 ml of MeOH at room temperature. A slight excess (2.3 mol %) of the TMSO was added in 3 ml MeOH. The solution was stirred at room temperature for one half hour, then put in a cold room overnight at −5°C. Dark green microcrystals formed overnight. The crystals were filtered off and the filtrate was placed over KOH at +5°C. Over a period of several weeks well-formed dark green prismatic crystals were formed. When crushed, the powder is a light yellow-green. Chemical analysis (16) confirmed the proposed stiochiometry. Calculated for $C_8H_{16}O_2CuBr_2$: C, 22.26; H, 3.73; O, 7.41; S, 14.85; Cu, 14.72; Br, 37.02; Found: C, 22.08; H, 3.68; H, 7.42; S, 14.90; Cu, 14,85; Br, 36.82. The use of methanol and the excess of TMSO are both necessary to prevent the determination of a separate black phase of as yet undetermined stoichiometry.

X-ray powder patterns of the $CuCl_2(TMSO)_2$ were compared to the pattern predicted for the lattice parameters of the corresponding chloride, as generated by the program PPPROG (17). The patterns matched very closely, with only slight differences in the two sets of values as would be expected from the differences in the ionic radii of the halide ions.

Experimental

The magnetic susceptibility of a 228 mg sample of $[CuBr_2(TMSO)_2]_2$ was measured between 4 and 260 K in a PAR model 155 Vibrating Sample Magnetometer. The temperatures were determined using a carbon glass resistance thermometer calibrated against magnetic standards. The magnetic field was measured using a Hall probe calibrated with NMR techniques. The susceptibilities were corrected for diamagnetism $(-193 \times 10^{-6}$ emu/mol) and the temperatures independent paramagnetism of the cupric ion $(+60 \times 10^{-6}$ emu/mol).

Results and Discussion

The magnetic susceptibility per mole of copper ions plotted against temperature in Figure 1. The susceptibility reaches a maximum near 29 K then descends rapidly to zero, indicating antiferromagnetic interactions. A Curie-Weiss analysis of the data above 100 K yielded $\theta = -25$ K and C = 0.43 emu-K/mol (g = 2.14).

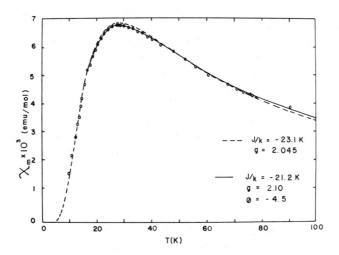

Figure 1. The molar magnetic susceptibility per mole of copper ions of the title compound is plotted versus temperature. The dashed line indicates the predicted susceptibility for non-interacting $S = \frac{1}{2}$ dimers which best approximates the experimental data. The mismatch at the peak is greater than three percent. The solid curve is the prediction for dimers which interact weakly antiferromagnetically. The two curves are indistinguishable below 20 K. Only the dashed curve is shown.

Based on the isomorphous nature of $[CuBr_2(TMSO)_2]_2$ with the chloride, the model chosen for initial comparison to the data was that of an isolated $S = \frac{1}{2}$ dimer (18) where both the exchange constant J and g were allowed to vary as independent parameters. For data over the entire range 4-260 K, a good fit was obtained with values J/k = −23.1 K and g = 2.05. This fit is shown as the dashed curve in the figure. The fit is several percent low at high temperatures and overshoots the data at the maximum by 3 percent. The data drop to zero faster than the predictions of the model which may indicate the existence of (weak) antiferromagnetic coupling between dimers. The model was altered to allow for the existence of a mean field due to interdimer exchange, equation 1.

$$\chi = \frac{N\,g^2\mu_\beta^2}{k(T - \theta)} \frac{e^x}{(1 + 3e^x)}, x = -2J/kT \tag{1}$$

Allowing all three parameters to vary gave the best fit to the values J/k = −21.2 K (−14.7 cm^{-1}) g = 2.10, θ = −4.5 K. This fit is shown as the solid line in the figure and is within the experimental scatter of the data between 10 and 260 K. The data below 10 K lie above the model but are subject to relatively large uncertainties due to the vanishing of the moments. Deleting the data below 10 K does not alter the best fit parameters. The value of   corresponds to an interdimer exchange interaction of 0.56 K, 0.39 cm^{-1} (from θ = 2ZJ′/k, Z = number of interacting dimers which is 4). The ratio of interdimer to intradimeric exchange is thus 0.026, indicating relatively good isolation.

Hatfield et al (19,20) have recently tabulated data for copper halide dimers of the types [CuL$_2$X$_2$]$_2$ or [CuAX$_2$]$_2$ where X=Cl, Br and L is a monodentate ligand, A a bidentate ligand. A linear correlation between bridging angle and exchange parameter was not observed for these compounds, unlike the case for the planar hydroxy bridge dimers in the earlier study (1). The magnetic exchange constant shows a close correlation to the ratio of the bridging angle to the internuclear separation ϕ/R for these dimers in which the copper coordinates is a (distorted) tetragonal pyramid. The [CuX$_2$(TMSO)$_2$]$_2$ dimers fall within this class of compounds. Although the chloride compound has an exchange strength (−8.3 cm^{-1}) more than twice that of the dimers tabulated, it nevertheless is in accord with the correlation observed. Since the structural parameters of the bromide are not yet determined, detailed comparison to the ϕ/R correlation will be done at a later time.

Acknowledgement

This work has been supported by the NSF, Grant DMR 83-06432. The magnetometer was purchased with a grant from the NSF Two and Four Year College Research Instrumentation Program, grant PRM-8109071.

References and Footnotes

1. V.H. Crawford, H.W. Richardson, J.R. Wasson, D.J. Hodgson and W.E. Hatfield, *Inorg. Chem. 15*, 2107 (1976).

2. P.J. Hay, J.C. Thibeault and R. Hoffman, *J. Am. Chem. Soc. 97,* 4884 (1975).
3. S.G.N. Roundhill, D.M. Roundhill, D.R. Bloomquist, C.P. Landee, R.D. Willett, D.M. Dooley and H.B. Gray, *Inorg. Chem. 18,* 831 (1979).
4. D.Y. Jeter and W.E. Hatfield, *J. Inorg. Nucl. Chem. 34,* 3055 (1972).
5. P. Bloembergen, *Physica 81B,* 205 (1976), see table I.
6. H.H. Goenendijk, H.W.J. Blote, A.J. van Duyneveldt, R.M. Gaura, C.P. Landee and R.D. Willett, *Physica 106B,* 47 (1981).
7. A.C. Phaff, H.C.W. Swuste, W.J.M. de Jonge, R. Hoogerbeets and A.J. van Duyneveldt, *J. Phys. C. 17,* 2583 (1984).
8. D.D. Swank, C.P. Landee and R.D. Willett, *Phys. Rev. B., 20,* 2154 (1979).
9. R.D. Willet and K. Chang, *Inorg. Chim. Acta, 4,* 447 (1970). .
10. R.D. Willett, R.H. Jardine and S.A. Roberts, *Inorg. Chim. Acta, 25,* 97 (1977).
11. W.E. Estes, W.E. Hatfield, J.A.C. van Ouijen and J. Reedijk, *J. Chem. Soc. Dalton 1980,* 2121 (1980).
12. C.P. Landee, A.C. Lamas, R.E. Greeney and P.S. Gahlawat, *J. Appl. Phys., 55,* 2473 (1984).
13. C.P. Landee, unpublished results.
14. D.D. Swank, G.F. Needham and R.D. Willett, *Inorg. Chem., 18,* 761 (1979).
15. R.D. Willett, unpublished results.
16. Galbraith Laboratories, Knoxville, Tenn. 37921
17. Quantum Chemistry Program Exchange, Indiana University, Program #307, authors J.S. Miller and S.Z. Goldberg
18. B. Bleaney and K.D. Bowers, *Proc. R. Soc. London 214A* 451 (1952).
19. W.E. Marsh, T.L. Bowman, W.E. Hatfield and D.J. Hodgson, *Inorg. Chim. Acta. 59,* 19 (1982).
20. W.E. Marsh, D.S. Eggleston, W.E. Hatfield and D.J. Hodgson, *Inorg. Chim. Acta. 70,* 137 (1982).